P208486

6911

£12·75

ML

or b n e

IEE TELECOMMUNICATIONS SERIES 5

SERIES EDITOR: PROF. J.E. FLOOD

Angle modulation:
the theory of system assessment

Angle modulation:
the theory of system assessment

J.H. Roberts, B.Sc., F.I.M.A.
Principal Mathematician
Plessey Avionics & Communications
Roke Manor
Romsey,
Hants., England

PETER PEREGRINUS LTD.
on behalf of the
Institution of Electrical Engineers

Published by Peter Peregrinus Ltd.,
Southgate House, Stevenage, Herts. SG1 1HQ, England

ISBN: 0 901223 95 6

Typeset by the Alden Press (London and Northampton) Ltd.,
Printed in England by A. Wheaton & Co., Exeter

D
621.3815'36
ROB

Preface

Angle modulation is the generic term applied to phase modulated (p.m.) and frequency modulated (f.m.) transmissions, and a large variety of present day communication systems use this means of conveying information in analogue or digital form, and, sometimes, in both.

The initials f.m. and p.m. are often encountered in the fields of Radar, T.V. local and police radio, satellite transmissions etc., and the rival amplitude modulation (a.m.) is now much less used. The early history of f.m. with its fervent championing in the USA by Major Armstrong (sometimes hampered, apparently, by equipment manufacturers who saw their sales slumping if the freedom from interference of f.m. compared with a.m. became too well known) and its misunderstandings regarding bandwidth, which were finally resolved by Carson, makes interesting reading.[1-3]

With both f.m. and p.m. the processes of modulation and demodulation are nonlinear so the analysis of performance of f.m. and p.m. systems when disturbed by noise and interference has long presented an attractive challenge to the analyst. This inherent nonlinearity means that, when decision theory is used to identify the optimum method of combatting noise and various types of system disturbances, a complicated receiver structure can emerge that is both difficult to analyse and build, but it would appear that, in many cases, conventional designs are near-optimum. Usually, rather special reasons have to exist for the optimum detector to be implemented and, more often, constraints imposed by date-lines and budgets force the designer to opt for tried and tested methods of detection, with the occasional variation in a conventional design. The analysis to be given here refers mainly to this latter situation.

Another consequence of the nonlinear nature is that the theory has developed in a piecemeal fashion with different approaches being tried from time to time. When a result is reported that accounts exactly for the nonlinearity, then this is particularly satisfying, but often a tractable theory can only be produced by taking steps that a determined critic can object to, and justification is strengthened by the results of computer simulation runs or laboratory measurements that are done to check the theoretical predictions. This is particularly the case when interest lies in the outcome of first filtering an f.m. wave and then demodulating it, and a survey of this problem is given here.

The monograph is principally concerned with the harmful effects of noise and interference, and many useful results from the large literature that now exists are quoted. It has become customary to include an extensive bibliography of pertinent literature, but it is becoming increasingly difficult to keep up to date (one recently published survey listed over eight hundred references on the phase lock loop alone) and here a unifying theory is developed which gives formal solutions to the performance assessment problems that are posed and which allows previously derived results to be credited to their originators at appropriate points during an overview of the subject.

The reader is assumed to be a practising engineer or graduate student and therefore familiar with such communication engineering concepts as power spectra, coherent and incoherent detection, Gaussian noise, error rates etc., but some of the mathematical tools used, such as the signum function (sgn $x = \pm 1$ according as x is positive or negative) or the Dirac delta function [d sgn $x/dx = 2\delta(x)$] may be a little unfamiliar. The Dirac delta is the most commonly encountered generalised function, and the discipline of generalised function theory, as described by Lighthill, is tacitly assumed here to gain freedom regarding multiple operations such as interchanging orders of integration or differentiating under the integral sign, and such steps will be taken without further comment with all limits being assumed to exist. A willingness to grapple with the double and quadruple integrals that need to be evaluated is therefore desirable but the aim is always to present a final result in as neat a form as possible so that its physical significance is apparent and it is usable to the reader. Moreover, the general availability of small but powerful desk calculators has greatly widened the class of performance formulae that can be easily handled.

In recognition of the increasing amount of data that is now transmitted in digital form, the subject matter is divided about equally between analogue and digital f.m. and p.m. signals, and the first three chapters develop the underlying theory. Then attention is given to predicting the performance of particular transmissions when disturbed by noise or adjacent channel interference in the situations commonly encountered by the systems analyst.

References

1 TUCKER, D.G.: 'The invention of frequency modulation in 1902', *J. Inst. Electron. & Radio Eng.*, 1970, **40**, (1), pp. 33–37
2 TUCKER, D.G.: 'The early history of amplitude modulation, side bands and frequency-division-multiplex', *J. Inst. Electron. & Radio Eng.*, 1971, **41**, (1), pp. 43–47
3 ANGUS, R.: 'Major Armstrong and the struggle for FM broadcasting', *Audio Scene Can.*, June 1974, pp. 30–34

Acknowledgments

The invitation to write this volume came from the IEE, and the author thanks them, and Dr. R. Hamer in particular, for the opportunity it afforded.

It is a pleasure to thank my colleagues for their help, David Randall for discussions and valuable checking, and especially Frank Gardner and Keith Wales who undertook to read the drafts and subsequently made a number of improvements.

At several points reference is made to computer programs but little attention is given to the detailed and careful work that lies behind them. For these I am indebted to Ann Griffiths.

The drawings were prepared by Neil Martin, and the general facilities made available to me by the Plessey Company through the offices of S.M. Cobb, are gratefully acknowledged.

Finally, I thank my wife Diana who typed the bulk of the manuscript and who never failed me in her support and encouragement.

Chandler's Ford   September 1976

Contents

List of principal symbols

Unless otherwise stated, frequencies are expressed in rad/s, and all power spectra as power/rad/s.

A	Carrier amplitude
a_1, a_2	Parameters of Tikhonov distribution
a_n, b_n	Coefficients in power series expansions of transfer characteristic
$\alpha(t)$	Phase modulation on unwanted transmission
$2\alpha p_m$	3 dB bandwidth of single-pole bandpass filter
βp_m	3 dB bandwidth of single-pole lowpass filter in d.t.f.
$B(t)$	Envelope of unwanted transmission
$B_1(\omega), \lambda$	Coherence factors (voltage ratios)
$2\omega_B$	Carson bandwidth
$c(t)$	Control voltage in d.t.f.
$\delta(x)$	Dirac delta function
w_d	r.m.s. test-tone deviation
ω_D	Carrier frequency separation
D/S	distortion-to-signal (power ratio)

$$\operatorname{erf}(x) = \frac{2}{\sqrt{\pi}} \int_0^x e^{-u^2} \, du$$

F	Feedback factor (voltage-wise)
$g(t)$	Impulse response function of equivalent lowpass filter
$\left\{ \dfrac{G(q)}{\frac{1}{2}A^2} \right\}$	Normalised r.f. power spectrum
h	Time interval that is made vanishingly small
$H(j\omega)$	Transfer characteristic of equivalent lowpass filter
$He_n(x)$	Hermite polynomial
I_c, I_s	In-phase and quadrature components of narrow-band Gaussian noise (understood to be time dependent)
$I_e(k, x)$	Rice's I_e function (see Appendix)

$I_n(x)$	Modified Bessel function of the first kind, of order n
j	$\sqrt{-1}$
$J_n(x)$	Bessel function of the first kind, of order n
k	a.m. to p.m. conversion factor (Section 5.9 and Section 8.2)
k	Binary f.m. deviation ratio (peak-to-peak frequency excursion, Hz, divided by the data rate)
L	Threshold
$2p_l$	Bandwidth of truncating filter
$L(j\omega)$	Transfer characteristic of lowpass filter
m	Parameter of Nakagami's m distribution
$M(t)$	Frequency modulation
M	Value of $M(t)$ at specific instant
$\mu(t)$	Phase modulation
$\dot{\mu}(t) = M(t)$	Frequency modulation
ν	Expected number of upward and downward f.m. clicks
n.p.r.	Noise power ratio
$\psi_N(0)$	Noise power
$\psi_N(\tau)$	Autocorrelation function of lowpass noise
p_m	Maximum modulating frequency
p_0	Minimum modulating frequency
p, q, ω	General baseband frequencies
$P(p)$	Pre-emphasis law (power-ratio) applied at baseband frequency p
$P(t), Q(t)$	In-phase and quadrature components of general narrow-band transmission
$Q(a, b)$	Marcum's Q function
$\phi(t)$	PLL phase error (Chapter 9)
$\phi(\omega)$	Phase characteristic of equivalent lowpass filter
r	Relative amplitude of interfering wave or relative echo amplitude
$r_N(\tau) = \dfrac{\psi_N(\tau)}{\psi_N(0)}$	
$R(\tau)$	Autocorrelation function
$R(t), R_s(t)$	Envelope functions
ρ	Carrier-to-noise (power ratio)
sgn (x)	$+1$ if $x > 0$, -1 if $x < 0$ zero if $x = 0$
$s(t)$	Signalling pulse in digital phase modulation
$S(\tau)$	Triangular wave
τ_0	Echo delay
T	General time period (Chapter 3)
T	Bit duration ($1/T$ Hz is the data rate: Chapter 10)

T_1 — Interval of time that contains many carrier cycles but is not long enough for the in-phase and quadrature components to have changed significantly

$\theta(t), \theta_s(t)$ — Phase functions

u — Dummy variable

$\Phi(u)$ — Univariate characteristic function

u_1, u_2 — Dummy variables

$\Phi(u_1, u_2)$ — Bivariate characteristic function

$W_\mu(\omega)$ — Power spectrum of $\mu(t)$

$\psi_\mu(\tau)$ — Autocorrelation function of $\mu(t)$

$W_M(\omega)$ — Power spectrum of $M(t)$

$\psi_M(\tau)$ — Autocorrelation function of $M(t)$

$W(\omega)$ — General power spectrum

$2\Delta_\omega$ — 3 dB static bandwidth of the d.t.f.

$\Delta(h) = \theta_s\left(t + \dfrac{h}{2}\right) - \theta_s\left(t - \dfrac{h}{2}\right)$

$\Delta_s = \mu(T) - \mu(0)$

ω_0 — Carrier frequency

ω_I — Intermediate frequency

$\omega_i(t)$ — Instantaneous frequency

ω_Δ — r.m.s. noiseband frequency deviation

$Z(j\omega)$ — Loop transfer characteristic

Z_0 — Expected number of zeros per second

Chapter 1

Introduction

The signal, noise, and interference waveforms to be considered are of the narrow-band type, by which it is meant that the carrier or intermediate frequency used greatly exceeds the occupied bandwidth. The general expression for a narrow-band wave, which will appear repeatedly in various guises through the monograph, is written as follows

$$V(t) = P(t) \cos \omega_0 t - Q(t) \sin \omega_0 t \qquad (1.1)$$

Here $P(t)$ and $Q(t)$ are called the in-phase and quadrature components, respectively, and it is important to appreciate two time scales (or, equivalently, two rates of change) associated with eqn. 1.1. The narrow-band assumption means that $P(t)$ and $Q(t)$ are to be regarded as slowly varying in the sense that in the time T_1, say, taken by $P(t)$ and/or $Q(t)$ to change significantly (one-half the reciprocal of the occupied bandwidth is representative of such a time period) a large number of cycles to $\cos \omega_0 t$ have gone by. The particular large number in question depends on the ratio of centre frequency (ω_0 rad/s) to the bandwidth that happens to be used, but many hundreds or many thousands would be typical; great precision is not necessary with this aspect of the theory and most of our results refer to the limiting situation in which the ratio of occupied bandwidth to centre frequency is vanishingly small. A consequence of the wide disparity in time scales is that it is often appropriate to perform an average over the time T_1 (thus smoothing out the fast variations) and produce a result which is time dependent but which varies at the slower rate. Of course, if a long-term time average is taken across many intervals of length T_1 [symbolised by $\lim_{n \to \infty} (nT_1)^{-1} \int_0^{nT_1} (\quad) dt$], then only the d.c. term, if any, is obtained.

Returning to eqn. 1.1, $[P^2(t) + Q^2(t)]^{1/2}$ is the envelope and $\tan^{-1}(Q(t)/P(t))$ is the instantaneous phase, and a representation such as eqn. 1.1 can be used for the transmitted signal as well as the wave appearing at the receiver terminals after limiting, amplification, filtering, and the addition of noise or interference have taken place.

The undistorted, unfiltered, and interference free angle modulated signal has the form

$$S(t) = A \cos [\omega_0 t + \mu(t)] \qquad (1.2)$$

where $\mu(t)$ is the information-bearing phase modulation and the frequency modulation is the time derivative of $\mu(t)$, i.e. $\dot{\mu}(t)$. It will be supposed that some form of additive narrow-band interference accompanies this wave so that the receiver input is given by

$$V(t) = A \cos [\omega_0 t + \mu(t)] + X(t) \cos \omega_0 t - Y(t) \sin \omega_0 t$$

$$= R(t) \cos [\omega_0 t + \theta(t)] \qquad (1.3)$$

$R(t)$ is the envelope and $\theta(t)$ is the instantaneous phase. The following identifications can then be made

$$\left. \begin{array}{l} R(t) = \{[A \cos \mu(t) + X(t)]^2 + [A \sin \mu(t) + Y(t)]^2\}^{1/2} \\[2mm] \theta(t) = \tan^{-1} \left\{ \dfrac{A \sin \mu(t) + Y(t)}{A \cos \mu(t) + X(t)} \right\} \end{array} \right\} \quad (1.4)$$

An investigation of system performance may be regarded as an exercise in which certain statistical features of eqn. 1.3 are compared with the corresponding features of eqn. 1.2 and some agreed yard-stick (such as a distortion level or an error-rate) is calculated as a measure of the comparison. Depending on the demodulation method (coherent or incoherent) and the form of the information transmitted (whether $\mu(t)$ represents an analogue signal or is a pulse train representing the digitised form of some analogue signal) so the method of calculation of the yard-stick can differ and, typically, interest may centre on one or more of the following:

(*a*) the spectral density of $\dot{\theta}(t)$
(*b*) the probability distribution of $\dot{\theta}(t)$
(*c*) the probability distribution of $\theta(t + \tau) - \theta(t)$ (τ a general delay)
(*d*) the expected number of zeros of $V(t)$

Also, with the radio spectrum becoming more and more congested there is often a need to establish the band over which significant frequency components of eqn. 1.2, or perhaps the hard limited version of eqn. 1.3, i.e. $K \cos [\omega_0 t + \theta(t)]$, extend. The latter could be of interest when $X(t)$ and $Y(t)$ (see eqn. 1.3) represent sums of the in-phase

and quadrature components of transmissions that share the use of a
hard limiting satellite transponder with a wanted signal $A \cos [\omega_0 t + \mu(t)]$.

For the major part of our development only second-order statistical
quantities have to be calculated, perhaps the most familiar of which
is the autocorrelation function. For $V(t)$ this is written

$$R(\tau) = \langle V(t)V(t + \tau)\rangle \qquad (1.5)$$

The angle brackets $\langle \ \rangle$ indicate an appropriate time average and an
ensemble average taken over any random parameters of $V(t)$ (associated with modulation, for example). The left-hand side of eqn. 1.5
has been shown as a function of τ only as this will be true of the cases
to be met here. However, this does not necessarily imply that $V(t)$ is
stationary.

By invoking the Wiener-Khinchine relationship the spectral density
of $V(t)$ [or power spectrum: $W(\omega)$ $\omega \geqslant 0$] is given by taking the
Fourier transform of $R(\tau)$

$$W(\omega) = \frac{2}{\pi} \int_0^\infty R(\tau) \cos \omega\tau d\tau \qquad (1.6)$$

With present day computing facilities this integral seldom presents
serious difficulty and here attention will be focussed on calculating
$R(\tau)$ in particular cases of interest.

The brackets $\langle \ \rangle$ will appear on numerous occasions and are not
confined to use when finding autocorrelation functions. Their mean-
ing will be clear from the context, and in some cases the time averaging
operation is not required. An example of this arises when item (b)
(the distribution of $\dot{\theta}(t)$) is under investigation.

If a signal, such as $\dot{\theta}(t)$, is sampled at some time instant $t = t_0$
then $\dot{\theta}(t_0)$ will often have a range of possible values. The probability
$Pr[\dot{\theta} > L]$ that $\dot{\theta}(t_0)$ exceeds a threshold L can then be expressed as

$$Pr[\dot{\theta} > L] = \langle \tfrac{1}{2} \{1 - \text{sgn} [L - \dot{\theta}(t_0)]\}\rangle \qquad (1.7)$$

Here sgn $(X) = \pm 1$ according as X is positive or negative and the
brackets $\langle \ \rangle$ evidently refer to an averaging operation in which each
possible value of $\dot{\theta}(t_0)$ is inserted in the expression $\tfrac{1}{2} \{1 - \text{sgn} [L - \dot{\theta}(t_0)]\}$ and the resulting 0 or 1 is weighted by the probability of that
particular $\dot{\theta}(t_0)$ arising. An alternative way of writing eqn. 1.7 is

$$Pr[\dot{\theta} > L] = \int_{-\infty}^{+\infty} \tfrac{1}{2} \{1 - \text{sgn} [L - \dot{\theta}(t_0)]\} \cdot p[\dot{\theta}(t_0)] d[\dot{\theta}(t_0)] \qquad (1.8)$$

but this implies knowledge of $p\,[\dot{\theta}(t_0)]$ the probability density function of $\dot{\theta}(t_0)$ and, as will be shown, the averaging can be performed without explicitly finding $p\,[\dot{\theta}(t_0)]$. For this reason the form shown in eqn. 1.7 is preferred.

In summary, we aim to consider a variety of statistical properties of eqn. 1.3 when $X(t)$ and $Y(t)$ refer to different noise and interference types. Some of the tools of probability theory that will be needed are discussed next.

Chapter 2

Preliminary theory

2.1 The characteristic function

Given a probability density function $p(x)$, the corresponding characteristic function $\Phi(u)$ is defined by

$$\Phi(u) = \int_{-\infty}^{+\infty} p(x) \exp{(jux)}dx \qquad (2.1)$$

where u is a dummy variable.

In communications analysis x usually stands for the value of a time dependent random variable $x(t)$ that is sampled at some definite instant, and, if this variable is stationary, then $p(x)$ will be independent of time. When $x(t)$ has the form shown in eqn. 1.3

$$\exp{[jux(t)]} = \exp{\{juR(t)\cos{[\omega_0 t + \theta(t)]}\}} \qquad (2.2)$$

Using the relationship

$$\exp{[ju\cos{\alpha}]} = \sum_{m=-\infty}^{+\infty} J_m(u)\exp{jm}(\alpha + \pi/2) \qquad (2.3)$$

where $J_m(u)$ is a Bessel function of the first kind of order m, we have

$$\exp{[jux(t)]} = \sum_{m=-\infty}^{+\infty} J_m(uR(t))\exp{jm}(\omega_0 t + \theta(t) + \pi/2) \quad (2.4)$$

Recalling the two time scales to be associated with a narrow-band waveform, an average of both sides of eqn. 2.4 taken across the time T_1 in which $R(t)$ and $\theta(t)$ show little variation but which contains many cycles of the centre frequency, will receive a significant contribution from only the $m = 0$ term of the summation on the right of eqn. 2.4, i.e. $J_0[uR(t)]$. Such an averaging process can be followed by an ensemble average over the possible values of $R(t)$, and these two forms of averaging will be denoted by angle brackets $\langle \ \rangle$. Thus,

$$\Phi(u) = \langle\exp{jux(t)}\rangle = \langle J_0[uR(t)]\rangle \qquad (2.5)$$

Higher-order forms of the characteristic function will be required. With u_1 and u_2 as dummy variables

$$\Phi(u_1, u_2) = \langle \exp j \, [u_1 x(t) + u_2 x(t + \tau)] \rangle \qquad (2.6)$$

where τ is a general time step, is called the bivariate characteristic function with obvious extensions to the trivariate and quadrivariate forms. Since

$$u_1 . R(t) \cos \, [\omega_0 t + \theta(t)] + u_2 . R(t + \tau) \cos \, [\omega_0(t + \tau) + \theta(t + \tau)]$$

$$= \{[u_1 R(t)]^2 + [u_2 R(t + \tau)]^2 + 2u_1 u_2 R(t) R(t + \tau)$$

$$\cos \, [\omega_0 \tau + \theta(t + \tau) - \theta(t)]\}^{1/2}$$

$$\cos \left[\omega_0 t + \tan^{-1} \left\{ \frac{u_1 R(t) \sin\theta \, (t) + u_2 R(t + \tau) \sin\theta \, (t + \tau)}{u_1 R(t) \cos\theta \, (t) + u_2 R(t + \tau) \cos\theta \, (t + \tau)} \right\} \right]$$

the result corresponding to eqn. 2.5 is

$$\Phi(u_1, u_2) = \langle J_0 \, [\{[u_1 R(t)]^2 + [u_2 R(t + \tau)]^2 \qquad (2.7)$$

$$+ 2u_1 u_2 R(t) R(t + \tau) \cos \, [\omega_0 \tau + \theta(t + \tau) - \theta(t)] \}^{1/2}] \rangle$$

Alternatively,

$$\Phi(u_1, u_2) = \langle J_0 \, [\{[u_1 P_1 + u_2(P_2 \cos \omega_0 \tau + Q_2 \sin \omega_0 \tau)]^2$$

$$+ [u_1 Q_1 + u_2(Q_2 \cos \omega_0 \tau - P_2 \sin \omega_0 \tau)]^2 \}^{1/2}] \rangle \quad (2.8)$$

where $P_1 = R(t) \cos \theta \, (t)$, $Q_2 = R(t + \tau) \sin \theta \, (t + \tau)$ etc., the use of suffix 1 for time t and suffix 2 for time $t + \tau$ being a convention introduced by S.O. Rice in Reference 1 where much of the background to the results quoted in this chapter may be found.

Now, $\Phi(u_1, u_2)$ is the bivariate characteristic function of a general narrow-band wave with envelope $R(t)$ and instantaneous phase $\theta(t)$. When (as in eqn. 1.3, for example) this wave is the sum of two statistically unrelated waves, the following relationship holds

$$\Phi_{s+I}(u_1, u_2) = \Phi_s(u_1, u_2) \cdot \Phi_I(u_1, u_2) \qquad (2.9)$$

where the suffices S and I stand, in a general way, for Signal and Interference.

Eqn. 2.9 is a consequence of the well-known property of characteristic functions in that the characteristic function of the sum of two independent variates is given by the product of their separate characteristic functions.

The role that these functions play in the theory will become clearer from subsequent chapters, but knowledge of the function $\Phi(u_1, u_2)$

identifies all the second-order moments between $V(t)$ and $V(t + \tau)$, typified by $\langle V^n(t) . V^m(t + \tau) \rangle$. In particular, $n = m = 1$ gives the autocorrelation function and for the narrow-band waves of interest here this will take the form $f(\tau) \cos \omega_0 \tau$. The first-harmonic terms in $\omega_0 \tau$ from $\Phi(u_1, u_2)$ are therefore to be associated with the auto-correlation function. Further, eqn. 2.7 shows a dependence upon $\theta(t + \tau) - \theta(t)$ which is the phase change that occurs in time τ. When τ is made equal to T, the bit or symbol duration of a digital data system, it will be shown how eqn. 2.7 can be exploited to calculate the probability that such a phase change is recorded in error by the decision circuitry (an application to differentially encoded phase shift keying is therefore apparent), and if τ is made small so that $\theta(t + \tau) - \theta(t) \approx \tau\dot{\theta}(t)$ it is plausible that the distribution of $\dot{\theta}(t)$ can be investigated.

A case to be frequently encountered is that in which the signal (eqn. 1.2) is passed through a bandpass filter. The result of this operation is yet another narrow-band wave such as eqn. 1.1 with in-phase and quadrature components that depend at time t on the prehistory of the unfiltered components and on the impulsive response function of the filter.

This involvement of the memory of the filter is an effect which, in general, can only be dealt with in an approximate way, but the effect of the filter on additive Gaussian noise or unmodulated c.w. inter-ference is easily accounted for. Thus, in a number of instances the filtered signal will be carried along in the analysis in a formal way until a point is reached at which further progress cannot be made unless some account of the filter is taken. This is often sufficiently far for useful conclusions to be drawn, however, and the case of filtered signal plus narrow-band Gaussian noise is considered in considerable detail here. As a concession to simplifying the working it will be assumed that the noise has a power spectrum that is symmetrical about ω_0. Then, for a general narrow-band signal accompanied by such noise:

$$\Phi_{S+N}(u_1, u_2) = \langle J_0 [\{[u_1 R_S(t)]^2 + [u_2 R_S(t + \tau)]^2$$
$$+ 2u_1 u_2 R_S(t) R_S(t + \tau)$$
$$\cos [\omega_0 \tau + \theta_S(t + \tau) - \theta_S(t)]\}^{1/2}] \rangle$$
$$\exp - \tfrac{1}{2} [\psi_N(0)(u_1^2 + u_2^2) + 2u_1 u_2 \psi_N(\tau) \cos \omega_0 \tau] \quad (2.10)$$

where $\psi_N(\tau) \cos \omega_0 \tau$ is the autocorrelation function of the noise and $\psi_N(0)$ is the noise power. For a general narrow-band signal accompanied by independent narrow-band interference of a general kind [with envelope $B(t)$, instantaneous phase $\alpha(t)$]

$$\Phi_{S+I}(u_1, u_2) =$$

$$\langle J_0 \left[\{ [u_1 R_S(t)]^2 + [u_2 R_S(t+\tau)]^2 + 2u_1 u_2 R_S(t) R_S(t+\tau) \right.$$

$$\left. \cos \left[\omega_0 \tau + \theta_S(t+\tau) - \theta_S(t) \right] \}^{1/2} \right] \rangle$$

$$\langle J_0 \left[\{ [u_1 B(t)]^2 + [u_2 B(t+\tau)]^2 + 2u_1 u_2 B(t) B(t+\tau) \right.$$

$$\left. \cos \left[\omega_0 \tau + \alpha(t+\tau) - \alpha(t) \right] \}^{1/2} \right] \rangle \tag{2.11}$$

2.2 Examples

Simple cases of eqns. 2.10 and 2.11 arise when the signal is a pure f.m. wave [making $R_S(t) = A$ and $\theta_S(t) = \mu(t)$, as in eqn. 1.2], and when the interference is noise or an off-set independent phase or frequency modulated transmission (the adjacent channel interference case). Then: for pure f.m. signal plus narrow-band Gaussian noise

$$\Phi_{S+N}(u_1, u_2) = \langle J_0 [A \{ u_1^2 + u_2^2 + 2u_1 u_2$$

$$\cos [\omega_0 \tau + \mu(t+\tau) - \mu(t)] \}^{1/2}] \rangle \tag{2.12}$$

$$\cdot \exp - \tfrac{1}{2} [\psi_N(0)(u_1^2 + u_2^2) + 2u_1 u_2 \psi_N(\tau) \cos \omega_0 \tau]$$

for pure f.m. signal plus off-set p.m. or f.m. interference

$$\Phi_{S+I}(u_1, u_2) =$$

$$\langle J_0 [A \{ u_1^2 + u_2^2 + 2u_1 u_2 \cos (\omega_0 \tau + \mu(t+\tau) - \mu(t)) \}^{1/2}] \rangle \tag{2.13}$$

$$\cdot \langle J_0 [rA \{ u_1^2 + u_2^2 + 2u_1 u_2 \cos [(\omega_0 + \omega_D)\tau + \alpha(t+\tau) - \alpha(t)] \}^{1/2}] \rangle$$

Here the carriers are separated by ω_D (rad/s), $\alpha(t)$ is the phase modulation [$\dot{\alpha}(t)$ the frequency modulation] on the interferer, r is the relative amplitude of the interferer.

If noise and adjacent channel interference both add to the wanted signal at the receiver input the corresponding bivariate function $\Phi_{S+I+N}(u_1, u_2)$ can be formed as a product of three functions. Further, the bivariate function pertaining to shot-noise can be identified (section 3.11 of Reference 1) and so this source of system interference can also, in principle, be accommodated by the theory. These examples considerably complicate the working, however, and will not be pursued.

2.3 Integral results

On recalling the Bessel function appearing in eqn. 2.7, which gives the completely general form of the bivariate characteristic function, some integral results are recorded for future reference. Firstly:

$$\frac{1}{2\pi} \iint_{-\infty}^{+\infty} J_0 \left[\{(u_1 R_1)^2 + (u_2 R_2)^2 + 2u_1 u_2 R_1 R_2 \cos(\omega_0 \tau + \theta_2 - \theta_1)\}^{1/2} \right]$$

$$\cdot \frac{du_1 du_2}{u_1 u_2} = |\omega_0 \tau + \theta_2 - \theta_1| - \pi/2 \qquad (2.14)$$

where the angle $(\omega_0 \tau + \theta_2 - \theta_1)$ lies in the range $-\pi$ to $+\pi$ and principal values are to be taken for the integral. Eqn. 2.14 is easily derived by using

$$J_0 \left[\{(u_1 R_1)^2 + (u_2 R_2)^2 + 2u_1 u_2 R_1 R_2 \cos\alpha\}^{1/2} \right]$$

$$= \sum_{m=-\infty}^{\infty} J_m(u_1 R_1) J_m(u_2 R_2) e^{jm(\alpha+\pi)} \qquad (2.15)$$

and

$$\int_{-\infty}^{+\infty} \frac{J_m(ax)}{x} \, dx = \frac{2}{m} \qquad \text{for } m \text{ odd } (a > 0)$$

$$= 0 \qquad \text{otherwise}$$

Then, replacing $\omega_0 \tau$ by Z, differentiating with respect to Z, and restoring the angled averaging brackets of eqn. 2.7 gives

$$\frac{1}{2\pi} \iint_{-\infty}^{+\infty} \frac{\partial}{\partial Z} \langle J_0 \left[\{(u_1 R_1)^2 + (u_2 R_2)^2 + 2u_1 u_2 R_1 R_2 \right.$$

$$\left. \cos(Z + \theta_2 - \theta_1)\}^{1/2} \right] \rangle \frac{du_1 du_2}{u_1 u_2} = \langle \text{sgn}(Z + \theta_2 - \theta_1) \rangle \qquad (2.16)$$

Thus, recalling eqn. 1.7, we have

$$P_r(-\pi < Z + \theta_2 - \theta_1 < 0) = \langle \tfrac{1}{2} [1 - \text{sgn}(Z + \theta_2 - \theta_1)] \rangle$$

$$= \tfrac{1}{2} \left[1 - \frac{1}{2\pi} \iint_{-\infty}^{+\infty} \frac{\partial \Phi(u_1, u_2)}{\partial Z} \cdot \frac{du_1 du_2}{u_1 u_2} \right]$$

$$(2.17)$$

Results like this that refer to statistical properties of a phase variable (reduced modulo 2π) can be described as transparent to any nonlinear operation that preserves phase (such as hard limiting) because the bivariate characteristic function used in the integral may be calculated for the signal in question or its modified form after the nonlinearity — whichever is the more convenient.* Further, R_1 and R_2 can be swapped (as is clear from eqn. 2.16), $\Phi(u_1, u_2)$ being the same for $R_1 \cos[\omega_0 t + \theta_1]$ and $R_2 \cos[\omega_0 t + \theta_2]$ as for $R_2 \cos[\omega_0 t + \theta_1]$ and $R_1 \cos[\omega_0 t + \theta_2]$.

A general integral result that is useful when $\Phi(u_1, u_2)$ has a product form as in eqn. 2.9 is

$$\frac{1}{2\pi} \iint_{-\infty}^{+\infty} \frac{\partial}{\partial Z} \{J_0 [\{(u_1 R_1)^2 + (u_2 R_2)^2 + 2u_1 u_2 R_1 R_2 \cos(\Delta + Z)\}^{1/2}]$$

$$\exp -\tfrac{1}{2}[K_1 u_1^2 + K_2 u_2^2 + 2C\sqrt{K_1 K_2} u_1 u_2 \cos Z]\} \frac{du_1 du_2}{u_1 u_2}$$

$$= \frac{1}{\gamma} \sin(\Delta + Z) \frac{R_1 R_2}{2\alpha} I_e\left(\frac{\beta}{\alpha}, \alpha\right) + \frac{1}{\gamma} \sin Z \cdot C\sqrt{K_1 K_2}\, e^{-\alpha} I_0(\beta) \quad (2.18)$$

where

$$\alpha = \frac{K_2 R_1^2 + K_1 R_2^2 - 2R_1 R_2 C\sqrt{K_1 K_2} \cos Z \cos(\Delta + Z)}{4\gamma^2}$$

$$\beta = \frac{\{[C(K_2 R_1^2 + K_1 R_2^2)\cos Z - 2R_1 R_2 \sqrt{K_1 K_2}\cos(\Delta + Z)]^2 + (K_2 R_1^2 - K_1 R_2^2)^2(1 - C^2 \cos^2 Z)\}^{1/2}}{4\gamma^2}$$

$$\gamma = \sqrt{K_1 K_2}\,\{1 - C^2 \cos^2 Z\}^{1/2}$$

The method of derivation is illustrated by the steps leading from eqn. 3.30 to eqns. 3.35 and 3.36. $I_0(x)$ is a modified Bessel function of order zero, while $I_e(k, x)$ is a tabulated integral (see the Appendix and eqn. 3.40). For $K_2 = C = 0$, the right hand side of eqn. 2.18 simplifies to

$$\mathrm{erf}\left[\frac{R_1}{\sqrt{2K_1}} \sin(\Delta + Z)\right] \quad \text{where} \quad \mathrm{erf}\, x = \frac{2}{\sqrt{\pi}} \int_0^x e^{-u^2}\, du$$

Using eqn. 2.15 it may also be shown that

$$\iint_0^\infty \frac{\partial J_0[\{x^2 + y^2 + 2xy \cos(Z + \gamma)\}^{1/2}]}{\partial Z} \frac{dxdy}{xy}$$

$$= -2 \sum_{m=1}^\infty \frac{\sin m(Z + \gamma + \pi)}{m} \quad (2.19)$$

$$= Z + \gamma \quad (2.20)$$

* This signal could be the carrier of a hybrid modulation method in which (independent) modulations are imposed on the amplitude and phase

here $Z + \gamma$ is an angle lying in $-\pi$ to π and the result may be compared with eqns. 2.14 and 2.17.

When angles are reduced modulo 2π, their probability density functions become periodic (with a period 2π), and there are occasions when we require to calculate the probability that such an angle lies in the sector defined by angles α and β ($\beta > \alpha$, α and β lying in $-\pi$ to π).

2.4 Distribution of angles reduced modulo 2π

Now, any density function $p(x)$ (with $-\infty < x < +\infty$) can be expressed as follows

$$p(x) = \int_{-\infty}^{+\infty} \delta(x - y) p(y) \, dy \tag{2.21}$$

and so may be interpreted as the expected value of the Dirac delta function $\delta(x - y)$. The counterpart of eqn. 2.21 for an angle θ which is reduced modulo 2π is

$$p(\theta) = \langle \sum_{k=-\infty}^{+\infty} \delta(\theta_a - 2k\pi - \theta) \rangle \tag{2.22}$$

where the expectation refers to values of θ_a which is the angle in question when it is not reduced modulo 2π. Such a sum of Dirac functions has an alternative representation (p. 67 of Reference 2) and

$$p(\theta) = \langle \frac{1}{2\pi} + \frac{1}{\pi} \sum_{k=1}^{\infty} \cos k(\theta_a - \theta) \rangle \tag{2.23}$$

so

$$\int_{\alpha}^{\beta} p(\theta) d\theta = \left(\frac{\beta - \alpha}{2\pi} \right) - \langle \frac{1}{\pi} \sum_{k=1}^{\infty} \frac{\sin k(\theta_a - \beta)}{k} \rangle + \langle \frac{1}{\pi} \sum_{k=1}^{\infty} \frac{\sin k(\theta_a - \alpha)}{k} \rangle$$

Using eqn. 2.19 $\tag{2.24}$

$$\int_{\alpha}^{\beta} p(\theta) d\theta = \left(\frac{\beta - \alpha}{2\pi} \right) + \frac{1}{2\pi} \iint_{0}^{\infty} \frac{\partial}{\partial \alpha}$$

$$\langle J_0 [\{x^2 + y^2 + 2xy \cos(\alpha - \theta_a + \pi)\}^{1/2}] \rangle \frac{dxdy}{xy}$$

$$- \frac{1}{2\pi} \iint_{0}^{\infty} \frac{\partial}{\partial \beta}$$

$$\langle J_0 [\{x^2 + y^2 + 2xy \cos(\beta - \theta_a + \pi)\}^{1/2}] \rangle \frac{dxdy}{xy}$$

$$\tag{2.25}$$

It is clear that the right-hand sides of eqns. 2.24 or 2.25 are not affected if the averaging is carried out with θ_a replaced by a θ angle as θ_a appears only in the argument of cosines, and thus it is evident that operations of differentiation and integration can be directly applied to the bivariate characteristic functions listed earlier in order to calculate the distribution of angles reduced modulo 2π.

Recalling eqn. 2.20, an alternative version of eqn. 2.25 is

$$\int_\alpha^\beta p(\theta)\, d\theta = \left(\frac{\beta - \alpha}{2\pi}\right) - \frac{1}{2\pi}\langle [\theta_a - \alpha - \pi] - [\theta_a - \beta - \pi]\rangle \tag{2.26}$$

where $[\theta_a - \alpha - \pi]$ and $[\theta_a - \beta - \pi]$ are angles lying in $-\pi$ to π and here, also, θ_a can be replaced by θ. $[\theta - \pi]$ will equal $\theta - \pi$ when θ is positive but when θ is negative its value will be $\pi + \theta$ and so with $\alpha = 0$ and $\beta = \pi$ (which gives the probability that θ is positive) the right-hand side of eqn. 2.25 becomes

$$\tfrac{1}{2} + \tfrac{1}{2}\langle \operatorname{sgn}(\theta)\rangle$$

However, in this case the expectation of the signum can be determined from eqn. 2.17, and this proves to be the easier approach when only the sign of an angle is of interest.

2.5 Zero-memory nonlinearity

Another result which will be required concerns the response of a zero memory nonlinearity to a Gaussian input. On writing the input-output relationship as

$$y(t) = F[x(t)] \tag{2.27}$$

the autocorrelation function of $y(t)$ is given by

$$R_y(\tau) = \langle y(t)y(t + \tau)\rangle = \langle F[x(t)] \cdot F[x(t + \tau)]\rangle \tag{2.28}$$

To progress further it is necessary to write $F(x)$ in a way that shows an explicit dependence on x. When $x(t)$ is a Gaussian variable a series of Hermite polynomials can then be particularly appropriate (Reference 3) but here we assume the following relationship

$$F(x) = \int_{-\infty}^{+\infty} f(z)\cdot e^{jxz}\, dz \tag{2.29}$$

and profit from the many cases in which the integral is known, $f(z)$ being the Fourier transform of $F(x)$.

Then

$$R_y(\tau) = \iint_{-\infty}^{+\infty} f(u_1)f(u_2)\,\Phi(u_1, u_2)\,du_1\,du_2 \qquad (2.30)$$

where $\Phi(u_1, u_2)$ is the joint characteristic function of $x(t)$ and $x(t + \tau)$. When these are zero mean Gaussian variates with the autocorrelation function $\psi(\tau)$

$$\Phi(u_1, u_2) = \langle \exp j\,[u_1 x(t) + u_2 x(t + \tau)]\rangle$$
$$= \exp -\tfrac{1}{2}\,[\psi(0)(u_1^2 + u_2^2) + 2\psi(\tau)u_1 u_2] \qquad (2.31)$$

$R_y(\tau)$ is seen to be a function of $\psi(0)$ and $\psi(\tau)$, and the development leading to eqn. 2.30 is often called the characteristic function method.[1,3,11]

The double integral is particularly easy to evaluate when $f(z)$ consists of Dirac delta functions and a case in point is

$$f(z) = \tfrac{1}{2}\,[\delta(z - A_1) + \delta(z + A_1)] \qquad (2.32)$$

which corresponds to $F(x) = \cos(A_1 x)$. This trigonometric nonlinearity is frequently encountered in f.m. and p.m. problems, and then

$$R_y(\tau) = \tfrac{1}{4}[\Phi(A_1, A_1) + \Phi(A_1, -A_1) + \Phi(-A_1, A_1) + \Phi(-A_1, -A_1)]$$
$$= \exp - [A_1^2 \psi(0)]\,\cosh\,[A_1^2 \psi(\tau)] \qquad (2.33)$$

when $\Phi(u_1, u_2)$ has the form of eqn. 2.31. Similarly, $F(x) = \sin(A_1 x)$ has the autocorrelation function

$$\exp - [A_1^2 \psi(0)]\,\sinh\,[A_1^2 \psi(\tau)]$$

If

$$y(t) = \sum_{n=0}^{\infty} a_n [x(t)]^n$$

the general result[4] is

$$R_y(\tau) = \sum_{q=0}^{\infty} B_q^2\,\frac{1}{q!}\,[\psi(\tau)]^q \qquad (2.34)$$

where

$$B_q = \sum_{h=0}^{\infty} a_{q+2h}\,\frac{(q + 2h)!}{2^h h!}\,[\psi(0)]^h$$

The aim of much of the work to come is to derive a series like eqn. 2.34 and then to obtain the corresponding power spectrum $W_y(\omega)$ through eqn. 1.6. Thus

$$W_y(\omega) = \sum_{q=0}^{\infty} B_q^2\,\frac{1}{q!}\,\frac{2}{\pi}\int_0^{\infty} [\psi(\tau)]^q\,\cos \omega\tau\,d\tau \qquad (2.35)$$

Integrals of the type appearing in eqn. 2.35 have received considerable study[5-7] and can be handled without difficulty for many forms of

$\psi(\tau)$. A useful result[7] corresponding to the case in which the power spectrum of $x(t)$, $W_x(\omega)$, is flat from d.c. to an angular frequency p_m [so making $\psi(\tau)/\psi(0) = \sin p_m \tau/(p_m \tau)$] is

$$\frac{2}{\pi} \int_0^\infty \left(\frac{\sin x}{x}\right)^q \cos(xy)\, dx = \frac{q}{2^{q-1}} \sum_{0 \leqslant r < \frac{y+q}{2}} (-1)^r \frac{[y+q-2r]^{q-1}}{r!(q-r)!}$$

$$(0 \leqslant y < q)$$
$$= 0 \qquad \text{otherwise} \qquad (2.36)$$

Alternatively, $W_y(\omega)$ can be developed as follows:

$$W_y(\omega) = 2B_0^2 \delta(\omega) + B_1^2 W_x(\omega) + \frac{B_2^2}{4} \int_0^\infty W_x(y_1)$$

$$[W_x(|\omega - y_1|) + W_x(\omega + y_1)]\, dy_1$$

$$+ \frac{B_3^2}{24} \iint_0^\infty W_x(y_1) W_x(y_2)[W_x(\omega + y_1 + y_2)$$

$$+ 2W_x(|\omega + y_1 - y_2|) + W_x(|\omega - y_1 - y_2|) dy_1 dy_2$$

$$+ \dots \qquad (2.37)$$

Here the leading term involving the Dirac delta corresponds to a d.c. component in $y(t)$, while the convolution integrals refer to the spectra of successively higher-order distortions of $x(t)$. Note that the undistorted component is multiplied by B_1^2 (in most of the examples to be considered $x(t)$ represents a signal that is to receive as little modification as possible as a result of being applied to the nonlinearity, and it is convenient to refer to $W_x(\omega)$ as the power spectrum of the undistorted or the wanted signal) consequently it is important that the coefficient B_1^2 should be large.

When the component parts of an f.m. or p.m. system are under investigation the combined effect of filtering and the presence of nonlinear elements can lead to nonlinearities that are frequency dependent and so are of a more complicated nature than the zero-memory power series device just treated. The output power spectrum can still be developed in a form such as eqn. 2.37 but the characteristic function method becomes less applicable and a technique known as a Volterra series approach is more fruitful.[3, 8-10] This technique is described in Chapter 7, and it leads to convolution-type integrals that are more complicated than those shown in eqn. 2.37 and B_1^2 usually turns out to depend on ω.

The term $B_1^2(\omega) . W_x(\omega)$ that then appears in the expression for the output power spectrum can be viewed as referring to a filtered version of $x(t)$, the filter in question having a power transfer characteristic given by $B_1^2(\omega)$, and $B_1^2(\omega)$ will be called a coherence factor.

2.6 Application to narrow-band waveforms

Cases are frequently encountered in which interest lies in the power spectrum of the envelope or of the hard-limited version of narrow-band waveforms, and knowledge of $\Phi(u_1, u_2)$ evaluated for $V(t)$ as given by eqn. 1.1 is the key to handling such problems.[11] In the case of the envelope, let

$$V_E(t) = \frac{V(t)}{2} \{1 + \text{sgn} [V(t)]\} \tag{2.38}$$

where $\text{sgn}(x) = +1$ if $x > 0$, -1 if $x < 0$ and is zero if $x = 0$. Then, by extracting the zero'th harmonic terms in $\omega_0 t$ (the low-frequency zone) from $V_E(t)$, the envelope $R(t)$ (or $[P^2(t) + Q^2(t)]^{1/2}$) is obtained

On applying the characteristic function method to $V_E(t)$ [$f(z)$ in eqn. 2.29 can be taken to be $1/j\pi z$ as this provides a convenient integral representation for $\text{sgn}(x)$. The principal value of the integral is to be taken, and this form is also used in eqn. 3.15 of Section 3.1], $R_E(\tau)$ the autocorrelation function of the envelope is obtained by extracting the zero'th harmonic term in $\omega_0 \tau$ from

$$\frac{1}{(2\pi)^2} \iint_{-\infty}^{+\infty} \frac{\Phi(u_1, u_2)}{(u_1 . u_2)^2} \, du_1 du_2 \tag{2.39}$$

This integral will not converge as it stands but removal of its limiting value as $\tau \to \infty$ will ensure convergence. This behaviour is due to the d.c. component which the envelope contains and which causes $R_E(\tau)$ to be finite when τ becomes infinitely large.

The autocorrelation function of the hard-limited version of a narrow-band signal is given by a very similar double integral that can be obtained as follows

Let
$$V_H(t) = \text{sgn} [V(t)] \tag{2.40}$$

Then $V_H(t)$ will contain frequency components that cluster around odd harmonics of $\omega_0 t$, and by accepting just the first-harmonic zone of this signal the result of hard limiting $V(t)$, i.e.

$$\frac{4}{\pi} \cos\left(\omega_0 t + \tan^{-1} \frac{Q(t)}{P(t)}\right)$$

in the case of eqn. 1.1, is obtained.

Applying the characteristic function method with the same integral representation as before for sgn(x), $R_H(\tau)$ the required autocorrelation function is obtained by extracting the first harmonic term in $\omega_0\tau$ from

$$-\frac{1}{\pi^2} \iint_{-\infty}^{+\infty} \frac{\Phi(u_1, u_2)}{u_1 u_2} du_1 du_2 \qquad (2.41)$$

Eqns. 2.39 and 2.41 are cases of eqn. 2.30 with the added instruction that particular harmonics of $\omega_0\tau$ are to be extracted and the similarity of eqn. 2.41 to eqns. 2.14 and 2.17 is to be noted. There is a difference in the mode of time averaging to be observed when calculating functions for insertion into these various integrals. An average over many cycles of $\cos \omega_0 t$ is always taken (the rapid variations are smoothed out) but eqn. 2.17 uses a characteristic function calculated at some definite point in time, typically a sampling instant of the waveforms $\theta(t)$ or $\dot{\theta}(t)$, while the functions to be used in eqns. 2.39 and 2.41 are the result of averaging over all time.

An example may help to illustrate this style of analysis and $R_H(\tau)$ for narrow-band noise will be calculated. Then (see eqn. 2.12)

$$\Phi(u_1, u_2) = \exp -\tfrac{1}{2} [\psi_N(0)(u_1^2 + u_2^2) + 2u_1 u_2 \psi_N(\tau) \cos \omega_0\tau]$$

$$= \exp -\tfrac{1}{2} [\psi_N(0)(u_1^2 + u_2^2)] \sum_{m=-\infty}^{+\infty} I_m(-u_1 u_2 \psi_N(\tau)) e^{jm\omega_0\tau} \qquad (2.42)$$

The required first harmonic terms are those for $m = \pm 1$, and, so, from eqn. 2.41

$$R_H(\tau) = \frac{2}{\pi^2} \iint_{-\infty}^{+\infty} \frac{I_1(u_1 u_2 \psi_N(\tau))}{u_1 u_2}$$

$$\exp -\left[\frac{\psi_N(0)}{2} (u_1^2 + u_2^2) \right] du_1 du_2 \cos \omega_0\tau \qquad (2.43)$$

Using the power series expansion of $I_1(x)$

$$R_H(\tau) = \frac{2}{\pi} \sum_{q=0}^{\infty} \left[\frac{\psi_N(\tau)}{\psi_N(0)} \right]^{2q+1} \frac{1}{(q+1)} \left(\frac{1}{2^{2q}} \binom{2q}{q} \right)^2 \cos \omega_0\tau \qquad (2.44)$$

The spectrum then follows as in eqn. 2.35, and if the amplitude after hard limiting is K the above is to be multiplied by $(K\pi/4)^2$.

When the noise accompanies a signal, $\Phi(u_1, u_2)$ has the form shown in eqn. 2.10 or 2.12. The working is more complicated (eqn. 13.83 of Reference 12) but a comparison of eqns. 2.41 and 2.18 then shows, formally, that the coefficient of $\sin Z$ (Z, it will be remembered, stands for $\omega_0\tau$) when extracted from the right-hand side of eqn. 2.18, and appropriately averaged, gives the expression corresponding to the series of eqn. 2.44.

2.7 References

1 RICE, S.O.: 'Mathematical analysis of random noise', *Bell Syst. Tech. J.* 1944, **23**, pp. 282–332 and 1945, **24**, pp. 46–157
2 LIGHTHILL, M.J.: 'Introduction to Fourier analysis and generalized functions' (Cambridge University Press, 1960)
3 DEUTSCH, R.: 'Non-linear transformations of random processes'. (Prentice Hall Applied Mathematics Series, 1962)
4 CODELUPI, R.: 'Spectral density of cross modulation noise', *Alta Freq.*, 1956, **25**, pp. 38–64
5 BENNETT, W.R., CURTIS, H.E., and RICE, S.O.: 'Interchannel interference in FM and PM systems under noise loading conditions'. *Bell Syst. Tech. J.,* 1955, **34**, pp. 601–636
6 ERDELYI, A. (Ed.) 'Tables of integral transforms – Vol. 1' (McGraw-Hill, 1954)
7 MEDHURST. R.G., and ROBERTS, J.H.: 'Evaluation of the integral
$$I_n(b) = \frac{2}{\pi} \int_0^\infty \left(\frac{\sin x}{x}\right)^n \cos bx \, dx\text{'}, \textit{Math. Comput.}, 1965, \mathbf{19}, (89),$$
pp. 113–117
8 ZADEH, L.A.: 'On the representation of non-linear operators' 1957 IRE WESCON Conference Record, Vol. 1, Pt. 2, pp. 105–113
9 BEDROSIAN, E., and RICE, S.O.: 'The output properties of Volterra Systems (Non-linear systems with memory) driven by harmonic and Gaussian inputs', *Proc. IEEE,* 1971, **59**, (12), pp. 1688–1707
10 MOJOLI, L.: 'Analysis of angle modulated transmission systems and identification of their Volterra Series'. *Alta Freq.* 1972, **41**, pp. 252–262 (82E–92E)
11 ROBERTS, J.H.: 'Autocorrelation functions arising in analysis of narrowband systems and their representation in terms of characteristic function', *Electron. Lett.,* 1970, **6**, (26), pp. 863–864
12 MIDDLETON, D.: 'An introduction to statistical communication theory' (McGraw-Hill, 1960)

Chapter 3

Instantaneous frequency

3.1 Zero-crossing approach

An oscillator is a device which provides at its output a steady wave represented as follows

$$V(t) = A \cos [\omega_0 t + \phi] \tag{3.1}$$

ϕ will be called the phase, although $\omega_0 t + \phi$ would more usually be given this title when ϕ is constant. The wave has zeros that are regularly spaced every π/ω_0 seconds, and its angular frequency is ω_0 rad/s.

A familiar interpretation of eqn. 3.1 is as a rotating vector in an Argand diagram, the value taken by $V(t)$ at any time being given by the projection of the vector on the horizontal axis. ϕ may suffer the addition or subtraction of any integer multiple of 2π radians without changing the value of $V(t)$, and when ϕ appears only in the argument of trigonometric functions it is usual to refer to it as a phase angle reduced modulo 2π.

When ϕ is constant the rate at which the vector rotates in the Argand diagram is ω_0 but taking our development a stage further to the case in which ϕ varies with time it is a natural extension to define $\dfrac{d}{dt}[\omega_0 t + \phi(t)]$ as the instantaneous frequency, $\omega_i(t)$.

$$\omega_i(t) = \omega_0 + \dot{\phi}(t) \tag{3.2}$$

The phase change that occurs between two neighbouring times t_1 and t_2 is given by $\int_{t_1}^{t_2} \dot{\phi}(x)dx = \phi(t_2) - \phi(t_1)$ but here $\phi(t_2) - \phi(t_1)$ is the absolute change in phase (not the change reduced modulo 2π) and so an integer multiple (positive or negative) of 2π may be included in $\phi(t_2) - \phi(t_1)$ corresponding to the net number of circulations of the origin executed by the moving point during t_1 to t_2.

Accordingly, the f.m. wave is written

$$V_{FM}(t) = A \cos\left[\omega_0 t + \int_{t_0}^{t} \dot{\phi}(y)dy \right] \qquad (3.3)$$

where t_0 is arbitrary. It may seem pedantic to show the integral of a derivative but in transmitting information by f.m. the message is identified with $\dot{\phi}(t)$ and an f.m. modulator is a device that can vary the frequency of an oscillator linearly according to eqn. 3.2 so producing the wave shown in eqn. 3.3.

Applying eqn. 3.2 to the general narrow-band wave shown in eqn. 1.1 gives

$$\begin{aligned} \omega_i(t) &= \omega_0 + \frac{d}{dt}\left\{ \tan^{-1}\left[\frac{Q(t)}{P(t)} \right] \right\} \\ &= \omega_0 + \left[\frac{P(t)\dot{Q}(t) - Q(t)\dot{P}(t)}{P^2(t) + Q^2(t)} \right] \end{aligned} \qquad (3.4)$$

A consequence of allowing ϕ to become time dependent is that the zero crossings of the wave no longer have a perfect regularity in their spacing, the narrow-band assumption means that the modulation represents only a small disturbance and so the zeros are, in general, only slightly perturbed. Since this jittering of the zero crossings is directly attributable to the modulation it should be possible to retrieve $\phi(t)$, the message waveform, from a record of where the crossings occur but this feature of f.m., although well recognised, has received little theoretical attention compared to the widespread use of eqn. 3.4. We shall show how it can be exploited to obtain a result very similar to eqn. 3.4.

Suppose that zeros occur at the successive times $t_1, t_2, t_3, \ldots, t_{N+1}$, so that

$$\left. \begin{aligned} \omega_0 t_1 + \phi(t_1) &= \pi/2 \\ \omega_0 t_2 + \phi(t_2) &= \pi/2 + \pi \\ \omega_0 t_3 + \phi(t_3) &= \pi/2 + 2\pi \\ \omega_0 t_{N+1} + \phi(t_{N+1}) &= \pi/2 + N \cdot \pi \end{aligned} \right\} \qquad (3.5)$$

If these zeros span the time period T_1 a density of zero crossings can be defined by forming N/T_1 and this ratio will depend to some extent on the particular portion of the waveform that has been examined. From the first and last of eqn. 3.5

$$\frac{N(T_1)}{T_1} = \frac{1}{\pi}\left[\omega_0 + \frac{\phi(t_{N+1}) - \phi(t_1)}{t_{N+1} - t_1} \right] \qquad (3.6)$$

Now, the narrow-band assumption means that when $N(T_1)$ is large, so that the left-hand side of eqn. 3.6 is a good estimate of the density of zeros, the change in $\phi(t)$ over the period t_1 to t_{N+1} will be sufficiently small for the right-hand side to be replaced by

$$\frac{1}{\pi} [\omega_0 + \dot\phi(t)]$$

where (by the mean-value theorem) t is an instant of time lying in the interval t_1 to t_{N+1}. Halving both sides then gives

$$\frac{1}{2} \left(\frac{N(T_1)}{T_1} \right) = \left[\frac{\omega_0 + \dot\phi(t)}{2\pi} \right] \tag{3.7}$$

and the form of this result prompted Stumpers[1] to define the instantaneous frequency (in Hz), at time t, as one half the ratio of the number of zeros in the time interval $t - T_1/2$ to $t + T_1/2$, to T_1.

To investigate this definition more fully some means of counting the zeros that are contained in a specified time interval is required. If $V(t)$ has a zero at a point $t = t_0$ in the interval $t - T_1/2$ to $t + T_1/2$ then $V(t_0 - h/2)$ and $V(t_0 + h/2)$ will be of opposite sign when the time step h is sufficiently small. This observation will be used to place a rectangle of width h and height $1/h$ on each zero so that by integrating across the time interval in question the number of zeros will be obtained.

This way of assessing $N(T_1)$ is rather more direct than the ingenious method originally used by Stumpers (who, in turn, credits Mann[2] with the basic ideas) and it has advantages when we come to calculate the autocorrelation function of $\omega_i(t)$.

To achieve the objective of forming an expression for $N(T_1)$, the following counting function is introduced

$$C(t_0) = \frac{1}{2} \left[1 - \text{sgn} \left\{ V\left(t_0 - \frac{h}{2}\right) V\left(t_0 + \frac{h}{2}\right) \right\} \right] \tag{3.8}$$

Then

$$N(T_1) = \lim_{h \to 0} \frac{1}{h} \int_{t-\frac{1}{2}T_1}^{t+\frac{1}{2}T_1} \frac{1}{2} \left[1 - \text{sgn} \left\{ V\left(t_0 - \frac{h}{2}\right) V\left(t_0 + \frac{h}{2}\right) \right\} \right] dt_0 \tag{3.9}$$

and so, using eqn. 3.7

$$\omega_i(t) = \lim_{h \to 0} \frac{\pi}{T_1} \left\{ \frac{1}{h} \int_{t-\frac{1}{2}T_1}^{t+\frac{1}{2}T_1} \frac{1}{2} \left[1 - \text{sgn} \left\{ V\left(t_0 - \frac{h}{2}\right) V\left(t_0 + \frac{h}{2}\right) \right\} \right] dt_0 \right\} \tag{3.10}$$

The limit as $h \to 0$ is taken in order to ensure that every zero is netted but in cases where the zeros are only slightly disturbed from a regular spacing, $h = \pi/4\omega_0$ for example, would seem adequate, but analytical results are easiest to express when h is reduced to zero.

When viewed as a function of t_0, $(1/h)C(t_0)$ consists of a sequence of unit area rectangles of height $1/h$, spaced nearly uniformly, and centred on the zeros of $V(t)$ that occur in $t - T_1/2$ to $t + T_1/2$. Correspondingly,

$$C(t_0) = K_0(t_0) + K_2(t_0) \cos [2\omega_0 t_0 + \beta(t_0)]$$
$$+ K_4(t_0) \cos [2(2\omega_0 t_0 + \beta(t_0))] + \ldots \quad (3.11)$$

where the Ks and $\beta(t_0)$ (see below eqn. 3.16) are functions of the slowly varying in-phase and quadrature signal components and are almost constant throughout the interval of length T_1. Thus

$$\omega_i(t) = \lim_{h \to 0} \frac{\pi}{h} \cdot \frac{1}{T_1} \int_{t-T_1/2}^{t+T_1/2} K_0(t_0) dt_0 + 0 \left(\frac{1}{\omega_0}\right)$$
$$\approx \lim_{h \to 0} \frac{\pi K_0(t)}{h} \quad (3.12)$$

Now, if we define a waveform $W_i(t)$ as follows

$$W_i(t) = \frac{\pi}{2h} \left[1 - \text{sgn} \left\{ V\left(t - \frac{h}{2}\right) V\left(t + \frac{h}{2}\right) \right\} \right] \quad (3.13)$$

then eqn. 3.12 shows that the instantaneous frequency $\omega_i(t)$ can be obtained by averaging $W_i(t)$ over the time period T_1, thus smoothing out the rapidly varying terms, and then taking a limit as $h \to 0$. This smoothing can also be viewed as a filtering operation in which the terms having frequencies $2\omega_0$, $4\omega_0$ etc. are removed from $W_i(t)$ (terms of such high frequency will not, in any case, play any part in the analysis) and in much of the working to follow $W_i(t)$ is used rather than $\omega_i(t)$ because eqn. 3.13 provides a direct link between the general narrow-band waveform $V(t)$ and the instantaneous frequency.

To reassure the reader that this unconventional view is in accord with the more familiar formulation of instantaneous frequency given in eqn. 3.4, it is convenient to have an integral representation of the signum function such as

$$\text{sgn}(x) = \frac{2}{\pi} \int_0^\infty \frac{\sin(xy)}{y} dy \quad (3.14)$$

If $\displaystyle\int_{-\infty}^{+\infty} \frac{\cos(xy)}{y} dy$ is defined to be zero (that is, the principal value is accepted) then a more convenient form still is obtained. This is

$$\text{sgn}(x) = \frac{1}{\pi} \int_{-\infty}^{+\infty} \left(\frac{e^{jxy}}{jy} \right) dy \qquad (3.15)$$

With $V(t) = P(t) \cos \omega_0 t - Q(t) \sin \omega_0 t$, as in eqn. 1.1

$$V\left(t - \frac{h}{2}\right) V\left(t + \frac{h}{2}\right) = \tfrac{1}{2} R_- R_+ \{\cos \alpha(t) + \cos [2\omega_0 t + \beta(t)]\}$$

where $\qquad (3.16)$

$$R_-^2 = P^2\left(t - \frac{h}{2}\right) + Q^2\left(t - \frac{h}{2}\right)$$

$$R_+^2 = P^2\left(t + \frac{h}{2}\right) + Q^2\left(t + \frac{h}{2}\right)$$

$$\alpha(t) = \omega_0 h + \tan^{-1}\left[\frac{Q(t + h/2)}{P(t + h/2)}\right] - \tan^{-1}\left[\frac{Q(t - h/2)}{P(t - h/2)}\right]$$

$$\beta(t) = \tan^{-1}\left[\frac{Q(t + h/2)}{P(t + h/2)}\right] + \tan^{-1}\left[\frac{Q(t - h/2)}{P(t - h/2)}\right]$$

Then, when eqn. 3.15 is used to represent the signum function appearing in eqn. 3.10 the integrand will contain $\exp [jyV(t - h/2) V(t + h/2)]$ and this may be expanded (using eqn. 3.16) into a series of even harmonics of $\omega_0 t$, as was the case with eqn. 3.11. The zero'th harmonic component (see eqn. 2.3) is

$$J_0\left(y\frac{R_+ . R_-}{2}\right) \exp\left[jy\frac{R_+ . R_-}{2} \cos \alpha(t)\right] \qquad (3.17)$$

Consequently, from eqn. 3.10

$$\omega_i(t) = \lim_{h \to 0} \frac{1}{h} \left\{ \frac{\pi}{2} - \int_0^\infty \frac{J_0(y)}{y} \sin [y \cos \alpha(t)] \, dy \right\} \qquad (3.18)$$

The integral is an even function of $\alpha(t)$ and has the value $\pi/2 - |\alpha(t)|$. Thus

$$\omega_i(t) = \lim_{h \to 0} \left| \frac{\alpha(t)}{h} \right|$$

$$= \lim_{h \to 0} \frac{1}{h} \left| \omega_0 h + \tan^{-1}\left\{\frac{Q(t + h/2)}{P(t + h/2)}\right\} - \tan^{-1}\left\{\frac{Q(t - h/2)}{P(t - h/2)}\right\} \right|$$

$$= \left| \omega_0 + \frac{P(t)\dot{Q}(t) - Q(t)\dot{P}(t)}{P^2(t) + Q^2(t)} \right| \qquad (3.19)$$

Clearly, when ω_0 is so large that the modulus signs can be dispensed with complete agreement with eqn. 3.4 is achieved, and since in many of the results to be quoted the centre frequency plays no part it is then convenient to regard ω_0 as being infinitely large.

There are other occasions, however, when the presence of the modulus signs in eqn. 3.19 can give rise to (usually small) perturbations of the results that would be achieved using eqn. 3.4.

3.2 Expected number of zeros per unit time

Before dealing with some of the statistical properties of the instantaneous frequency $\omega_i(t)$ it is appropriate to consider the closely related statistics of $N(T)$ the number of zeros that lie in a time interval of specified length.

Through eqn. 3.9 a means is available for counting the zeros that occur in a time period T^*, and on dividing by T, $N(T)/T$, the number of zeros occurring per unit time, can be simply expressed. Then by suitably averaging this ratio, the expected number of zeros per unit time Z_0 may be calculated. Using eqns. 3.9, 3.13 and assuming h to be sufficiently small

$$\frac{N(T)}{T} = \frac{1}{\pi} \cdot \frac{1}{T} \int_{-T/2}^{T/2} W_i(t + x)\,dx \qquad (3.20)$$

where the time interval in question is $t - T/2$ to $t + T/2$. $W_i(t)$ is given by eqn. 3.13, and eqn. 3.20 holds irrespective of whether $V(t)$, the waveform whose zeros are to be counted, is of the narrow-band variety or not. Provided the statistical features of $W_i(t)$ do not vary with time, i.e. $W_i(t)$ is stationary, we have

$$Z_0 = \langle \frac{N(T)}{T} \rangle = \langle \frac{W_i(t)}{\pi} \rangle \qquad (3.21)$$

From eqn. 3.13,

$$\langle \frac{W_i(t)}{\pi} \rangle = \frac{1}{h} [1 - P_2(t - h/2, t + h/2)]$$

where $P_2(t - h/2, t + h/2)$ is the probability that two samples of $V(t)$, spaced in time by h, are of the same sign. h is to be made so small that no zeros are missed by the counting process, so

$$Z_0 = \lim_{h \to 0} \left[\frac{1 - P_2(h)}{h} \right] \qquad (3.22)$$

Here $P_2(h)$ stands for $P_2(t - h/2, t + h/2)$ and emphasises the assumption that P_2 depends only upon the time spacing h. A rather more

*T is general here

convenient form of eqn. 3.22 is obtained by applying L'Hôpital's rule, then

$$Z_0 = \lim_{h \to 0} (Z_h) \quad \text{where} \quad Z_h = -\frac{\partial P_2(h)}{\partial h} \qquad (3.23)$$

To evaluate eqn. 3.23 in particular cases it is expedient to express $P_2(h)$ in terms of $\Phi(u_1, u_2)$ the joint characteristic function of $V(t - h/2)$ and $V(t + h/2)$. Noting that sgn $(a \cdot b) = $ sgn $a \cdot$ sgn b

$$\tfrac{1}{2} [1 - \text{sgn} \{V(t - h/2) \, V(t + h/2)\}]$$
$$= \frac{1}{2} + \frac{1}{2\pi^2} \iint_{-\infty}^{+\infty} \frac{\exp j \{u_1 V(t - h/2) + u_2 V(t + h/2)\}}{u_1 u_2} du_1 du_2$$
$$(3.24)$$

where the representation of sgn (x) given in eqn. 3.15 has been used. Thus

$$P_2(h) = \frac{1}{2} - \frac{1}{2\pi^2} \iint_{-\infty}^{+\infty} \frac{\Phi(u_1, u_2)}{u_1 u_2} du_1 du_2 \qquad (3.25)$$

and

$$Z_h = \frac{1}{2\pi^2} \iint_{-\infty}^{+\infty} \frac{\partial \Phi(u_1, u_2)}{\partial h} \frac{du_1 du_2}{u_1 u_2} \qquad (3.26)$$

This is a general result, and by a simple extension the expected number of upward and downward crossings per unit time of a level L is given by including $\exp jL(u_1 + u_2)$ in the integrand of eqn. 3.26. The forms for $\Phi(u_1, u_2)$ listed in Chapter 2 can now be used to evaluate eqn. 3.26 and then, on taking the limit as $h \to 0$, the final result for Z_0 is obtained. Two important examples of this calculation are now given.

3.3 Expected number of zeros per unit time of the sum of two independent frequency modulated waves

The expected number of zeros per unit time of the sum of two statistically unrelated frequency modulated waves can be evaluated with the help of $\Phi(u_1, u_2)$ as given in eqn. 2.13.

τ is replaced by h and, as h is ultimately to be reduced to zero, we replace* $\mu(t + h) - \mu(t)$ by $h\dot{\mu}(t)$ and $\alpha(t + h) - \alpha(t)$ by $h\dot{\alpha}(t)$. The assumption that $P_2(h)$ and therefore $\Phi(u_1, u_2)$ is only a function of h is then satisfied if $\dot{\mu}(t)$, and $\dot{\alpha}(t)$ are stationary processes so that the ensemble averages, denoted by the angle brackets in eqn. 2.13, are independent of time.

---

*Working to this order in h is adequate here and shortens the presentation

With eqn. 2.13 in eqn. 3.26, the differentiation with respect to h produces a term involving J_0 and a term involving J_1 (as a result of $J_0' = -J_1$) and the changes of variable $u_1 + u_2 = x, u_1 - u_2 = y$, then prove to be fruitful. The following integral result given by Watson (p. 411 of Reference 3)

$$\int_0^\infty J_1(ax) J_0(bx) J_0(cx)\, dx = \frac{A}{a\pi} \qquad (3.27)$$

A is 0, $\cos^{-1}\left(\dfrac{b^2 + c^2 - a^2}{2bc}\right)$, or π according as a^2 is less than lies

between, or exceeds $(b-c)^2$ and $(b+c)^2$, then produces

$$Z_h = \left\langle \left(\frac{\theta_2}{\pi}\right) \alpha_1(h) + \left(\frac{\theta_1}{\pi}\right) \alpha_2(h) \right\rangle \qquad (3.28)$$

where
$$\theta_1 = \omega_0 + \dot{\mu}(t), \qquad \theta_2 = \omega_0 + \omega_D + \dot{\alpha}(t)$$
and
$$\alpha_1(h) = \left\{ 0, \frac{1}{\pi}\cos^{-1}\left(\frac{1 - \cos(\theta_1 h)\cos(\theta_2 h) - r^2 \sin^2(\theta_2 h)}{|\cos(\theta_1 h) - \cos(\theta_2 h)|}\right) \text{ or } 1 \right\}$$

the choices being taken according as 1 lies below, between, or above

$$\frac{1}{r^2}\left[\frac{1 + \cos(\theta_1 h)}{1 + \cos(\theta_2 h)}\right] \quad \text{and} \quad \frac{1}{r^2}\left[\frac{1 - \cos(\theta_1 h)}{1 - \cos(\theta_2 h)}\right]$$

$$\alpha_2(h) = \left\{ 0, \frac{1}{\pi}\cos^{-1}\left(\frac{r^2[1 - \cos(\theta_1 h)\cos(\theta_2 h)] - \sin^2(\theta_1 h)}{r^2|\cos(\theta_1 h) - \cos(\theta_2 h)|}\right) \text{ or } 1 \right\}$$

the choices being taken according as 1 lies below, between, or above

$$r^2\left[\frac{1 + \cos(\theta_2 h)}{1 + \cos(\theta_1 h)}\right] \quad \text{and} \quad r^2\left[\frac{1 - \cos(\theta_2 h)}{1 - \cos(\theta_1 h)}\right]$$

Taking h down to zero the final result is

$$Z_0 = \left\langle \left(\frac{\theta_2}{\pi}\right) \alpha_1(0) + \left(\frac{\theta_1}{\pi}\right) \alpha_2(0) \right\rangle \qquad (3.29)$$

where
$$\alpha_1(0) = \left\{ 0, \frac{1}{\pi}\cos^{-1}\left[\frac{\theta_1^2 + (1 - 2r^2)\theta_2^2}{|\theta_1^2 - \theta_2^2|}\right] \text{ or } 1 \right\}$$

$$\alpha_2(0) = \left\{ 0, \frac{1}{\pi}\cos^{-1}\left[\frac{r^2(\theta_1^2 + \theta_2^2) - 2\theta_1^2}{r^2|\theta_1^2 - \theta_2^2|}\right] \text{ or } 1 \right\}$$

The choices in $\alpha_1(0)$ are taken according as 1 lies below, between, or above, $1/r^2$ and $[(1/r)(\theta_1/\theta_2)]^2$, and in $\alpha_2(0)$ according as 1 lies below, between, or above r^2 and $(r\theta_2/\theta_1)^2$.

If $\dot{\mu}(t)$ and $\dot{\alpha}(t)$ are constant, the angle brackets of eqn. 3.29 are redundant; a case in which they are easy to implement is when $\dot{\mu}(t)$ and $\dot{\alpha}(t)$ each adopt only two values, the example of binary data considered in Chapter 10.

3.4 Expected number of zeros per unit time of the sum of a pure f.m. signal and narrow-band Gaussian noise

For this case $\Phi(u_1, u_2)$ is given by eqn. 2.12 [with h again replacing τ, and $\mu(t + h) - \mu(t)$ being replaced by $h\,\dot{\mu}(t)$], so

$$\Phi_{S+N}(u_1, u_2) = \langle J_0\left[\sqrt{f_1(\omega_0 h)}\right]\rangle \exp{-f_2(\omega_0 h)} \qquad (3.30)$$

where

$$f_1(\omega_0 h) = A^2\{u_1^2 + u_2^2 + 2u_1 u_2 \cos{[(\omega_0 + \dot{\mu}(t))h]}\}$$

$$f_2(\omega_0 h) = \tfrac{1}{2}\left[\psi_N(0)(u_1^2 + u_2^2) + 2u_1 u_2 \psi_N(h) \cos{(\omega_0 h)}\right]$$

$$\frac{\partial \Phi_{S+N}(u_1, u_2)}{\partial h} = -\langle J_0\left[\sqrt{f_1(\omega_0 h)}\right]\frac{\partial f_2(\omega_0 h)}{\partial h} + \frac{J_1\left[\sqrt{f_1(\omega_0 h)}\right]}{\sqrt{f_1(\omega_0 h)}}$$

$$\cdot \frac{1}{2}\frac{\partial f_1(\omega_0 h)}{\partial h}\rangle \exp{-f_2(\omega_0 h)} \qquad (3.31)$$

with

$$\frac{\partial f_1(\omega_0 h)}{\partial h} = -2u_1 u_2 A^2\left[\omega_0 + \dot{\mu}(t)\right] \sin{[(\omega_0 + \dot{\mu}(t))h]}$$

$$\frac{\partial f_2(\omega_0 h)}{\partial h} = -\omega_0 \psi_N(h) u_1 u_2 \sin{(\omega_0 h)} + \psi_N'(h) u_1 u_2 \cos{(\omega_0 h)}$$

The working is being shown in more detail here because, as will become clear in Chapter 10, the end result has direct application to the exercise of determining the error probability of binary f.m. and p.m. digital signals operating in the presence of narrow-band Gaussian noise.

When eqn. 3.31 is inserted in eqn. 3.26, two basic integrals emerge for consideration. These are:

$$\mathcal{I}_0 = \frac{1}{2\pi}\iint_{-\infty}^{+\infty} J_0\left[\sqrt{f_1(\omega_0 h)}\right] \exp{-f_2(\omega_0 h)}\, du_1 du_2 \qquad (3.32)$$

and

$$\mathcal{I}_1 = \frac{1}{2\pi}\iint_{-\infty}^{+\infty} \frac{J_1\left[\sqrt{f_1(\omega_0 h)}\right]}{\sqrt{f_1(\omega_0 h)}} \exp{-f_2(\omega_0 h)}\, du_1 du_2 \qquad (3.33)$$

As $J_1(x)/x = \int_0^1 v J_0(xv)\,dv$, however, $\mathcal{I}_1$ can be obtained in a simple way once $\mathcal{I}_0$ has been dealt with and again the changes of variables $u_1 + u_2 = x$, $u_1 - u_2 = y$, $2du_1 du_2 = dx\,dy$ are helpful.

An exercise in elementary integration assisted by

$$\int_0^\infty e^{-\lambda x^2} J_0(\alpha x) J_0(\beta x) x\,dx = \frac{1}{2\lambda} \exp -\left(\frac{\alpha^2+\beta^2}{4\lambda}\right) I_0\left(\frac{\alpha\beta}{2\lambda}\right)$$

shows that $\qquad\qquad\qquad\qquad\qquad\qquad\qquad\qquad$ (3.34)

$$\mathcal{G}_0 = \frac{1}{\gamma_1} I_0(\beta_1) \exp -\alpha_1 \qquad (3.35)$$

$$\mathcal{G}_1 = \frac{1}{2\alpha_1\gamma_1} I_e\left(\frac{\beta_1}{\alpha_1}, \alpha_1\right) \qquad (3.36)$$

Where

$$\alpha_1 = \rho\left\{\frac{1 - r_N(h)\cos\omega_0 h \cos\overline{[\omega_0+\dot\mu(t)]h}}{1 - r_N^2(h)\cos^2\omega_0 h}\right\} \qquad (3.37)$$

$$\beta_1 = \rho\left\{\frac{\cos\overline{[\omega_0+\dot\mu(t)]h} - r_N(h)\cos\omega_0 h}{1 - r_N^2(h)\cos^2\omega_0 h}\right\} \qquad (3.38)$$

$$\gamma_1 = \psi_N(0)\{1 - r_N^2(h)\cos^2\omega_0 h\}^{1/2} \qquad (3.39)$$

$$r_N(h) = \frac{\psi_N(h)}{\psi_N(0)}$$

Here $I_e(k, x)$ is defined by

$$I_e(k, x) = \int_0^x e^{-u} I_0(ku)\,du \qquad (3.40)$$

and this function of two variables was used and tabulated by Rice[4] when considering this same problem for the case of an unmodulated carrier plus noise [see the Appendix for a table of $I_e(k,x)$]. Putting these results together and taking the limit as $h \to 0$ gives

$$Z_0 = \frac{1}{\pi}\sqrt{\omega_0^2 - r_N''(0)}\langle e^{-\alpha}I_0(\beta) + \left(\frac{\alpha^2-\beta^2}{\alpha\rho}\right)I_e\left(\frac{\beta}{\alpha}, \alpha\right)\rangle \quad (3.41)$$

where

$$\alpha = \frac{\rho}{2}\left[\frac{\omega_0^2 - r_N''(0) + [\omega_0+\dot\mu(t)]^2}{\omega_0^2 - r_N''(0)}\right]$$

$$\beta = \frac{\rho}{2}\left|\frac{\omega_0^2 - r_N''(0) - [\omega_0+\dot\mu(t)]^2}{\omega_0^2 - r_N''(0)}\right| \qquad (3.42)$$

Note $\dfrac{1}{\pi}\sqrt{\omega_0^2 - r_N''(0)}$ is the expected number of zeros per unit time of the noise alone and $-r_N''(0)$ stands for $-\left.\dfrac{\partial^2 r_N(h)}{\partial h^2}\right|_{h=0}$. Eqn. 3.41 is an extension of the result orginally given as eqn. 2.8 of Reference 4 in that the angle brackets offer the opportunity to perform a final ensemble average over the stationary distribution of values adopted by $\dot\mu(t)$, and thus the case of modulated carrier plus noise can be investigated.

$\mathfrak{I}_0$ and $\mathfrak{I}_1$ are integrals that appear repeatedly in the analysis, enabling results like eqn. 2.18 to be obtained. It is important to notice, however, that in using eqn. 3.26 to calculate Z_0 (the expected number of zeros per unit time), $\Phi(u_1, u_2)$ is differentiated partially with respect to h, but when applying eqn. 2.17 the partial differentiation is done with respect to $\omega_0 h$ (and, usually, we place $\omega_0 h = Z$). In the former case, terms like $\cos \omega_0 h$ and $\psi_N(h)$ become $-\omega_0 \sin \omega_0 h$ and $\psi'_N(h)$, respectively, but in the latter case the results are $-\sin \omega_0 h$ and zero. In many instances these different styles of differentiation lead only to different multiplying factors being applied to $\mathfrak{I}_0$ and $\mathfrak{I}_1$, and many of our results have a striking similarity of form (compare eqns. 2.18, 3.41 and 6.6).

Results for Z_0 of still greater generality can be produced by starting with $\Phi(u_1, u_2)$ as given by eqn. 2.10, that is when the noise accompanies a general narrow-band signal. The working follows through straight-forwardly using eqn. 3.26 but is complicated by the appearance of the first and second derivatives of the envelope.

The method of arriving at eqn. 3.41 shown here differs from that employed by Rice in his paper of 1948. Alternative derivations of this interesting formula are to be found in Reference 5 (pp. 318–320) and, more recently, in Reference 6 where a geometrical approach is described.

The function $I_0(\beta)$ appearing in eqn. 3.35 is extensively tabulated, but this is not the case with $I_e(k, x)$. A short table of this function is given in Appendix I of Reference 4, but a more extensive tabulation is given in this volume in the Appendix. This table can facilitate the averaging operation $\langle \ \rangle$ shown in eqn. 3.41 as this is likely to be best accomplished by numerical means.

As a final comment, comparing eqns. 3.9, 3.10, 3.19 and 3.21, it is seen that an alternative form for Z_0 is

$$Z_0 = \frac{1}{\pi} \langle |\omega_0 + \dot{\theta}(t)| \rangle \tag{3.43}$$

Z_0 is positive by definition but if the modulus signs are ignored on the grounds that ω_0 greatly exceeds $\dot{\theta}(t)$, we have

$$Z_0 = \frac{\omega_0}{\pi} + \frac{1}{\pi} \langle \dot{\theta}(t) \rangle \tag{3.44}$$

and, usually, $\langle \dot{\theta}(t) \rangle$ is zero.

In practical cases the presence of the modulus signs seldom gives rise to departures from the value ω_0/π that are large (witness the leading factor of eqn. 3.41), and, while retention of the signs is necessary for a strict observance of the theory, it is sometimes convenient to remove them and regard the results then obtained as holding for an infinitely large ω_0. An example of this occurs in the next section which considers the variance of $N(T)$.

3.5 Variance of $N(T)$ for narrow-band processes

Using eqn. 3.20 the number of zeros in a time T, which is assumed initially to equal or exceed the period T_1, is given by

$$N(T) = \frac{1}{\pi} \int_{-T/2}^{+T/2} W_i(t + y)\,dy \qquad (3.45)$$

Under the narrow band assumption, however, the integral will receive a significant contribution only from the zero'th harmonic component of $\omega_0 t$ in a Fourier development of $W_i(t)$ (this is the $K_0(t)$ term in eqn. 3.11) and so

$$N(T) \approx \int_{-T/2}^{T/2} \frac{K_0(t + y)}{h}\,dy \qquad (3.46)$$

In the limit of $h \to 0$, therefore, this gives (using eqns. 3.12 and 3.19)

$$N(T) \approx \int_{-T/2}^{T/2} \left| \frac{\omega_0 + \dot{\theta}(t + y)}{\pi} \right| dy \qquad (3.47)$$

The modulus signs prove difficult to cope with and so we agree to make ω_0 so large that $\omega_0 + \dot{\theta}(t)$ is negative for a negligible fraction of the time. Then (supposing $\langle \dot{\theta}(t) \rangle = 0$) the variance of $N(T)$ is given by:

$$Var\,[N(T)] = \langle N^2(T) \rangle - [\langle N(T) \rangle]^2$$

$$\approx \frac{1}{\pi^2} \iint_{-T/2}^{+T/2} \langle \dot{\theta}(t + y_1) \dot{\theta}(t + y_2) \rangle\,dy_1 dy_2 \qquad (3.48)$$

and on assuming that $\dot{\theta}(t)$ is a stationary process

$$Var\,[N(T)] \approx \frac{1}{\pi^2} \iint_{-T/2}^{T/2} R_{\dot{\theta}}(y_1 - y_2)\,dy_1 dy_2 \qquad (3.49)$$

Double integrals of the kind of eqn. 3.49 can be rewritten as a single integral by simple changes of variable (Section 3.9 of Reference 9) and so

$$\frac{Var\,[N(T)]}{T} \approx \frac{2}{\pi^2} \int_0^T \left(1 - \frac{x}{T}\right) R_{\dot{\theta}}(x)\,dx \qquad (3.50)$$

For T sufficiently large, and assuming $R_{\dot{\theta}}(x)$ decreases to zero at an appropriate rate, we then have

$$\underset{T \to \infty}{\text{Lim}} \frac{Var\ [N(T)]}{T} \approx \frac{2}{\pi^2} \int_0^\infty R_{\dot\theta}(x)\,dx \qquad (3.51)$$

On comparison with eqn. 1.6 this is seen to give $\frac{1}{\pi}W(0)$, where $W(0)$ is the power spectrum of the instantaneous frequency of a general narrow-band process evaluated at vanishingly small values of ω.

A case in which the explicit form of $R_{\dot\theta}(\tau)$ is known is that of narrow-band Gaussian noise (see eqn. 3.75) and

$$R_{\dot\theta}(\tau) = -\frac{1}{2}\left\{\left[\frac{r_N'(\tau)}{r_N(\tau)}\right]^2 - \left[\frac{r_N''(\tau)}{r_N(\tau)}\right]\right\} \cdot \log_e[1 - r_N^2(\tau)] \quad (3.52)$$

On inserting this expression in eqn. 3.50, a result for $Var\ [N(T)]$ is obtained that is to be regarded as a limiting form for $\omega_0 \to \infty$ (having built in this assumption the interval T always contains an infinitely large number of carrier cycles). An integration by parts yields

$$Var\ [N(T)] \approx \frac{2}{\pi^2}\int_0^T \frac{(T-x)[r_N'(x)]^2}{1 - r_N^2(x)}\,dx + I \qquad (3.53)$$

where

$$I = \frac{1}{12} - \frac{1}{2\pi^2}\sum_{m=1}^\infty \frac{[r_N(T)]^{2m}}{m^2}$$

I of eqn. 3.53 is zero when $T = 0$ and assumes its maximum value of $1/12$ when T is infinitely large, but then the integral is dominant, and for large T

$$\frac{Var\ [N(T)]}{T} \approx \frac{2}{\pi^2}\int_0^\infty \frac{[r_N'(x)]^2}{1 - r_N^2(x)}\,dx \qquad (3.54)$$

The analysis in References 7 and 8 examines the behaviour of $Var\ [N(T)]$ for noise when $\omega_0 T$ is kept finite and the narrow-band assumption is made. Results for the variance differ in certain respects (when $\omega_0 T/\pi$ is an integer, I is replaced by $(1/4) - \{(1/\pi)\sin^{-1}[r_N(T)]\}^2$ in eqn. 3.53) but the integral of eqn. 3.54 is common to both approaches. Blachman provides a table of $\{Var\ [N(T)]/T\}$ as calculated from eqn. 3.54 for several autocorrelation function types, that is, various power spectra for the noise: see p. 71 of Reference 7. In particular, for a power spectrum that is flat from $\omega_0 - \omega_B$ to $\omega_0 + \omega_B$

$$Var\ [N(T)] \approx 0\cdot612\left[\frac{2\omega_B T}{2\pi}\right] \qquad (3.55)$$

Here, and above, large T means that the product of T (seconds) and the bandwidth (Hz) exceeds unity.

3.6 Inclusion of a carrier

The variance of the expected number of zeros appearing in a long time
interval T for the sum of an unmodulated carrier and narrow-band
Gaussian noise can be expressed by a simple modification to the
integral in eqn. 3.54. The reader is referred to Blachman's work for
details of the ingenious way (Price's back-door method[6-8]) by which
eqn. 3.54 is extended and the result, for large T, is

$$Var\ [N(T)] = \frac{2T}{\pi^2}\int_0^\infty \frac{[r_N'(x)]^2}{1-r_N^2(x)}\exp-\left(\frac{2\rho}{1+r_N(x)}\right)dx \quad (3.56)$$

An alternative derivation of this integral is given here in eqn. 5.4.

3.7 Autocorrelation function of the instantaneous frequency

Having noted that $W_i(t)$ as given in eqn. 3.13 has the instantaneous
radian frequency $\omega_i(t)$ as its low frequency component it follows, on
proceeding with an analysis of the power spectrum of $W_i(t)$, that the
low-frequency portion of this spectrum will refer to the power spectrum
of $\omega_i(t)$. Thus, $R_W(\tau)$ the autocorrelation function of $W_i(t)$, which is
to be calculated by averaging $W_i(t) . W_i(t+\tau)$, can be developed
(compare eqn. 3.11) in the form

$$R_W(\tau) = R_0(\tau) + R_2(\tau)\cos 2\omega_0\tau + R_4(\tau)\cos 4\omega_0\tau + \ldots$$
$$(3.57)$$

As interest lies solely in $R_0(\tau)$, this term can be obtained through
dropping terms encountered in the calculation of $R_W(\tau)$ that contribute
spectral components near to $2\omega_0$, $4\omega_0$ etc. (such terms being
recognised through their association with $\cos 2\omega_0\tau$, $\cos 4\omega_0\tau$ etc.)

The ensemble averaging is assumed to depend only on time
differences, and when applied to $W_i(t) \cdot W_i(t+\tau)$, it gives

$$2\left(\frac{\pi}{2h}\right)^2 \{1 - P_2(h) + P_4(h,\tau,\tau-h,\tau+h)\} \quad (3.58)$$

where $P_4(h,\tau,\tau-h,\tau+h)$ is the probability that the product
$V(t-h/2) . V(t+h/2) . V(t+\tau-h/2) . V(t+\tau+h/2)$ is positive. As
usual, in order to obtain only the continuously distributed part of
the spectrum, the limiting expression as $\tau \to \infty$ is removed. When this
is done and the assumption regarding stationarity is met, the long-term
time averaging is redundant, and

$$R_W(\tau) = \frac{1}{2}\left(\frac{\pi}{h}\right)^2 \{P_4(h, \tau, \tau - h, \tau + h) - P_2^2(h) - [1 - P_2(h)]^2\}$$

$$(3.59)$$

The approach taken here is to express P_4 in terms of the quadrivariate characteristic function $\Phi(u_1, u_2, u_3, u_4)$ where

$$\Phi(u_1, u_2, u_3, u_4) = \langle \exp j \, [u_1 V(t - h/2) + u_2 V(t + h/2)$$

$$+ u_3 V(t + \tau - h/2) + u_4 V(t + \tau + h/2)] \rangle$$

and

$$P_4 = \frac{1}{2} + \frac{1}{2 \cdot \pi^4} \int\!\!\!\int\!\!\!\int\!\!\!\int_{-\infty}^{+\infty} \frac{\Phi(u_1, u_2, u_3, u_4)}{u_1 u_2 u_3 u_4} \, du_1 du_2 du_3 du_4$$

$$(3.60)$$

This is a direct extension of eqn. 3.25 where P_2 was expressed in terms of $\Phi(u_1, u_2)$, and use of eqns. 3.25 and 3.60 then gives the compact result

$$R_W(\tau) = \lim_{h \to 0} \frac{1}{(2\pi h)^2} \int\!\!\!\int\!\!\!\int\!\!\!\int_{-\infty}^{+\infty}$$

$$\left[\frac{\Phi(u_1, u_2, u_3, u_4) - \Phi(u_1, u_2)\,\Phi(u_3, u_4)}{u_1 u_2 u_3 u_4}\right] du_1 du_2 du_3 du_4$$

$$(3.61)$$

Eqn. 3.61 allows the multiplicative property of characteristic functions to be exploited to investigate the effects of additive disturbances at the receiver input, but the integration presents a formidable problem. However, an important case in which considerable progress can be made is that of a general narrow-band signal plus narrow-band Gaussian noise. The angle brackets that then appear refer to averages to be taken over the statistical parameters of the signal.

3.8 Case of a general narrow-band signal plus noise

For the general narrow-band wave-form of eqn. 1.1 a form akin to eqn. 2.8 is obtained for $\Phi(u_1, u_2, u_3, u_4)$ and is as follows:

$$\Phi(u_1, u_2, u_3, u_4) = \langle J_0(\sqrt{X_h^2 + Y_h^2}) \rangle \qquad (3.62)$$

where

$$X_h = u_1 P(t) + u_2 \, [P(t + h) \cos \omega_0 h + Q(t + h) \sin \omega_0 h]$$

$$+ u_3 \, [P(t + \tau) \cos \omega_0 \tau + Q(t + \tau) \sin \omega_0 \tau]$$

$$+ u_4 \, [P(t + \tau + h) \cos \omega_0(\tau + h) + Q(t + \tau + h) \sin \omega_0(\tau + h)]$$

$$Y_h = u_1 Q(t) + u_2 \left[-P(t+h) \sin \omega_0 h + Q(t+h) \cos \omega_0 h \right]$$
$$+ u_3 \left[-P(t+\tau) \sin \omega_0 \tau + Q(t+\tau) \cos \omega_0 \tau \right]$$
$$+ u_4 \left[-P(t+\tau+h) \sin \omega_0 (\tau+h) + Q(t+\tau+h) \cos \omega_0 (\tau+h) \right]$$

For narrow-band Gaussian noise with a power spectrum that is symmetrically disposed about ω_0, and with the autocorrelation function $\psi_N(\tau) \cos \omega_0 \tau$

$$\Phi_N(u_1, u_2, u_3, u_4) = \exp - F_N(h) \qquad (3.63)$$

where

$$F_N(h) = \tfrac{1}{2} \psi_N(0) [u_1^2 + u_2^2 + u_3^2 + u_4^2] + (u_1 u_2 + u_3 u_4) \psi_N(h) \cos \omega_0 h$$
$$+ (u_1 u_3 + u_2 u_4) \psi_N(\tau) \cos \omega_0 \tau + u_1 u_4 \psi_N(\tau+h) \cos \omega_0 (\tau+h)$$
$$+ u_2 u_3 \psi_N(\tau-h) \cos \omega_0 (\tau-h)$$

The product of eqns. 3.62 and 3.63 provides the quadrivariate characteristic function that is required if the autocorrelation function of the instantaneous frequency of the sum of a general narrow-band wave and narrow-band Gaussian noise is to be calculated. This is the most involved case that will be treated and the formal expression is given so that cases of lesser complication can be pared off from it. The quadruple integration is a task of considerable complication, and it is attacked here by first extracting all terms of order h^2 and then applying an appropriate transformation to the integration variables u_1, u_2, u_3, and u_4.* Taking the product of eqns. 3.62 and 3.63, a double differentiation with respect to h followed by placing $h = 0$ in the nontrigonometrical terms gives:

$$\tfrac{1}{2} \langle J_0 (\sqrt{X_0^2 + Y_0^2}) \rangle \left[(F_N'(0))^2 - F_N''(0) \right] e^{-F_N(0)}$$
$$- \left\langle \left(\frac{X_0 X_0' + Y_0 Y_0'}{\sqrt{X_0^2 + Y_0^2}} \right) J_0'(\sqrt{X_0^2 + Y_0^2}) \right\rangle F_N'(0) e^{-F_N(0)}$$

$$+ \frac{1}{2} \left\langle \left\{ \frac{X_0 X_0'' + Y_0 Y_0''}{\sqrt{X_0^2 + Y_0^2}} + \frac{[X_0 Y_0' - Y_0 X_0']^2}{(X_0^2 + Y_0^2)^{3/2}} \right\} J_0'(\sqrt{X_0^2 + Y_0^2}) \right.$$

$$\left. + \frac{[X_0 X_0' + Y_0 Y_0']^2}{X_0^2 + Y_0^2} J_0''(\sqrt{X_0^2 + Y_0^2}) \right\rangle e^{-F_N(0)} \qquad (3.64)$$

*For example, $\psi_N(h)$ is replaced by $\psi_N(0) + h^2/2 \, \psi_N''(0)$, but $\sin \omega_0 h$ and $\cos \omega_0 h$ are left as they are because of the underlying assumption that ω_0 is large without bound. When this procedure is followed the final result is found not to involve $\omega_0 h$

where X_0'', for example, is $\left.\dfrac{\partial^2 X(h)}{\partial h^2}\right|_{h=0}$ and

$$F_N'(0) = \psi_N'(\tau) [u_1 u_4 \cos \omega_0 (\tau + h) - u_2 u_3 \cos \omega_0 (\tau - h)]$$

$$F_N''(0) = \psi_N''(0) [u_1 u_2 + u_3 u_4] \cos \omega_0 h + \psi_N''(\tau)$$
$$\{u_1 u_4 \cos \omega_0(\tau + h) + u_2 u_3 \cos \omega_0(\tau - h)\}$$

Changes of variable that prove to be especially helpful are:

$$u_1 = -\frac{x \sin (\theta_1 - \omega_0 h)}{\sin \omega_0 h} \qquad u_2 = \frac{x \sin \theta_1}{\sin \omega_0 h}$$

$$u_3 = -\frac{y \sin (\theta_2 - \omega_0 h)}{\sin \omega_0 h} \qquad u_4 = \frac{y \sin \theta_2}{\sin \omega_0 h}$$

Then

$$\frac{du_1 du_2 du_3 du_4}{u_1 u_2 u_3 u_4} = \frac{\sin^2 \omega_0 h \, d\theta_1 d\theta_2 dx dy}{xy \sin \theta_1 \sin (\theta_1 - \omega_0 h) \sin \theta_2 \sin (\theta_2 - \omega_0 h)}$$

and it is found that both $F_N(0)$ and $\sqrt{X_0^2 + Y_0^2}$ become periodic functions of the angle combination $(\theta_2 - \theta_1 + \omega_0 \tau)$, namely,

$$F_N(0) = \frac{\psi_N(0)}{2} (x^2 + y^2) + xy \psi_N(\tau) \cos (\theta_2 - \theta_1 + \omega_0 \tau)$$

and

$$(3.65)$$

$$X_0^2 + Y_0^2 = (x r_1)^2 + (y r_2)^2 + 2 x y r_1 r_2 \cos (\theta_1 - \theta_2 + \omega_0 \tau + \Delta)$$

where

$$(3.66)$$

$$r_1^2 = P^2(t) + Q^2(t)$$

$$r_2^2 = P^2(t + \tau) + Q^2(t + \tau)$$

$$\tan \Delta = \frac{Q(t) P(t + \tau) - P(t) Q(t + \tau)}{P(t) P(t + \tau) + Q(t) Q(t + \tau)}$$

In view of eqn. 3.64 it is convenient to let

$$\frac{J_l(\sqrt{X_0^2 + Y_0^2})}{(\sqrt{X_0^2 + Y_0^2})^l} e^{-F_N(0)} = \frac{a_0(l)}{2}$$

$$+ \sum_{m=1}^{\infty} a_m(l) \cos m\gamma + b_m(l) \sin m\gamma$$

$$(3.67)$$

where $\gamma = \theta_2 - \theta_1 + \omega_0 \tau$ and the coefficients $a_m(l)$ and $b_m(l)$ are given by:

$$a_m(l) = \frac{1}{\pi} \int_{-\pi}^{\pi} \frac{J_l(\sqrt{X_0^2 + Y_0^2})}{(\sqrt{X_0^2 + Y_0^2})^l} e^{-F_N(0)} \cos m\gamma \, d\gamma \left.\vphantom{\int_{-\pi}^{\pi}}\right\}$$

$$b_m(l) = \frac{1}{\pi} \int_{-\pi}^{\pi} \frac{J_l(\sqrt{X_0^2 + Y_0^2})}{(\sqrt{X_0^2 + Y_0^2})^l} e^{-F_N(0)} \sin m\gamma \, d\gamma \quad (3.68)$$

with $F_N(0)$ given by eqn. 3.65, and $X_0^2 + Y_0^2$ by eqn. 3.66.

The Fourier development (eqn. 3.67) allows the zero'th harmonic components in $\omega_0 \tau$ to be extracted from each term of eqn. 3.64 once the three combinations $(X_0 X_0' + Y_0 Y_0')$, $(X_0 X_0'' + Y_0 Y_0'')$ and $[(X_0')^2 + (Y_0')^2]$ have also been expressed harmonically. The θ_1 and θ_2 integrations prove to be easy to handle, a typical integral result being

$$\iint_{-\pi}^{\pi} \frac{\sin(\theta_1 - \omega_0 h) \sin \theta_2 \cos 2(\theta_2 - \theta_1 - \omega_0 h)}{\sin \theta_1 \sin(\theta_2 - \omega_0 h)} \, d\theta_1 d\theta_2 = -4\pi^2 \sin^2 \omega_0 h$$

$$(3.69)$$

and it is convenient to make the following definitions:

$$P_1 = Q(t)\dot{P}(t) - P(t)\dot{Q}(t)$$

$$P_3 = Q(t+\tau)\dot{P}(t+\tau) - P(t+\tau)\dot{Q}(t+\tau)$$

$$P_5 = Q(t)\dot{P}(t+\tau) - P(t)\dot{Q}(t+\tau)$$

$$P_6 = P(t)\dot{P}(t+\tau) + Q(t)\dot{Q}(t+\tau)$$

$$P_7 = Q(t+\tau)\dot{P}(t) - \dot{Q}(t)P(t+\tau)$$

$$P_8 = \dot{P}(t)P(t+\tau) + \dot{Q}(t)Q(t+\tau) \quad (3.70)$$

Then, $R(\tau)$ the autocorrelation function of the continuously distributed components of the instantaneous frequency of the sum of a general narrow-band transmission and narrow-band Gaussian noise, is given by

$$R(\tau) = \Big\langle \iint_0^\infty \Big\{ a_1(2)[x^2 P_1 P_5 + y^2 P_3 P_7] + b_1(2)[x^2 P_1 P_6 - y^2 P_3 P_8]$$

$$+ \frac{xy}{2} \left(\frac{a_0(2)}{2} [2P_1 P_3 - P_6 P_8 + P_5 P_7] + \frac{a_2(2)}{2} [P_6 P_8 + P_5 P_7] \right.$$

$$\left. - \frac{b_2(2)}{2} [P_5 P_8 - P_6 P_7] \right) \Big\} dx dy \Big\rangle$$

$$- \Big\langle \iint_0^\infty \Big\{ \frac{a_1(1)}{2} [\dot{P}(t)\dot{P}(t+\tau) + \dot{Q}(t)\dot{Q}(t+\tau)]$$

$$+ \frac{b_1(1)}{2} [\dot{P}(t)\dot{Q}(t+\tau) - \dot{Q}(t)\dot{P}(t+\tau)] \Big\} dx dy \Big\rangle$$

$$+ \psi_N'(\tau) \langle \iint_0^\infty \left([x^2 P_1 + y^2 P_3] \, b_1(1) \right.$$

$$+ \left\{ \left[\frac{a_0(1) - a_2(1)}{2} \right] (P_6 - P_8) + \frac{b_2(1)}{2} (P_5 + P_7) \right\} xy \right) dx dy \rangle$$

$$+ [\psi_N'(\tau)]^2 \langle \iint_0^\infty \left(\frac{a_0(0) - a_2(0)}{2} \right) \frac{xy}{2} \, dx dy \rangle$$

$$- \psi_N''(\tau) \langle \iint_0^\infty \frac{a_1(0)}{2} \, dx dy \rangle \tag{3.71}$$

with $a_m(l)$ and $b_m(l)$ given by eqn. 3.68.

3.9 Unmodulated carrier plus noise

For an unmodulated carrier plus narrow-band Gaussian noise the autocorrelation function $R(\tau)$ is given by the final two terms of eqn. 3.71:

$$R(\tau) = [\psi_N'(\tau)]^2 \iint_0^\infty \left[\frac{a_0(0) - a_2(0)}{2} \right] \frac{xy}{2} \, dx dy$$

$$- \psi_N''(\tau) \iint_0^\infty \frac{a_1(0)}{2} \, dx dy \tag{3.72}$$

$$a_m(0) = \frac{1}{\pi} \int_{-\pi}^{\pi} J_0(\sqrt{X_0^2 + Y_0^2}) e^{-F_N(0)} \cos m\gamma \, d\gamma \quad m = 0, 1 \text{ and } 2$$

where
$$\tag{3.73}$$
$$\sqrt{X_0^2 + Y_0^2} = A\sqrt{x^2 + y^2 + 2xy \cos \gamma}$$

and $F_N(0)$ is given by eqn. 3.65 with γ replacing $(\theta_2 - \theta_1 + \omega_0 \tau)$. It is evident from a comparison of eqns. 3.73 and 2.12 that $a_m(0)$ is the coefficient of $\cos m\gamma$ in the bivariate characteristic function of signal plus noise.

Here A is the amplitude of the unmodulated carrier (as in eqn. 3.1), and if A is made zero so that only noise is present, the coefficients $a_m(0)$ are easy to identify, in fact

$$a_m(0) = 2 I_m(xy \psi_N(\tau)) e^{-\psi_N(0)(x^2 + y^2)/2} \, m = 0, 1 \text{ and } 2 \tag{3.74}$$

Substitution into eqn. 3.72 then gives the autocorrelation function of the instantaneous frequency of narrow-band Gaussian noise

$$R(\tau) = \left\{ \frac{[\psi_N'(\tau)]^2 - \psi_N(\tau) \psi_N''(\tau)}{\psi_N(\tau)} \right\} \iint_0^\infty I_1(xy \psi_N(\tau)) e^{-\psi_N(0)(x^2 + y^2)/2} \, dx dy$$

$$= -\frac{1}{2} \left\{ \left[\frac{r'_N(\tau)}{r_N(\tau)} \right]^2 - \left[\frac{r''_N(\tau)}{r_N(\tau)} \right] \right\} \log_e \left\{ 1 - [r_N(\tau)]^2 \right\} \quad (3.75)$$

where

$$r_N(\tau) = \frac{\psi_N(\tau)}{\psi_N(0)}$$

This result was first obtained by Rice[4] and Wang[11] during investigations of the unmodulated carrier plus noise case. Note that $R(0)$, which gives the variance, is infinite, thus implying that the tails of the probability density function of the instantaneous frequency fall away relatively slowly. This distribution is given by eqn. 6.9 of Section 6.1.

It is the Fourier transform of $R(\tau)$ that is of principal interest as this gives the power spectrum $W(\omega)$, and using eqn. 1.6 with $R(\tau)$, given by eqn. 3.72, the power spectrum of the instantaneous frequency of the sum of a sine wave and narrow-band Gaussian noise is given by

$$W(\omega) = \frac{2}{\pi} \int_0^\infty \left\{ [\psi'_N(\tau)]^2 \left\langle \iint_0^\infty \left(\frac{a_0(0) - a_2(0)}{2} \right) \frac{xy}{2} dx dy \right\rangle \right.$$

$$\left. - \psi''_N(\tau) \left\langle \iint_0^\infty \frac{a_1(0)}{2} dx dy \right\rangle \right\} \cos \omega \tau \, d\tau \quad (3.76)$$

Unfortunately, the coefficients $a_m(0)$ are simply related only when A, the sine-wave amplitude, is zero (then eqn. 3.74 holds) and, in general, the spectrum has to be determined by numerical means. The quoted references (especially References 1, 4 and 11) show the results of considerable numerical investigation of the spectrum. An important case that can be handled analytically is that of $\omega \to 0$, and this exercise is carried out in Chapter 5. The spectrum at vanishingly small frequencies proves to be of great practical interest, and its level can be expressed in terms of elementary functions if certain realistic approximations are made and a more intuitive approach is taken (f.m. click theory), as described in Chapter 5.

3.10 References

1 STUMPERS, F.L.H.M.: 'Theory of frequency-modulation noise', *Proc. IRE*, 1948, **36**, pp. 1081–1092
2 MANN, P.A.: 'Der Zeitablauf von Rauschspannungen', *Elek Nach Tech*, 1943, **20**, pp. 232–237
3 WATSON, G.N.: 'A treatise on the theory of Bessel functions' (Cambridge University Press, 1962, 2nd edn.)
4 RICE, S.O.: 'Statistical properties of a sine wave plus random noise', *Bell Syst. Tech. J.* 1948, **27**, pp. 109–157

5 CRAMER, H., and LEADBETTER, M.R.: 'Stationary and related stochastic processes' (Wiley, 1967)

6 BLACHMAN, N.M.: 'Zero crossing rate for the sum of two sinusoids or a signal plus noise', *IEEE Trans.*, 1975, **IT-21**, (6), pp. 671–675

7 BLACHMAN, N.M.: 'Noise and its effect upon communication' (McGraw-Hill, 1966)

8 BLACHMAN, N.M.: 'FM reception and the zeros of narrow-band Gaussian noise', *IEEE Trans.*, 1964, **IT-10**, (3), pp. 235–241

9 RICE, S.O.: 'Mathematical analysis of random noise', *Bell Syst. Tech. J.* 1944, **23**, pp. 282–332, and 1945, **24**, pp. 46–157

10 BEDROSIAN, E., and RICE, S.O.: 'Distortion and cross talk of linearly filtered angle-modulated signals', *Proc. IEEE*, 1968, **56**, (1), pp. 2–13

11 LAWSON, J.L., and UHLENBECK, G.E.: 'Threshold signals' (McGraw-Hill, 1950)

Chapter 4

Analogue modulation and its representation by a band of Gaussian noise

4.1 Types of analogue modulation

A great variety of analogue signals are currently used to modulate the f.m. systems operated by the commercial, civil, and military authorities, ranging from one or a few voice channels or music to a full television transmission, and it would be very convenient if one all-embracing modulation could be assumed for theoretical purposes. Aside from the obvious differences in the bandwidth requirements, however, there are fundamental differences in the fidelity criteria for these various signals, a television transmission, for example, may be far less tolerant of echoes or frequency-dependent delays than an assembly of audio channels arranged in frequency division multiplex (f.d.m.).

A common characteristic of the signals used in practice is, of course, that they are information bearing and this feature should be kept to the fore when a suitable model for the modulation is being sought. The adoption of single tone or two-tone modulating waveforms is far from adequate, therefore, unless the pilot or monitoring tones that are used on a system enter our considerations. It has occasionally been the unfortunate practice to draw conclusions from an analysis of the single tone case and regard these as being appropriate to situations in which the modulation is clearly of a much more complicated kind. Again, it is well known that the expression for the r.f. spectrum of a carrier frequency or phase modulated by as few as two tones is cumbersome and this hindrance would have to be carried through the analysis.

Thus, the use of one or two tones is to be rejected as a model in the great majority of cases and, with Shannon's pioneering work in information theory in the background, it is inevitable that we should turn to a statistical description of the modulation.

Now Gaussian noise and the Gaussian process have both received exhaustive attention in the communications literature and their benign properties, so far as mathematical analysis is concerned, are widely recognised. Some of these properties have already been referred to in the foregoing chapters where the additive noise at the receiver input has been modelled by a band of Gaussian noise centred on the carrier frequency, and it is very convenient to have a common mathematical discipline covering the statistical properties of both the modulation and the noise. Further, such a model is often intuitively satisfying as it is not uncommon to encounter situations in which precise statistical data concerning the modulation is not available and about all that is known is that it is noise-like.

Over and above these analytical conveniences, however, is the fact that it has been internationally agreed that a band of Gaussian noise should be adopted as the test signal for specifying the performance of radio-relay systems which are now installed world-wide. The essential transmission properties of such systems, e.g. microwave carrier frequencies, intermediate frequencies, modulation characteristics and distortion-to-signal (D/S) ratios, have been standardised by international agreement and these standards are issued in the form of recommendations by the CCIR (Comité Consultatif International des Radio-communications).

The Gaussian noise model is not appropriate in every case (for example, it is unlikely to be acceptable when one or a few voice channels constitute the modulation) but it comes close to satisfying our requirement of an all-embracing modulation. It has been widely adopted in theoretical investigations for the reasons given above, especially in microwave radio-relay applications, and in later sections considerable attention will be given to its use in defining the performance of such systems. A Gaussian modulation will be assumed almost exclusively from now on.

4.2 R.F. spectra

Before describing the particular measurement technique which is employed on radio relay equipments, it is of interest to examine the r.f. spectrum that results when a carrier is phase or frequency modulated by a band of Gaussian noise. If the modulated carrier wave is written

$$S(t) = A \cos [\omega_0 t + \mu(t)] \qquad (4.1)$$

then $R(\tau)$ the autocorrelation function is given (using eqn. 1.5) by

$$R(\tau) = \langle \frac{A^2}{2} \cos \left[\omega_0 \tau + \mu(t+\tau) - \mu(t) \right] \rangle$$

$$+ \langle \frac{A^2}{2} \cos \left[2\omega_0 t + \omega_0 \tau + \mu(t+\tau) + \mu(t) \right] \rangle \quad (4.2)$$

On interpreting the pointed brackets as referring to both a long term time average as well as an ensemble average, it is evident that with τ fixed the second member on the right-hand side will make no contribution, and if $\mu(t)$ has a zero mean value

$$R(\tau) = \frac{A^2}{2} \langle \cos \left[\mu(t+\tau) - \mu(t) \right] \rangle \cos \omega_0 \tau \quad (4.3)$$

The averaging to be carried out is seen to be simply the characteristic function of the variate $\mu(t+\tau) - \mu(t)$, and when $\mu(t)$ is a zero mean Gaussian process

$$\langle \cos \left[\mu(t+\tau) - \mu(t) \right] \rangle = \exp - \tfrac{1}{2} \langle \left[\mu(t+\tau) - \mu(t) \right]^2 \rangle$$

$$= \exp - \left[\psi_\mu(0) - \psi_\mu(\tau) \right] \quad (4.4)$$

where $\psi_\mu(\tau)$ is the autocorrelation function of the phase modulation $\mu(t)$. Alternatively, this result comes from eqn. 2.31 in the special instances of $x(t) = \mu(t)$, $-u_1 = +u_2 = 1$. Using eqn. 1.6 the required power spectrum is given by

$$W(\omega) = \frac{2}{\pi} \int_0^\infty \frac{A^2}{2} \exp - \left[\psi_\mu(0) - \psi_\mu(\tau) \right] \cos \omega_0 \tau \cdot \cos \omega \tau \, d\tau$$

$$= \frac{A^2}{2\pi} \int_0^\infty \exp - \left[\psi_\mu(0) - \psi_\mu(\tau) \right]$$

$$\cdot \left\{ \cos \left(\overline{\omega_0 + \omega} \tau \right) + \cos \left(\overline{\omega_0 - \omega} \tau \right) \right\} \, d\tau \quad (4.5)$$

Usually interest lies only in the spectral levels in the vicinity of ω_0 and then, on writing $\omega = \omega_0 + q$ the contribution made by the first term in the curly bracket is overwhelmed by that from the second and much more slowly oscillating term, and a spectrum $G(q)$ is defined as follows

$$\left\{ \frac{G(q)}{\tfrac{1}{2} A^2} \right\} = \frac{1}{\pi} \int_0^\infty \exp - \left[\psi_\mu(0) - \psi_\mu(\tau) \right] \cos q\tau \, d\tau \quad (4.6)$$

Then $\left\{ \left[G(q) \, dq \right] / (\tfrac{1}{2} A^2) \right\}$ gives the fractional power that is contributed to the small frequency interval dq centred on a frequency that has a separation of q (rad/s) from ω_0, the centre frequency. Note $\int_{-\infty}^{+\infty} G(q) \, dq = \tfrac{1}{2} A^2$ is the total power transmitted. Eqn. 4.6 can be inverted, and sometimes it is convenient to call on the relationship

$$\exp - [\psi_\mu(0) - \psi_\mu(\tau)] = \int_{-\infty}^{+\infty} \left\{ \frac{G(q)}{\frac{1}{2}A^2} \right\} \cos q\tau \, dq \qquad (4.7)$$

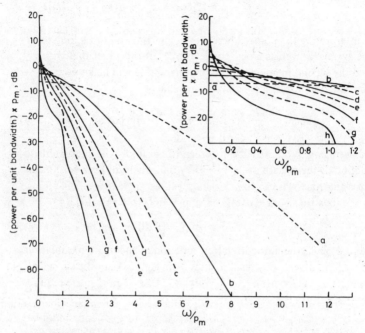

Fig. 4.1 Spectral distribution of a carrier frequency modulated with flat noise having a maximum modulating frequency p_m and a zero minimum modulating frequency

Power in modulated carrier $= 1$ ω_Δ is the r.m.s. frequency deviation
$a\ \omega_\Delta/p_m = 2\cdot0.\ b\ \omega_\Delta/p_m = 1\cdot0.\ c\ \omega_\Delta/p_m = 0\cdot7.\ d\ \omega_\Delta/p_m = 0\cdot5.$
$e\ \omega_\Delta/p_m = 0\cdot4.\ f\ \omega_\Delta/p_m = 0\cdot3.\ g\ \omega_\Delta/p_m = 0\cdot2.\ h\ \omega_\Delta/p_m = 0\cdot1$

The integral in eqn. 4.6 is seen to be a function of the autocorrelation function of the phase modulation and the resulting spectrum therefore depends ultimately on the power spectrum that is ascribed to $\mu(t)$. When $\psi_\mu(0) < 1$, $\exp \psi_\mu(\tau)$ can be replaced by its first two or three terms, and then

$$\left\{ \frac{G(q)}{\frac{1}{2}A^2} \right\} = \exp - [\psi_\mu(0)] \cdot \left\{ \delta(q) + \tfrac{1}{2} W_\mu(q) \right.$$

$$\left. + \frac{1}{8} \int_0^\infty W_\mu(x) \left[W_\mu(|q - x|) + W_\mu(q + x) \right] dx + \ldots \right\}$$
$$(4.8)$$

The delta function refers to the residual carrier which is seen to have a power level determined by $\exp - \psi_\mu(0)$, and the integral refers to the second-order sideband spectra which derive from $\cos \mu(t)$ (in addition to the term $-1/2! \, \mu^2(t)$, the terms $1/4! \, \mu^4(t), -1/6! \, \mu^6(t)$ etc. all contribute to the 2nd-order spectrum and the factor $\exp - \psi_\mu(0)$ accounts correctly for the net result). Higher terms in the series,[1] which require double and treble integrals for their specification, refer to the third- and higher-order sideband spectra.

In most cases it is necessary to resort to numerical analysis and the use of a computer to evaluate the integral that defines the spectrum $G(q)$, and, the further out in the tail regions it is necessary to go, the more exacting the numerical procedure has to be.

$W_M(q)$ the power spectrum of the frequency modulation is related to $W_\mu(q)$ through

$$W_M(q) = q^2 W_\mu(q) \qquad (4.9)$$

and when $W_M(q)$ is constant over a specified angular frequency range p_0 to p_m we shall write

$$W_M(q) = \frac{\omega_\Delta^2}{(p_m - p_0)} \qquad p_0 \leqslant q \leqslant p_m \qquad (4.10)$$

So

$$W_\mu(q) = \frac{\omega_\Delta^2}{(p_m - p_0)q^2} \qquad p_0 \leqslant q \leqslant p_m \qquad (4.11)$$

and ω_Δ is a parameter that fixes the total power (the mean square value) of the flat band of Gaussian noise that is used to frequency modulate the carrier. The mean square phase deviation is, accordingly, given by

$$\psi_\mu(0) = \langle \mu^2(t) \rangle = \int_{p_0}^{p_m} \frac{\omega_\Delta^2}{(p_m - p_0)q^2} \, dq = \frac{\omega_\Delta^2}{p_0 \cdot p_m} \qquad (4.12)$$

Spectra for this situation, i.e. flat f.m., are shown in Fig. 4.1. The numerical procedure used to obtain these curves is described in Reference 2 and they refer to a limiting situation in which the minimum modulating frequency p_0 has become vanishingly small. Note that this causes $\psi_\mu(0)$ to become infinite and so the spectra contain no residual carrier components, but it is only in the immediate vicinity of the carrier frequency that differences appear when p_0 is non-zero and $p_0 \ll p_m$.

Fig. 4.2 shows a set of curves for a pre-emphasised baseband, that is, the power spectrum of the frequency-modulating noise is not flat. It is seen that for a given value of ω_Δ/p_m the spectra in Figs. 4.1 and 4.2 do not differ greatly. The particular shaping of the modulation for which Fig. 4.2 is drawn is discussed in Section 5.4 of Chapter 5.

The tails of the spectra are particularly interesting. It is known[1-3] that the tails can fall away in a variety of ways depending on the particular modulation parameters (p_0, p_m and ω_Δ) to hand, while near to the carrier the spectral shape can, under certain conditions,[3-5] follow the probability density function of the frequency modulation. This behaviour is seen on Figs. 4.1 and 4.2 for the larger values of ω_Δ/p_m, for which a Gaussian law is closely followed.

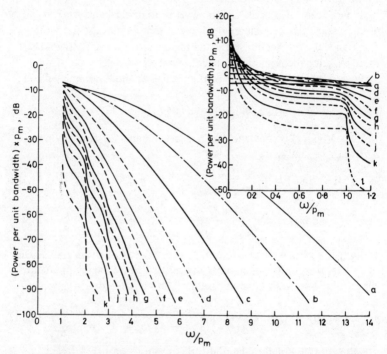

Fig. 4.2 Spectral distribution of a carrier frequency modulated with noise shaped according to the CCIR pre-emphasis law

Power in modulated carrier = 1
Pre-emphasis law $P(p) = 0.4 \cosh\left(2.55\,\dfrac{p}{p_m}\right)$ (Section 5.4)

ω_Δ is the r.m.s. frequency deviation, p_m is the maximum modulating frequency, and the minimum modulating frequency is zero

a ω_Δ/p_m = 2.0. b ω_Δ/p_m = 1.5. c ω_Δ/p_m = 1.0. d ω_Δ/p_m = 0.7.
e ω_Δ/p_m = 0.5. f ω_Δ/p_m = 0.4. g ω_Δ/p_m= 0.30. h ω_Δ/p_m = 0.25.
i ω_Δ/p_m = 0.2. j ω_Δ/p_m = 0.15. k ω_Δ/p_m = 0.10. l ω_Δ/p_m = 0.05

In theory these spectra extend infinitely far to either side of the carrier but in practice the tail region beyond a certain frequency will be of very low level and so is unlikely to be of interest.

It is highly desirable that some finite bandwidth be associated with the spectrum, however, and one widely adopted rule of thumb for achieving this aim is known as Carson's law. This states:

$$2\omega_B = 2p_m \left[1 + 3{\cdot}162 \left(\frac{\omega_\Delta}{p_m} \right) \right] \qquad (4.13)$$

$2\omega_B$ (or $\pm \omega_B$) is the bandwidth and Carson's original formulation applied to single-tone modulation producing a definite peak deviation. In eqn. 4.13, $3{\cdot}162\omega_\Delta$ is taken for the corresponding peak deviation of a frequency modulation with a Gaussian distribution of amplitudes ($3{\cdot}162$ or $\sqrt{10}$ is usually agreed to be an appropriate peak-to-r.m.s. factor for a Gaussian process) and the law is seen to be in the form of a factor multiplying twice the highest modulating frequency.

Eqn. 4.13 gives no information as to the fraction of the total power that is contained in the band $2\omega_B$ nor, more importantly, does it indicate how much distortion is introduced if spectral components beyond $\pm \omega_B$ are ignored or filtered away.

With these provisos in mind the law will be frequently employed here as it predicts bandwidths that prove to be realistic for system design purposes and because of its extreme simplicity.

Estimates of the amount of power contained within a specified bandwidth are best obtained with the aid of inequalities. A bound derived by Blachman,[6] which is both simpler and tighter than most others, can be written

$$\int_{-p}^{+p} \left\{ \frac{G(q)}{\frac{1}{2}A^2} \right\} dq > 1 - 2 \left[\frac{e}{2} \left(\frac{\omega_\Delta}{p_m} \right)^2 \frac{p_m}{p} \right]^{p/p_m} \qquad (4.14)$$

This is for use in the tail region of spectra, on the left is the fraction of the total power that is contained within the band $\pm p$ rad/s and the bound applies equally well to pre-emphasised and non-pre-emphasised cases.

Eqns. 4.13 and 4.14 give the figures in Table 4.1, from which it is seen that the Carson bandwidth contains a very large percentage of the power when $\omega_\Delta/p_m < 2$.

Table 4.1   Spectrum occupancy and Carson bandwidth

$\dfrac{\omega_\Delta}{p_m}$	Fraction of total power exceeded on truncating at the Carson bandwidth
0·5	0·9893
1·0	0·9810
2·0	0·7747

The question of the distortion suffered by spectrum truncation is considered in Chapter 7, but, before closing, we remark that the spectra of Figs. 4.1 and 4.2 carry the assumption that the modulator employed is linear, i.e. the instantaneous frequency varies linearly with $\dot{\mu}(t) = M(t)$.

This is an assumption which will always be made hereafter, but the effect of a nonlinear modulator can be investigated using the tools of Section 2.5 (the instantaneous frequency can be postulated to be of the form $\omega_0 + \dot{\mu}(t) + a_2 [\dot{\mu}(t)]^2$, for example, where a_2 specifies a parabolic nonlinearity) and some information on the resulting r.f. spectrum may be found in Reference 7.

4.3 F.M. F.D.M.

Having supplied some information on the spectrum of a noise modulated carrier, a closer discussion of a situation in which random noise is a good model for the modulating signal is now given.

F.M. trunk radio systems, both terrestrial and satellite, commonly make use of a technique known as frequency-division multiplex (f.d.m.) to carry telephony speech channels. In this system, each channel is translated in frequency so as to occupy one of a number of adjacent 4 kHz bands, and the resulting composite signal frequency modulates a carrier, usually located in the range 2 GHz to 12 GHz.

If the number of speech channels is sufficiently large, the statistical properties of the f.d.m. signal are similar to those of random noise, and detailed investigations have been conducted into the amplitude distribution that prevails, perhaps the most widely recognised study being that reported in Reference 8. The distribution of the f.d.m. assembly is generally agreed to be sufficiently close to the Gaussian law for practical purposes when more than about 60 of the channels are active simultaneously. Studies have shown, however, that the time taken up when the other party is talking, and by the pauses that naturally occur in speech, mean that each channel is active for only about 25% of the time, and, thus, the system design can be based on the supposition that only a small fraction of the total number of channels will be used at any one time. The agreed criterion is that for less than 1% of the time (the busiest hour) no more than n of the N channels shall be supposed active. With an activity factor of 0·25, the probability that more than n channels are active is given by

$$\sum_{r=n+1}^{N} \binom{N}{r} \cdot \left(\frac{1}{4}\right)^r \cdot \left(\frac{3}{4}\right)^{N-r}$$

It is accepted practice to equate a probability such as this to the fraction of time in question (0·01 in this case) and so interest lies in the values of N and n for which

$$\sum_{r=n+1}^{N} \binom{N}{r} \cdot \left(\frac{1}{4}\right)^{r} \cdot \left(\frac{3}{4}\right)^{N-r} < 0\cdot01 \qquad (4.15)$$

When this inequality is satisfied, the value of n may be used to determine the peak voltage that can reasonably be expected to occur and which must not cause unacceptable distortion by overloading the equipment.

With an activity factor of 0·25, the expected number of active channels is $N/4$, and Table 4.2 shows the relationship between N, $N/4$ and n for some typical system capacities.

Table 4.2   System capacity and number of simultaneously active channels

N (system capacity)	$\dfrac{N}{4}$ (The expected number of active channels)	n (The probability that more than n channels are active simultaneously is less than 1%)
60	15	23
120	30	41
240	60	76
300	75	93
600	150	175
960	240	272
1 800	450	493
2 700	675	728

From this table it is seen that, for system capacities of 240 channels and above, it is fair to assume that more than 60 channels are always active, and this is the number which ensures that the f.d.m. signal is a close approximation to a Gaussian process. Consequently, the CCIR have stated that, for capacities of 240 channels and above, the f.d.m. signal is to be modelled by a band of Gaussian noise covering the appropriate frequency range and having a level which is given by N times the mean power level in a single telephone channel. As a result of tests made on systems installed in various parts of Europe, this latter quantity has been standardized at $-15\,$dBmO. (Decibels referred to 1 mW at a point of zero relative level). dBmO is an example of the notation now widely used for specifying power levels

in telephone systems and dBrn, dBa are other examples.* These and
phrases such as 'point of zero relative level' are all part of the jargon of
multichannel telephony, and a considerable service has been performed
by the author of Reference 9 in collecting together the various
definitions and discussing most of the terminology now commonly
used.

Strictly, when N is less than 240, the f.d.m. signal is not well
approximated by a Gaussian process but, due perhaps to the lack of
any other easily specifiable alternative, it has become accepted
practice still to use the Gaussian model but with a level specified by a
law given below, in eqn. 4.17.

The f.d.m. assembly of audio channels is used to frequency modulate
the carrier and some way of specifying the amount by which the
carrier is then deviated is now required. Essentially a voltage/frequency
conversion factor k, say, is necessary, and we start by supposing that
an audio tone $A \sin \omega_1 t$ is converted by the modulator into the
frequency modulating tone $kA \sin \omega_1 t$. If the r.m.s. frequency deviation so produced is w_d, we then have

$$\tfrac{1}{2}(kA)^2 = w_d^2 \qquad (4.16)$$

If, further, the input audio tone has a power of 1 mW, it is seen that
$k = w_d$ or, put in words, the conversion factor is the r.m.s. frequency
deviation produced when a 1 mW tone is applied at the input to the
modulator. In practice this tone is chosen to have a frequency of
800 Hz (in the lower half of the audio band) and w_d is called the r.m.s.
test-tone deviation. Typical values of $w_d/2\pi$ for terrestrial systems are
140 kHz or 200 kHz, and, on assuming the modulator to be linear, the
CCIR have proposed two rules for calculating ω_Δ the r.m.s. frequency
deviation produced when the carrier is frequency modulated by
Gaussian noise modelling the f.d.m. signal.

$$20 \log_{10}\left(\frac{\omega_\Delta}{w_d}\right) = \begin{cases} -1 + 4\log_{10}N & \text{for } N < 240 \\ -15 + 10\log_{10}N & \text{for } N \geqslant 240 \end{cases} \qquad (4.17)$$

Similar laws[9] have been recommended in the cases of basebands made
up primarily from data or telegraph signals (the right-hand side of
eqn. 4.17 is then to be taken as $-10 + 10\log_{10}N$ for $N > 12$), but the
presentation will now continue on the assumption that a value for ω_Δ
is known or is sought. For flat noise band f.m., therefore, the spectral
densities of the frequency modulation and the corresponding phase

---

*dBrn refer to decibels above reference noise: dBa decibels above adjusted
reference noise.

modulation are given by eqns. 4.10 and 4.11, respectively, where p_0 and p_m are the minimum and maximum modulating frequencies, and the spectral occupancy is largely governed by the value of ω_Δ/p_m. The corresponding spectra are shown in Fig. 4.1.

4.4 Measurement procedure for f.m. f.d.m. operation

The interference that falls into the channels of a radio relay system arises as a consequence of the nonlinear nature of frequency modulation and can be attributed to a number of sources such as the non-linearity of transmission equipment, bandwidth limitation, discriminator nonlinearity, echoes, adjacent channel interference etc. Ideally all of these, in addition to the effects of the thermal noise that inevitably accompanies the transmitted signal, are to be accounted for and the interference manifests itself as a continuous spectrum that underlies and extends well beyond the baseband frequency range.

Accordingly, the measurement technique consists of inserting band-stop filters into the spectrum of Gaussian noise used to simulate the f.d.m. signal before modulation takes place, and then measuring the level of interference in these 'silent' gaps after demodulation. The White-Noise Test Set which enables this procedure to be carried out is now standard laboratory equipment and the band-stop filters used conform to standards laid down by the CCIR.[9] They usually allow three positions (slots) in the baseband to be examined, near the bottom, the middle and the top channels.

The most widely used yard-stick of performance is the noise power ratio (n.p.r.) and this is defined to be the decibel ratio of the level recorded after demodulation in a measurement slot with the baseband fully noise loaded, to the level recorded in the same slot with the baseband fully loaded except for the channel corresponding to the measurement slot.

The slot filters have bandwidths which are comparable to the width of an audio channel (2 kHz or 3 kHz, say) and, generally, the spectrum of the interference varies only slowly across the baseband frequency range. The ratio that is determined by a measurement of n.p.r. is therefore given with acceptable accuracy, in most cases, by forming the quotient of the spectral densities with and without the band-stop filter. In any case, this ratio of spectral densities provides the means whereby finite slot widths or particular filter loss characteristics can be investigated theoretically.

In making a measurement of n.p.r. many factors contribute to the accuracy obtained. Of these, the most important are the finite slot width, the uniformity of the power spectrum of the noise model, and the minimum modulating frequency (ideally, the noise modulation frequency components are strictly confined to the baseband range, p_0 to p_m.) A filter that provides a well-defined p_0 is therefore required, and the ratio $p_0/(p_m - p_0)$ is an important parameter.[10] Several papers have appeared[10-12] that discuss the accuracy of n.p.r. measurements but we shall work in terms of spectral densities, writing

$$\text{n.p.r.} = 10 \log_{10} \left[\frac{D + S}{D} \right] \qquad (4.18)$$

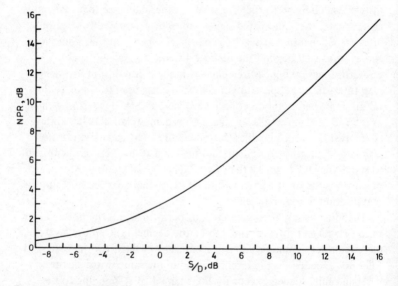

Fig. 4.3 n.p.r. versus *S/D*

$$\text{n.p.r.} = \log_{10} \left(1 + \frac{S}{D} \right)$$

n.p.r. and *S/D* are, effectively, the same number of positive decibels when either exceeds 16 dB

Here S stands for that part of the power spectrum determined in a measurement slot that has not suffered a nonlinear transformation as a result of passage through the system under examination, while D stands in a general way for distortion, interference, noise, or distortion × noise interactions. Thus S can be viewed as the useful output, while D is the unwanted output. In much of the future analysis the quantity D/S will be determined (the distortion/signal ratio), and Fig. 4.3 shows the relationship between S/D (when expressed in decibels) and n.p.r.

Several expressions for D/S are to be given, perhaps the most important one being eqn. 5.25 which gives D/S at any spot frequency in the baseband of a multi-channel radio relay system disturbed by additive Gaussian noise.

4.5 Linearly filtered term

It is important to establish just how much of the signal $M(t)$ is present in the demodulator output in an undistorted form, and, having discussed the suitability of a band of Gaussian noise as a model for the frequency modulation, an explicit expression for S, as used in the definition of n.p.r. given by eqn. 4.18, is required. In terms of $R(\tau)$, the autocorrelation function of the instantaneous frequency, when no noise is present and the wave is not filtered we have

$$R(\tau) = \langle M(t) M(t+\tau) \rangle = \psi_M(\tau)$$

but in the general case, in which both noise and filtering are present, $R(\tau)$ is given by eqn. 3.71 and now we wish to identify those parts which contribute to an undistorted version of $M(t)$ and which therefore constitute S. To do this it is convenient to introduce $g(t)$, the impulse response of the low-pass equivalent of the bandpass filter, [see Chapter 7 for further discussion of $g(t)$]. Then $g(t)$, and $P(t)$ and $Q(t)$, as used in eqn. 3.70, are related by

$$P(t) + jQ(t) = A \int_{-\infty}^{+\infty} g(x) e^{j\mu(t-x)} dx \qquad (4.19)$$

When the filter bandwidth becomes indefinitely large $g(x) \to \delta(x)$, so it could be conjectured that with a noise free signal the autocorrelation function of the undistorted term is given by

$$\langle \iint_{-\infty}^{+\infty} g(x) g(y) M(t-x) M(t+\tau-y) \, dx dy \rangle$$

$$= \iint_{-\infty}^{+\infty} g(x) g(y) \psi_M(\tau + x - y) dx dy \qquad (4.20)$$

as, when $g(x)$ is $\delta(x)$, eqn. 4.20 reduces to $\psi_M(\tau)$.

When the filtering cannot be regarded as light, or if noise is present, a further departure from eqn. 4.20, or its equivalent, can be expected. Unfortunately, the portion of eqn. 3.71 that is required is difficult to

identify directly and so a linear operator $h(x)$ and the instantaneous
frequency $\omega_i(t)$ are combined as follows.

Let
$$Z(t) = \omega_i(t) - \int_0^\infty h(x) M(t-x) \, dx \qquad (4.21)$$

Then $Z(t)$ is to consist entirely of distortion or unwanted noise and
interference, and $h(x)$ may be identified through forming the cross-
correlation of $Z(t)$ with $M(t+\tau)$ where τ is a general time lag.[13]
From eqn. 4.21 the requirement is then $\langle Z(t) M(t+\tau) \rangle = 0$, or

$$\int_0^\infty h(x) \psi_M(\tau+x) \, dx = \langle \omega_i(t) M(t+\tau) \rangle \qquad (4.22)$$

Evaluation of the right-hand side is expedited by using $W_i(t)$ as given by
eqn. 3.13 in place of $\omega_i(t)$. The now familiar operations of extracting
the low-frequency terms followed by taking the limit as $h \to 0$ then
give

$$\langle \omega_i(t) M(t+\tau) \rangle = \langle M(t+\tau) \cdot \left\{ \frac{P(t)\dot{Q}(t) - Q(t)\dot{P}(t)}{P^2(t) + Q^2(t)} \right\}$$
$$\left[1 - \exp - \left(\frac{P^2(t) + Q^2(t)}{2\psi_N(0)} \right) \right] \rangle \qquad (4.23)$$

The expression in curly brackets may be recognised as the instantaneous
frequency of the narrow-band transmission, and so the square bracket
is a factor that is introduced by the noise.

Strict observance of the angle brackets in eqn. 4.23 demands information on the way $\mu(t), M(t), P(t)$ and $Q(t)$ are cross-correlated at
general time spacings, but, for even the simplest filtering operation,
the memory of the filter debars any easy way of specifying these
correlations and some approximate approach is required. One such
approach derives from noticing that the averaging is most seriously
impeded by the presence of the factor $P^2(t) + Q^2(t)$ in the
denominator of the curly bracket. This factor, however, is the square
of the envelope of the narrow-band signal, and in those cases where
this envelope differs little from the unfiltered amplitude A, a first
approximation to eqn. 4.23 is

$$\langle \iint_{-\infty}^{+\infty} g(x)g(y)M(t+\tau)M(t-x) \cos [\mu(t-x) - \mu(t-y)] \, dx dy \rangle$$
$$\times \left[1 - \exp - \left(\frac{A^2}{2\psi_N(0)} \right) \right] \qquad (4.24)$$

Now, $\cos [\mu(t-x) - \mu(t-y)]$ can be expanded as $1 - \frac{1}{2} [\mu(t-x) - \mu(t-y)]^2 + \ldots$ etc., but, when contributions from the higher-degree terms to the lower are accounted for, the complete d.c. term is given (as eqn. 2.31 shows) by $\exp - [\psi_\mu(0) - \psi_\mu(x-y)]$. Here $\psi_\mu(\tau)$ is the autocorrelation function of $\mu(t)$. Consequently eqn. 4.24 will contribute

$$\iint_{-\infty}^{+\infty} g(x)g(y)\,\psi_M(\tau+x)\exp - [\psi_\mu(0) - \psi_\mu(x-y)]\,dxdy\,[1-e^{-\rho}]$$
(4.25)

and on comparison with the left-hand side of eqn. 4.22

$$h(x) = g(x)\int_{-\infty}^{+\infty} g(y)\exp - [\psi_\mu(0) - \psi_\mu(x-y)]\,dy\,[1-e^{-\rho}]$$
(4.26)

Casting this result into the form of a frequency characteristic rather than an impulse function shows that the spectral distribution of $M(t)$ at an angular frequency ω is multiplied by

$$\left| \int_{-\infty}^{+\infty} \left\{ \frac{G(q)}{\frac{1}{2}A^2} \right\} [H(jq)H(j(\omega-q))]dq \right|^2 \,[1-\exp-\rho]^2 \qquad (4.27)$$

where $H(j\omega)$ is the transfer characteristic of the equivalent low-pass filter and $G(q)$ is the power spectrum of the unfiltered transmission. ($\int_{-\infty}^{+\infty} G(q)dq = \frac{1}{2}A^2$, the total power). Eqn. 4.27 is the coherence factor when envelope variations in the denominator of eqn. 4.23 are ignored, and it is the counterpart of B_1^2 in the series shown in eqn. 2.37. Thus, with flat f.m., S is given by the product of eqns. 4.27 and 4.10.

An alternative approach to deriving a factor like eqn. 4.27 and one which, in principle, can be made to yield any desired accuracy, is realised through the use of a Volterra series to represent the instantaneous frequency in the curly bracket of eqn. 4.23 before the averaging is done. The Volterra-series technique is taken up more fully in Chapter 7 [for the case in which both $M(t)$ and $\mu(t)$ are Gaussian processes] and here we shall quote the appropriate results.[*] In place of eqn. 4.27, the spectral distribution of the modulating signal is multiplied by

$$\left| H(j\omega) - \frac{1}{4}\int_{-\infty}^{+\infty} W_\mu(x)G_3(\omega,x,-x)dx + \ldots \right|^2 \times [1-\exp-\rho]^2$$
(4.28)

---

[*]For ease of presentation we assume $H(j\omega) = H^*(-j\omega)$. The instructions given above eqn. 7.18 cover the general case

where $W_\mu(x)$ is the power spectrum of the phase modulation $\mu(t)$ of the filtered narrow-band signal.

$$G_3(\omega, x, -x) = 2H(j\omega)H(jx)H(-jx) - H(jx)H(j(\omega - x))$$
$$- H(-jx)H(j(\omega + x))$$

and in the integral $W_\mu(x)$ is defined to be equal to $W_\mu(-x)$. Clearly, the factor $[1 - e^{-\rho}]^2$ comes into play only at very small values of ρ and so it can be omitted when, as will now be assumed, the effect of the filter is of primary interest. Then eqn. 4.28 can be written

$$|H(j\omega)|^2 \cdot \left|\left\{1 - \frac{1}{4}\int_{-\infty}^{+\infty} W_\mu(x)G_3^1(\omega, x, -x)dx + \dots\right\}\right|^2 \quad (4.29)$$

where $H(j\omega)G_3^1(\omega, x, -x) = G_3(\omega, x, -x)$. Usually $|H(j\omega)|^2$ is close to unity for all baseband frequencies ($p_0 \leqslant \omega \leqslant p_m$) but if the filter bandwidth is made too small the curly bracket in eqn. 4.29 will depart significantly from a value of unity. This is an important consideration in the design of threshold extending demodulators, as will be explained in Section 9.7.

Further terms within the modulus signs of eqn. 4.28 can be included if required,[14,15] but the labour involved in their computation greatly exceeds that which is required to handle the terms shown, so in most cases the series is terminated at G_3.

Two estimates of the true coherence factor are therefore available and with regard to eqn. 4.27 some information about $G(q)$ is usually to hand. The spectrum may contain a large residual carrier component so $G(q) \approx \frac{1}{2}A^2\delta(q)$ or perhaps be almost Gaussian in shape, whereupon eqn. 7.26 holds. Such knowledge can be used to evaluate eqn. 4.27 and in the former case we obtain $|H(j\omega)|^2$ which is the leading term of eqn. 4.29. This simple result for the coherence factor can be derived in a number of ways (compare the first term of eqn. 7.12, for example) and it is often accepted as providing sufficient accuracy in published treatments of this topic.[16,18] The conjecture (eqn. 4.20) corresponds to $S = W_M(\omega)|H(j\omega)|^2$ and so is in agreement too.

Now, the Volterra-series approach is best suited to systems which are in the low deviation class (this point is discussed more fully in Section 7.9), that is, the carrier wave that is filtered has a power spectrum that falls away very rapidly on both sides of the centre frequency, and it is in a situation like this that one or two terms of the Volterra series are often adequate and the factor $|H(j\omega)|^2$ is most acceptable. When a carrier that is significantly deviated is passed into the filter the inference is that additional terms will be required in the series shown in eqn. 4.28, for example, but due to the difficulty of

handling such terms (see Chapter 7) this effectively annuls the usefulness of the Volterra-series approach. These extra terms can be viewed
as being a consequence of the need to correctly account for the
altering shape of the r.f. spectrum as the deviation is increased.

This is accounted for in the former method, however, as, on
retrieving eqn. 4.27, it is seen that a direct dependence upon $G(q)$ is
exhibited, although it must be remembered that envelope variations
have been ignored through replacing $P^2(t) + Q^2(t)$ by A^2. As a rough
measure of when such a move is acceptable we can compare the
average value of $P^2(t) + Q^2(t)$ with A^2.

$$\langle P^2(t) + Q^2(t) \rangle = A^2 \iint_{-\infty}^{+\infty} g(x) g(y) \exp - [\psi_\mu(0) - \psi_\mu(x-y)] \, dx dy$$

(4.30)

and this double integral can be transformed into

$$A^2 \int_{-\infty}^{+\infty} |H(j\omega)|^2 \left\{ \frac{G(\omega)}{\frac{1}{2} A^2} \right\} d\omega \qquad (4.31)$$

Thus, if the filter removes only a small fraction of the spectral power,
eqn. 4.27 is likely* to give an acceptable estimate of the factor by
which the useful power at frequency ω is suppressed.

As a final comment it is seen from eqn. 4.23 that if the noise level is
so high that $[1 - \exp - \{P^2(t) + Q^2(t)/2\psi_N(0)\}]$ can be replaced by
$\{P^2(t) + Q^2(t)/2\psi_N(0)\}$ then the error introduced as a result of
ignoring envelope variations is eliminated and the coherence factor is
given by eqn. 4.27 with $[1 - e^{-\rho}]^2$ replaced by ρ^2.

4.6 References

1 MEDHURST, R.G.: 'RF Spectra and interfering carrier distortion in FM
trunk radio systems with low modulation ratios', *Trans. IRE*, 1961, **CS-9**,
(2), pp. 107–115

2 MEDHURST, R.G. 'R.F. Spectra of waves frequency modulated by white
noise', *Proc. IEE*, 1960, 107C, pp. 314–323 (IEE Monograph 380E)

3 HAMER, R., and ACTON, R.A.: 'Power spectrum of a carrier modulated in
phase or frequency by white noise', *Electron. & Radio Eng.*, July 1957,
pp. 246–253

4 BLACHMAN, N.M., and McALPINE, G.A.: 'The spectrum of a high-index
FM waveform: Woodward's theorem revisited', *IEEE Trans.*, 1969, **COM-17**,
(2), pp. 201–208

5 SLEPIAN, D.: 'An expansion of FM spectra', *IEEE Trans*, 1971, **COM-19**,
pp. 223–225

*In Section 7.3 this style of approximation is discussed further

6 BLACHMAN, N.M.: 'New bound for the spectrum of an f.m. wave', *Proc. IEE*, 1974, **121**, (9), pp. 920–922

7 WITTKE, P.H.: 'The autocorrelation function of the output of a non-linear angle modulator', *IEEE Trans.*, 1964, **IT-10**, pp. 67–72

8 HOLBROOK, B.D., and DIXON, J.T.: 'Load rating theory for multi-channel amplifiers', *Bell Syst. Tech. J.*, 1939, **18**, p. 624

9 TANT, M.J.: 'The White Noise Book' (Marconi Instruments Ltd., 1974)

10 TANT, M.J.: 'Further advances in noise power ratio measurements', *Telecommunications*, 1973, **7**, (7), pp. 39–42

11 SPINDLER, W.: 'Noise loading measuring procedures and error sources', *Telecommunications*, 1974, **8**, (7), pp. 32C-32F

12 OLIVER, W.: 'Noise loading of multi-channel communication systems', *Electron. Engineering*, November 1965, pp. 714–717

13 BLACHMAN, N.M.: 'The signal × signal, noise × noise and signal × noise output of a non-linearity', *IEEE Trans.*, 1968, **IT-14**, pp. 21–27

14 BEDROSIAN, E., and RICE, S.O.: 'The output properties of Volterra-systems (non-linear systems with memory) driven by harmonic and Gaussian inputs', *Proc. IEEE*, 1971, **59**, (12), pp. 1688–1707

15 MIRCEA, A., and SINNREICH, H.: 'Distortion noise in frequency-dependent nonlinear networks', *Proc. IEE*, 1969, **116**, (10), pp. 1644–1648

16 SHIMBO, O., and LOO, C.: 'Digital computation of FM Distortion due to linear networks'. IEEE International Conference on Communications, Philadelphia, 1968, pp. 482–486

17 RAINAL, A.J.: 'Computing distortion in analog FM communication systems'. *Bell Syst. Tech. J.*, 1973, **52**, pp. 627–648

Effects of noise, echoes, and adjacent channel interference on the conventional f.m. receiver

5.1 Power spectrum of the instantaneous frequency when narrow-band Gaussian noise is present

As has been discussed in Chapter 4, it is the power spectrum, $W(\omega)$, of the instantaneous frequency that is usually of interest in an analogue f.m. system. In this section, the case of unmodulated carrier plus narrow-band Gaussian noise is considered and $W(0)$, that is, the power spectrum for vanishingly small frequencies, is calculated using the final pair of terms in eqn. 3.71. From the Wiener-Khinchine relationship eqn. 1.6

$$W(0) = \frac{2}{\pi} \int_0^\infty R(\tau) \, d\tau \tag{5.1}$$

and $R(\tau)$ is given by eqn. 3.72. To enable the coefficients $a_0(0), a_1(0)$ and $a_2(0)$ to be handled easily it is convenient to use the following representation for the Bessel function appearing in eqn. 3.73. (Entry 3·868 of Reference 1, holding for $A \neq 0$):

$$J_0(A\sqrt{x^2 + y^2 + 2xy \cos \gamma})$$
$$= \frac{1}{\pi} \int_0^\infty \sin\left[\frac{A^2}{4V}(x^2 + y^2 + 2xy \cos \gamma) + V \right] \frac{dV}{V} \tag{5.2}$$

Then $R(\tau)$ can be written

$$R(\tau) = R_e \left\{ \frac{1}{4\pi j} \int_{-\infty}^{+\infty} e^{jv} \frac{\partial}{\partial \tau} \left[\frac{-r'_N(\tau)}{vr_N(\tau) - j\rho} \right] \times \right.$$
$$\left. -\log_e \left[1 - \left(\frac{vr_N(\tau) - j\rho}{v - j\rho} \right)^2 \right] dv \right\} \tag{5.3}$$

where R_e means 'real part of'.

$$\rho = \frac{A^2}{2\psi_N(0)} \qquad \text{is the carrier-to-noise power ratio}$$

$$r_N(\tau) = \frac{\psi_N(\tau)}{\psi_N(0)} \qquad \text{is the noise covariance function}$$

$$r'_N(\tau) = \frac{\psi'_N(\tau)}{\psi_N(0)} \qquad \text{etc.}$$

substituting eqn. 5.3 in eqn. 5.1 and integrating by parts gives

$$W(0) = \frac{2}{\pi}\int_0^\infty \frac{[r'_N(\tau)]^2}{1-r_N^2(\tau)}$$

$$\left\{ \frac{1}{\pi}\int_0^\infty \left[\frac{\frac{2\rho}{1+r_N(\tau)}\cos v + v\sin v}{v^2 + \left(\frac{2\rho}{1+r_N(\tau)}\right)^2} \right] dv \right\} d\tau$$

$$= \frac{2}{\pi}\int_0^\infty \frac{[r'_N(\tau)]^2}{1-r_N^2(\tau)}\exp - \left[\frac{2\rho}{1+r_N(\tau)} \right] d\tau \qquad (5.4)$$

This result appears to have been derived first by Blachman[2,3] who points out that for ρ large ($\rho > 2$, say) the major contribution to the integral comes from the small τ region (where $r_N(\tau) \approx 1 + \tau^2/2r''_N(0) + ..$), and then

$$W(0) \approx 2\sqrt{\frac{-r''_N(0)}{\pi\rho}}\, e^{-\rho} \qquad (5.5)$$

Blachman obtained eqn. 5.5 from an investigation of the variance of $N(T)$ the number of zeros of a narrow-band process that occur in time T, and comparing eqn. 5.4 with 3.56 it is clear that

$$W(0) = \lim_{T\to\infty} \frac{\pi}{T}\, Var\,[N(T)] \qquad (5.6)$$

At first sight it might appear undesirably restrictive to confine attention to $W(0)$ but the fact that $W(0)$ is non-zero is significant when it is remembered that the instantaneous frequency is the time derivative of $\theta(t)$, the instantaneous phase, and the power spectrum of $\dot\theta(t)$ could therefore be expected to have a multiplying factor of ω^2 so rendering $W(\omega)$ zero when $\omega = 0$. The reason for $W(\omega)$ not being of this form is the multi-valued nature of $\theta(t)$ in that at any instant it can be viewed as the sum of two parts, the first part being $\theta(t)$ reduced modulo 2π, and the second part an integer multiple (positive or negative) of 2π. As time goes by this multiple changes, with the next integer value above or below being adopted abruptly in step-like fashion, and with $\theta(t)$, when reduced modulo 2π, remaining close to its value before the jump occurred. These steps of 2π in $\theta(t)$ give rise to sharp pulses in $\dot{\theta}(t)$ that have considerable low-frequency content and which provide the non-zero value of $W(0)$.

It has long been observed that a very marked change takes place in the output of an f.m. receiver fed with the sum of a modulated (or unmodulated) carrier and narrow-band noise when ρ passes through a critical region usually near $\rho = 10$. Above this value the wanted intelligence is accompanied by a background hiss, but below it (exactly where is often a matter of subjective judgement) the hiss is joined by what have been variously described as splutterings, pops, or clicks. These individual spike-like pulses in $\dot{\theta}(t)$ rapidly increase in their frequency of occurrence as ρ becomes smaller still until they merge with the hiss into a continuously distributed non-Gaussian interference.

This description is seen to be in accord with the explanation given earlier for $W(0)$ being non-zero and the value of ρ at which the clicks can be said to first appear is often referred to as the f.m. threshold point.

In many practical situations a knowledge of the performance above the f.m. threshold and a short way into the threshold region where clicks may be individually distinguished, suffices; indeed, the notion of a click becomes inappropriate if ρ is too small and events such as the phase almost accumulating 2π by a forward rotation only to be counteracted by a rotation in the reverse sense, are no longer very rare. When ρ is this small ($\rho < 2$, say) the spectral distribution is given, strictly, by all the terms in eqn. 3.71 (except for subtraction of the linearly filtered part) and the situation well below threshold will be considered later. (Section 5.5)

Using the observation that as the demodulator approaches its threshold the output changes rapidly in character in the way outlined above, Cohn[4] and Rice[5] developed theory that provides expressions for ν the expected number of upward and downward clicks that occur per second. Using a phasor diagram in which the envelope R and instantaneous phase θ of the carrier plus noise sum are taken as polar coordinates, Cohn argued that, for an impulsive disturbance or pop to appear in $\theta(t)$, the origin of the phasor diagram must be enclosed by the locus of the resultant R so that a net gain or loss of one complete cycle is registered compared with the phase of the undisturbed carrier.

Now take eqn. 1.3 with $X(t)$ and $Y(t)$ replaced by $I_c(t)$ and $I_s(t)$ the low-pass components of narrow-band Gaussian noise. The assumption (Section 2.1) that the noise power spectrum is symmetrical about the nominal carrier frequency ω_0 ensures that I_c, I_s, and the derivatives $\dot{I}_c, \dot{I}_s$, are four mutually uncorrelated variates. Should this symmetry be satisfied only for some neighbouring r.f. frequency $\omega_0 - \omega_L$, we may re-express the signal by resolving it about $\omega_0 - \omega_L$. The results obtained in this section then apply with the instantaneous frequency $M(t)$ replaced by $M(t) + \omega_L$. The sum of f.m. signal and noise is written

$$[A + P_1(t)] \cos [\omega_0 t + \mu(t)] - Q_1(t) \sin [\omega_0 t + \mu(t)] \qquad (5.7)$$

where

$$P_1(t) = I_c \cos \mu(t) + I_s \sin \mu(t)$$

$$Q_1(t) = I_s \cos \mu(t) - I_c \sin \mu(t)$$

$$\langle I_s^2 \rangle = \langle I_c^2 \rangle = \psi_N(0)$$

The derivatives $\dot{I}_s$ and $\dot{I}_c$ will be independent Gaussian variates, and

$$\langle (\dot{I}_s)^2 \rangle = \langle (\dot{I}_c)^2 \rangle = -r_N''(0) \cdot \psi_N(0)$$

The inverse tangent with argument $[Q_1(t)]/[A + P_1(t)]$ gives the phase error measured relative to the phase of the undisturbed carrier, and if this angle should pass through π [so $A + P_1(t)$ is negative] it is likely that a complete encirclement of the origin will ensue. Such a passage through π is not an unconditional guarantee of a click, but when ρ is large such events are rare, and a return to the neighbourhood of the undisturbed phase without completing the rotation is extremely unlikely.[4-6] ν, the expected number of pops or clicks that occur per second, can therefore be equated with the expected number of zeros of $Q_1(t)$ that occur per second when $A + P_1(t)$ is negative.

Then the following double integral, in which the angle brackets indicate an expectation to be taken over the modulation parameters, gives the probability of a click in the interval $(0, dt)$

$$\left\langle \int_{-\infty}^{-A} \int_{-\infty}^{+\infty} |\dot{Q}_1| \, p(\dot{Q}_1, P_1, 0) \, d\dot{Q}_1 \, dP_1 \right\rangle dt \qquad (5.8)$$

(this type of integral was introduced by Rice (Section 3.3 of Reference 7) in his early work on the expected number of zeros occurring per second).

Now $\dot{Q}_1$ and P_1 are both Gaussian and their joint density function $p(\dot{Q}_1, P_1)$ is given by

$$p(\dot{Q}_1, P_1) = \frac{1}{2\pi(\sqrt{-r_N''(0)})\,\psi_N(0)} \exp\left[\frac{-1}{2\psi_N(0)[-r_N''(0)]}\right.$$
$$\left. \{(\dot{Q}_1)^2 + 2M(t)\dot{Q}_1 P_1 + [M^2(t) - r_N''(0)]\,P_1^2\}\right] \quad (5.9)$$

where, as earlier, $M(t)$ is $\dot{\mu}(t)$, the frequency modulation.

$$p(\dot{Q}_1, P_1, Q_1) = p(\dot{Q}_1, P_1)\,p(Q_1)$$

so, in eqn. 5.8,

$$p(\dot{Q}_1, P_1, 0) = \frac{1}{\sqrt{2\pi\psi_N(0)}}p(\dot{Q}_1, P_1)$$

The integration is straightforward requiring only standard integral results, and dividing by dt, the click rate ν is given* by

$$\nu = \langle \frac{\sqrt{-r_N''(0)}}{2\pi} \cdot \sqrt{1 + \frac{[M(t)]^2}{-r_N''(0)}}\left\{1 - \mathrm{erf}\left(\sqrt{\rho\left\{1 + \frac{[M(t)]^2}{-r_N''(0)}\right\}}\right)\right\}$$
$$+ \frac{M(t)}{2\pi}\exp -\rho\;\mathrm{erf}\left(\frac{M(t)}{\sqrt{-r_N''(0)}}\sqrt{\rho}\right)\rangle \quad (5.10)$$

for large ρ, therefore

$$\nu \approx \langle \frac{1}{2\pi}\left\{\sqrt{\frac{-r_N''(0)}{\pi\rho}}\exp\left[-\rho\left\{1 + \frac{[M(t)]^2}{-r_N''(0)}\right\}\right]\right.$$
$$\left. + M(t)\,\mathrm{erf}\left[\frac{M(t)}{\sqrt{-r_N''(0)}}\sqrt{\rho}\right]\exp -\rho\right\}\rangle \quad (5.11)$$

When $M(t)$ is constant the $\langle\;\rangle$ brackets are redundant and then eqn. 5.10 agrees with a result given by Rice (add the two members of expression 71 of Reference 5) for the expected number of times per second that $\theta(t)$ passes through an odd multiple of π, while the extension to eqn. 5.11 can be inferred in Cohn's paper where experimental evidence that formulae of this type predict the click rate accurately is given.

Noting that the curly bracket of the exponential in eqn. 5.9 can be written $\{[\dot{Q}_1 + P_1 M(t)]^2 - r_N''(0)P_1^2\}$ the change of variable $\dot{Q}_1 + P_1 M(t) = y\;\; d\dot{Q}_1 = dy$ gives

$$\nu = \frac{1}{\sqrt{2\pi\psi_N(0)}}\langle\frac{1}{\sqrt{2\pi\psi_N(0)}}\int_{-\infty}^{-A}|P_1|\exp -\frac{P_1^2}{2\psi_N(0)}$$
$$\left(\frac{1}{\sqrt{2\pi\cdot -r_N''(0)\psi_N(0)}}\int_{-\infty}^{+\infty}\left|M(t) - \frac{y}{P_1}\right|\exp -\frac{y^2/2}{-r_N''(0)\psi_N(0)}\,dy\right)dP_1\rangle$$

*This formulation presupposes that $M(t)$ is stationary. When it is not the click rate is obtained by taking a long-term average

A much simplified expression for v is obtained if P_1 is replaced by $-A$ in the inner integral (on the grounds that $A + P_1$ will be a very small negative quantity for the majority of clicks), for then the right-hand side separates into two integrals with clear interpretations, and

$$v \approx \frac{1}{2\pi} \left\langle \left| M(t) + \frac{\dot{I}_s}{A} \right| \right\rangle \exp - \rho \qquad (5.12)$$

This form reproduces eqn. 5.11 when the expectation on $\dot{I}_s$ is carried through (as was pointed out in Reference 8) and an independent derivation is given in Reference 9. The calculation of the expectation on $M(t)$ is greatly facilitated when eqn. 5.12 is used, and when $M(t)$ is a zero mean Gaussian process with r.m.s. value ω_Δ we have

$$v = \frac{1}{2\pi} \sqrt{-r_N''(0)} \left\{ \frac{1 + 2b\rho}{\pi\rho} \right\}^{1/2} \exp - \rho \qquad (5.13)$$

where

$$b = \frac{\omega_\Delta^2}{-r_N''(0)}$$

When $M(t)$ is a sine-wave modulation of amplitude A

$$v = 2(L_1 + L_2) \qquad (5.14)$$

where

$$L_1 = \frac{1}{4\pi} \sqrt{\frac{-r_N''(0)}{\pi\rho}} I_0(a\rho) e^{-(1+a)\rho}$$

$$L_2 = \frac{1}{4\pi} \sqrt{\frac{-r_N''(0)}{\pi\rho}} 2a\rho \{I_0(a\rho) + I_1(a\rho)\} e^{-(1+a)\rho}$$

with

$$a = \frac{A^2/2}{-r_N''(0)}$$

Further, the working given in References 5 and 9 allows the rates v_+, v_- of upward and downward clicks to be individually determined and

$$v_+ - v_- = \left\langle -\frac{M(t)}{2\pi} e^{-\rho} \right\rangle \qquad (5.15)$$

(note, $v_+ > v_-$ when $\langle M(t) \rangle$ is negative) with $v_+ + v_- = v$ being given by eqns. 5.10 or 5.11.

Our preoccupation with v at this point stems from another aspect of the theory developed by Rice. On picturing the train of impulses in $\dot{\theta}(t)$ as a succession of positive and negative delta functions with arrival times that constitute a Poisson process (v arrivals/s), Rice combined Cambell's theorem with this model and showed (Reference 5 and Sections 1.3 and 2.6 of Reference 7) that

$$W(0) = 4\pi v \qquad (5.16)$$

and this will be seen to be in agreement with eqn. 5.5 when ν is provided by eqn. 5.11 with $M(t) = 0$.

Thus, two alternative ways of obtaining $W(0)$ are offered: either eqn. 5.1 is used, or ν is calculated and placed in eqn. 5.16.

In principle the former method will give the result corresponding to eqn. 5.4 when the carrier is modulated. Firstly replace γ in eqn. 5.2 by $(\gamma + \Delta)$ where Δ is given by $\mu(t + \tau) - \mu(t)$, as follows from three lines below eqn. 3.66 when $P(t) = A \cos \mu(t)$ and $Q(t) = A \sin \mu(t)$. It is then found that the cross term in eqn. 3.71 [that is, the term leading with $\psi_N'(\tau)$] has to be included and that additional contributions come from the pair of terms that eventually led to eqn. 5.4. No neat way of presenting the final result has been found but Shimbo[10] has shown that for Gaussian modulation a form closely similar to 4π times eqn. 5.13 can be obtained for large ρ. Thus, the three terms with which eqn. 3.71 concludes provide the interference components at low-frequencies, but $W(0)$ is more easily calculated using ν as given by one of the formulae eqns. 5.10, 5.11, 5.12, 5.13 or 5.14, and then applying eqn. 5.16.

It is seen that $\sqrt{-r_N''(0)}$ is a parameter of the noise that plays a prominent role in the theory and that it has the dimensions of an angular frequency. In terms of $H(j\omega)$, the transfer characteristic of the bandpass filter stages of the receiver before any nonlinear operations such as limiting, $-r_N''(0)$ is given by

$$-r_N''(0) = \frac{\int_{-\infty}^{+\infty} N(\omega) \cdot \omega^2 |H(j\omega)|^2 \, d\omega}{\int_{-\infty}^{+\infty} N(\omega) |H(j\omega)|^2 \, d\omega} \qquad (5.17)$$

where ω is measured from the centre frequency ω_0, and $N(\omega)$ is the power spectrum of the noise before it is filtered. A commonly encountered case is that of flat noise received in a filter having unity transfer for frequencies in the range $\omega_0 - \omega_B$ to $\omega_0 + \omega_B$, and zero transfer elsewhere. Then

$$-r_N''(0) = \frac{\omega_B^2}{3}$$

so

$$\sqrt{-r_N''(0)} = \frac{\omega_B}{\sqrt{3}}$$

$-r_N''(0)$ as given by eqn. 5.17 may be recognised as $\left. \dfrac{-\partial^2 \psi_N(h)/(\partial h^2)}{\psi_N(h)} \right|_{h=0}$

in accordance with the definitions quoted earlier below eqns. 3.39 and 3.42.

5.2 Definitions of spectral density

The various treatments that have appeared in the literature have differed in their definitions of spectral density. It is recalled that $\dot{\theta}(t)$ is measured in radians/s thus $W(\omega)$ as given by eqn. 3.76 has the units $(\text{rad/s})^2 \times$ s, i.e. $(2\pi)^2$ Hz or 2π rad/s. So when $W(\omega)$ is divided by any convenient frequency a dimensionless quantity is obtained and $\sqrt{-r_N''(0)}$ as calculated from eqn. 5.17 (sometimes referred to as the radius of gyration of the power spectrum assumed for the input noise) serves this purpose, as it is a characteristic of the receiver i.f. filter stages before the limiter.

Some authors prefer to work entirely in terms of Hertz rather than rad/s and Wang[11] uses a dimensionless quantity which he writes as $G(f)/4\pi B$ where B is the bandwidth in Hz of a rectangular i.f. filter. It turns out that Wang's $G(f)/4\pi B$ is the quantity $W(f)/[4\pi\beta]$ in notation adopted by Rice[3] and both of these are equivalent to $\pi/4E_1(u)/\Delta_\omega^2$ of Stumpers.[12]

The click theory is expected to offer adequate accuracy at carrier-to-noise power ratios that exceed 2 or so, and, for the case of a Gaussian i.f. filter characteristic, Rice gives a table which shows an agreement of better than 1 dB with exact spectral levels obtained by numerical integration (Table II of Reference 13).

In the case of a rectangular i.f. pass-band the click theory gives eqn. 5.18, below, which can be compared directly with $G(f)/4\pi B$ (see Table 13.2 of Reference 11) and with $\pi/4E_1(u)/\Delta_\omega^2$ (see Table III of Reference 12)

$$\frac{\pi W(\omega)}{2\omega_B} = \frac{\pi}{\sqrt{3}}\left[1 - \text{erf}\left(\sqrt{\rho}\right)\right] + \frac{\pi}{\rho}\left(\frac{\omega}{2\omega_B}\right)^2 \qquad (5.18)$$

A comparison of results is given in Table 5.1.
Usually interest lies in frequencies in the demodulator output that are much smaller than the i.f. bandwidth, and $\omega/2\omega_B \leqslant 0.2$ is representative.

It is seen that agreement is generally good, the largest discrepancy being at $\rho = 5$, with $\omega/2\omega_B = 0$ where the entry in the final column seems rather low. At this point with a Gaussian i.f. filter the click theory gives 0·00314, Table IV of Reference 12 gives $\pi/4 (0\cdot06681)^2 = 0\cdot0035$, and the exact result is 0·003017. With a change in pass-band shaping therefore very close agreement is retrieved and it is perhaps significant that Stumpers' numerical attack involved the summation of series which converge much more rapidly for the Gaussian pass-band than for the rectangular shape.

Table 5.1   Spectral density of instantaneous frequency of
unmodulated carrier + noise

ρ (power ratio)	$\dfrac{\omega}{2\omega_B}$	Click theory	Theory of Wang	Theory of Stumpers
1·5	0	0·1532	0·134	
2·0	0	0·0834		0·060
5·0	0	0·0028		0·0013
10·0	0	$1·469 \times 10^{-5}$	$1·38 \times 10^{-5}$	
1·5	0·2	0·2370	0·182	
2·0	0·2	0·1462		0·1063
5·0	0·2	0·0279		0·0283
10·0	0·2	0·0140	0·0132	

Rectangular i.f. filter of width $2\omega_B$ rad/s. Table entries calculated from eqn. 5.18
for click theory.

5.3 Regions in and above the f.m. threshold

Above the threshold $\theta(t)$ the instantaneous phase, may be regarded as
always lying the range $-\pi$ to π, as the jumps of 2π occur so rarely they
can be ignored. Then with reference to eqn. 5.7, because ρ is now
envisaged as exceeding 10, say, $P_1(t)$ can be neglected in relation to A.
Then

$$\theta(t) = \mu(t) + \tan^{-1}\left[\frac{Q_1(t)}{A + P_1(t)}\right]$$

can be replaced by

$$\theta(t) \approx \mu(t) + \frac{Q_1(t)}{A} = \mu(t) + \frac{I_s}{A}\cos\mu(t) - \frac{I_c}{A}\sin\mu(t) \quad (5.19)$$

whence

$$\dot{\theta}(t) \approx \dot{\mu}(t) + \frac{\dot{Q}_1(t)}{A} \quad (5.20)$$

This result is in accord with the conceptual description given earlier
that above threshold the wanted intelligence $\dot{\mu}(t)$ is accompanied by
a background hiss, and eqn. 5.20 will be seen to be a linear relationship
in that $\dot{Q}_1(t)/A$ is an additive disturbance which is itself a linear function
of the in-phase and quadrature components of the noise and their
derivatives. For this reason operation above the threshold is often
referred to as the linear region of the receiver.

As the in-phase and quadrature noise components are Gaussian
variables, it is a simple exercise to calculate the autocorrelation function
of Q_1/A (assuming $\mu(t)$ to be a stationary modulation process) and
then use eqn. 1.6 to obtain $W_1(\omega)$, say, the spectral distribution.

With $C(\tau) = \langle \cos [\mu(t + \tau) - \mu(t)] \rangle$ and assuming the noise to have a flat spectrum covering the range $\omega_0 - \omega_B$ to $\omega_0 + \omega_B$

$$W_1(\omega) = \frac{\omega^2}{\rho\pi} \int_0^\infty \left(\frac{\sin \omega_B \tau}{\omega_B \tau} \right) C(\tau) \cos (\omega\tau) \, d\tau$$

The equivalent of eqn. 4.7 then transforms this into

$$W_1(\omega) = \frac{\omega^2}{\rho(A^2/2)} \frac{1}{2\omega_B} \left\{ \int_0^{\omega_B - \omega} G(y) dy + \int_0^{\omega_B + \omega} G(y) dy \right\} \quad (5.21)$$

where $\int_{-\infty}^{+\infty} G(y) dy = A^2/2$ and $G(y)$ is the power spectrum of the modulated carrier $A \cos [\omega_0 t + \mu(t)]$. $\frac{1}{2}A^2$ is the total power transmitted and the bandwidth of $2\omega_B$ will generally be sufficient to adequately accommodate the modulated carrier so $\int_{-\omega_B}^{\omega_B} G(y) dy$ will very closely approximate to $\frac{1}{2}A^2$. It follows that for $\omega \ll \omega_B$ the curly bracket in eqn. 5.21 can be replaced by $\frac{1}{2}A^2$ with little error, and then

$$W_1(\omega) = \frac{\omega^2}{\rho 2\omega_B} \quad \omega \ll \omega_B \quad (5.22)$$

This result (with the inequality replaced by $\omega \leqslant \omega_B$) is obtained, however, if $\dot{Q}_1(t)/A$ is taken to be $\dot{I}_s(t)/A$, that is, the modulation $\mu(t)$ is placed equal to zero (the carrier is unmodulated). Thus, taking the modulation into account has a negligible effect on the spectral distribution of the interference at frequencies that are small in comparison with the semi-bandwidth. In qualitative terms the interference is, in fact, slightly reduced in level by the presence of the modulation.

In the f.m. f.d.m. situation described in Chapter 4, the measure of system performance is given by forming the ratio of $W_1(\omega)$ to the spectral density of $\dot{\mu}(t)$ at the same value of ω. Thus, above threshold

$$\frac{D}{S} = \frac{(p_m - p_0)}{\omega_\Delta^2} \cdot \frac{\omega^2}{\rho \cdot 2\omega_B} \quad (5.23)$$

D/S stands for distortion-to-signal ratio which, strictly, is a misnomer as here we are assuming no bandwidth restriction and therefore no distortion, but this is a practice that is now well established. When distortion is present, and noise too, S stands for the linearly-filtered component (the undistorted version of $\dot{\mu}(t)$ that was discussed in Section 4.5) while D refers to the spectral density of all terms in eqn. 3.71, for example, after the linearly filtered part has been subtracted out.

The combination of inphase and quadrature noise components in eqn. 5.19 will be met in other rather similar guises later (see eqns. 9.17

and 9.45) and the fact that the spectral distribution hardly differs (at least, for frequencies over the baseband range) from that of I_s/A together with the fact that the mean square value is also independent of $\mu(t)$, prompts us to place $\mu(t)$ (or its non-Gaussian equivalent in other cases) equal to zero in order to obtain a useful simplification, i.e. $(I_s/A) \cos \mu(t) + (I_c/A) \sin \mu(t)$ is replaced by I_s/A. When rather broad-brush statistical features suffice, this is a very helpful approximation and it may also be noted that the peak value, which, strictly, is given by the maximum of $(I_s^2 + I_c^2)^{1/2}/A$, is exchanged for the peak value of I_s/A.

By integrating eqn. 5.23 across the information bandwidth p_m, the total noise power falling into the baseband is obtained, and many writers refer to $3(\omega_\Delta/p_m)^2 (2\omega_B/p_m)\rho$ as the above threshold signal-to-noise ratio of f.m. The factor of 3 is then a reliable indicator that this integration has been done and a definition of S/D differing from the one used here is in force.

5.4 Useful formula for D/S

Now, by adding eqns. 5.16 and 5.22 consider

$$\frac{D}{S} = \frac{4\pi\nu + \dfrac{\omega^2}{2\omega_B} \cdot \dfrac{1}{\rho}}{\left(\dfrac{\omega_\Delta^2}{p_m - p_0}\right)[1 - e^{-\rho}]^2} \qquad 0 < \omega \leqslant p_m, \rho > 2 \quad (5.24)$$

When ρ is above the threshold this becomes eqn. 5.23, effectively, showing a dependence on ω, the spot frequency at which D/S is calculated. When ρ becomes smaller and the threshold region is entered, the interference is dominated by clicks having a flat spectrum across the baseband, and, when ρ is smaller still, the coherence factor $[1 - e^{-\rho}]^2$ (coming from eqn. 4.28 with $H(j\omega) \equiv 1$ as no filtering is currently assumed) becomes important in deciding the linearly filtered component.

This simple formula for D/S is therefore seen to offer a highly plausible way of approximating the D/S ratio. Indeed, it has been widely used in system assessments, proving to be in good agreement with measurements (which are usually presented in terms of n.p.r. rather than S/D or D/S) and with the results of a Monte Carlo approach to calculating distortion levels in f.m. f.d.m. trunk radio systems.[14] Gor greement was maintained even when ρ fell a little below the valu ₁ 2 (3 dB carrier-to-noise ratio) which Rice considered to be the lower limit of validity of the theory (Reference 5 and Table 5.1).

The most useful form of eqn. 5.24 pertains to the case in which a flat band of noise is taken as a model for the frequency modulation and the additive noise has a flat spectrum over the range $\omega_0 - \omega_B$ to $\omega_0 + \omega_B$. Then, using eqn. 5.13

$$\frac{D}{S} = \frac{(p_m - p_0)}{\omega_\Delta^2} \cdot \frac{2\omega_B}{[1 - e^{-\rho}]^2} \left\{ \frac{1}{\sqrt{3\pi}} e^{-\rho} \sqrt{24 \left(\frac{\omega_\Delta}{p_m}\right)^2 \left(\frac{p_m}{2\omega_B}\right)^2 + \frac{1}{\rho}} \right.$$
$$\left. + \frac{1}{\rho}\left(\frac{p}{2\omega_B}\right)^2 \right\} \tag{5.25}$$

and this gives the distortion-to-signal power ratio at a general baseband position $(p_0 \leqslant p \leqslant p_m)$ at the output of an f.m. f.d.m. system.

As is seen from eqn. 5.22, the above-threshold interference has a 6 dB-per octave slope, and it follows that audio channels near the top end of the baseband receive a greater interference contribution than channels placed lower down. To share this penalty more evenly it is customary to shape the baseband spectral distribution of $\dot{\mu}(t)$ by applying a pre-emphasis which leaves ω_Δ, the r.m.s. frequency deviation, unaltered. The pre-emphasis law recommended by the international body known as CCIR (Comité Consultatif International des Radio Communications) can be well approximated[15] by

$$P(p) = 0\cdot4 \cosh\left(2\cdot55 \cdot \frac{p}{p_m}\right) \tag{5.26}$$

thus when $p = p_m$, for example, $+4$ dB of pre-emphasis is applied, but this falls smoothly to -4 dB when $p \approx p_0$.

As this law leaves ω_Δ unchanged

$$\left(\frac{\omega_\Delta^2}{p_m - p_0} \int_{p_0}^{p_m} 0\cdot4 \cosh\left(2\cdot55 \frac{p}{p_m}\right) dp \approx \omega_\Delta^2\right)$$

the sole modification to eqn. 5.25 to account for pre-emphasis is the inclusion of $P(p)$ in the denominator of the right-hand side.

Fig. 5.1 shows eqn. 5.25 plotted for a 240 channel non-pre-emphasised system (baseband range 60 kHz – 1052 kHz; 200 kHz r.m.s. test-tone deviation). The threshold point ρ_τ is usually defined as the value of ρ at which a 1 dB departure from the above-threshold linear performance takes place; in the 1002 kHz channel $\rho_\tau = 7\cdot6$ dB, in the 70 kHz channel $\rho_\tau = 11\cdot6$ dB.

For general cases, Fig. 5.2 shows ρ_τ plotted against $(p/2\omega_B)$ for an unmodulated carrier. This is justified by the observation that the threshold point is not critically dependent on the presence of the modulation (the formulae given in eqns. 5.13 and 5.14 can be used for particular modulations) and a simplification in presentation is then achieved since ρ_T is the value of ρ that satisfies

$$\left(\frac{2\omega_B}{p}\right)^2 \sqrt{\frac{\rho}{3\pi}} e^{-\rho} = 0.259 \qquad (5.27)$$

Fig. 5.2 provides a datum against which the performance of threshold extending devices (see Chapter 9) can be measured.

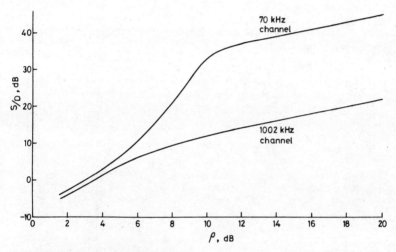

Fig. 5.1 Baseband curves of *S/D* versus ρ

  240 channel non-pre-emphasised f.m. f.d.m. system with the baseband
  range 60 kHz to 1052 kHz. The r.m.s. test-tone deviation is 200 kHz,
  making $\omega_\Delta/p_m = 0.52$
  Threshold occurs in the 1002 kHz channel when $\rho = 7.6$ dB, and in the
  70 kHz channel when $\rho = 10.6$ dB

5.5 Well below the f.m. threshold

The region that is many decibels below the threshold point can be of importance when deep fading occurs on a link or when severe jamming is experienced, and it is given a brief treatment here for reasons of completeness.

  The carrier-to-noise power ratio will be considered as lying in the range 0 to 4 and the interference will be assumed to have a flat power spectrum, specified by $W(0)$, over the baseband frequencies.

  In the limit of zero carrier power (so only noise in input) a result for the spectral distribution of the instantaneous frequency at $\omega = 0$

is available by combining eqns. 5.6 and 3.55 but then, of course, it is immaterial whether or not the carrier is modulated.

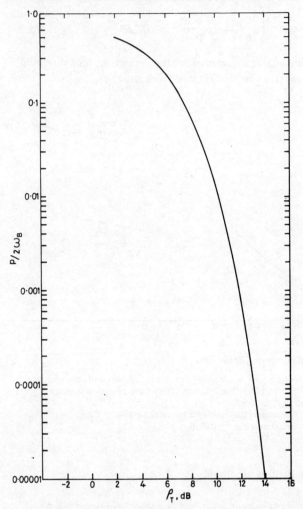

Fig. 5.2 Values of ρ at which the f.m. threshold occurs

$\rho/2\omega_B$ is the ratio of the baseband frequency of interest to the noise bandwidth at the detector input. The noise is measured in the bandwidth $2\omega_B$

With non-zero carrier power and a phase modulation $\mu(t)$ the in-phase and quadrature components of carrier + noise are given by $A \cos \mu(t) + I_c$ and $A \sin \mu(t) + I_s$, and when $\mu(t)$ is a Gaussian process these have respective mean values of $A \exp -\frac{1}{2} \psi_\mu(0)$ and zero, and variances which each differ little from that of the noise when $\rho < 1$.

In the case of an unmodulated carrier the interference spectrum is given for all values of ρ by eqn. 3.76 and numerical results are well documented (see Table 5.1, for example). In this case the in-phase component is given by $A + I_c$ and the quadrature component by I_s. It seems likely therefore that on examining the distribution densities of $A \cos \mu(t) + I_c$ and $A \sin \mu(t) + I_s$ a simple perturbation technique would enable the required interference spectrum to be estimated from the results available for the unmodulated case.

Letting $W_m(\omega, \rho)$ be the power spectrum to be estimated (the suffix m indicating the presence of modulation and ω being a general baseband frequency) the relationship used is

$$W_m(\omega, \rho) \approx W(\omega, \rho_e) \qquad (5.28)$$

where $W(\omega, \rho_e)$ is the spectrum in the unmodulated case and ρ_e is an 'equivalent' carrier-to-noise power ratio in which the 'equivalent' carrier power is taken as $\frac{1}{2} A^2 \exp - \psi_\mu(0)$. The 'equivalent' noise power is obtained by first calculating the distribution densities of $f_D = A \cos \mu(t) + I_c$ and $f_N = A \sin \mu(t) + I_s$ (Reference 16) and seeing how they compare to the distributions of $A + I_c$ and I_s.

Almost independently of the r.m.s. phase deviation applied to the carrier, interference levels up to a value of ρ approaching 0 dB can be estimated by this method. Beyond this point two effects become noticeable that cause a breakdown: when $\psi_N(0)$ is small the peaks in the density curves of f_D and f_N become incomparable, and when $\psi_\mu(0)$ is large the distributions are not sufficiently bell like.

Fig. 5.3 shows the results obtained. $[\pi W_m(0, \rho)]/[2\omega_B]$ is plotted against ρ (as a power ratio), the multiplying factor of π being included to gain uniformity with the dimensionless quantity $G(0)/4\pi B$ of Wang[11] and $W(0)/4\pi\beta$ as used by Rice.[5] From eqns. 5.13 and 5.16, when $\rho > 2 \ [\pi W_m(0, \rho)]/[2\omega_B]$ is given by

$$\frac{\pi W_m(0, \rho)}{2\omega_B} = \sqrt{\frac{\pi}{3}} e^{-\rho} \sqrt{24 \left(\frac{\omega_\Delta}{p_m}\right)^2 \left(\frac{p_m}{2\omega_B}\right)^2 + \frac{1}{\rho}} \qquad (5.29)$$

Two curves obtained from this are shown on Fig. 5.3, and, on ignoring variation with baseband frequency,

$$\frac{D}{S} \approx \frac{(p_m - p_0) \, W_m(0, \rho)}{\omega_\Delta^2 [1 - e^{-\rho}]^2} \qquad (5.30)$$

The tacit assumption has been made that the input bandwidth is sufficiently large to adequately accommodate the carrier no matter how large the f.m. index ω_Δ/p_m becomes. Carson's rule as shown in eqn. 4.13 is often used to assess this bandwidth and the factor of $3 \cdot 162$ is an accepted peak-to-r.m.s. figure for Gaussian noise. Other factors of comparable magnitude can be used equally well and the original formulation[16] of the present theory adopted a factor of 4. This will be retained here, and then, if the f.m. index is made very large, the

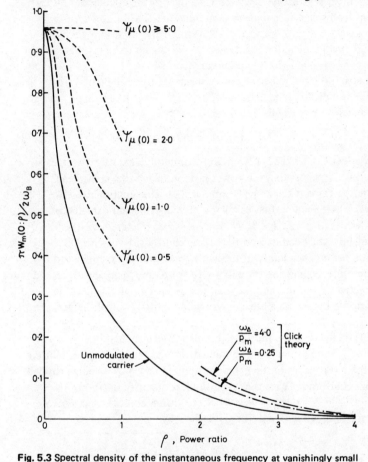

Fig. 5.3 Spectral density of the instantaneous frequency at vanishingly small baseband frequencies and for small values of the carrier-to-noise ratio

$\psi_\mu(0)$ is the mean square phase deviation
The i.f. filter is rectangular, of width $2\omega_B$ (rad/s), and perfect limiting is assumed

following simple limiting form is obtained for $[\pi W_m(0, \rho)]/[2\omega_B]$

$$\frac{\pi W_m(0, \rho)}{2\omega_B} \approx \sqrt{\frac{\pi}{3}} e^{-\rho} \left\{ \frac{3}{8} + \frac{1}{\rho} \right\}^{1/2} \qquad (5.31)$$

When the f.m. index is large, the mean square phase deviation will also be large, and Fig. 5.3 suggests that in such situations a drop of about 9 dB in the interference level will accompany an increase in the carrier-to-noise ratio from 0 dB to 3 dB. The dotted line on Fig. 5.4 offers a plausible join-up between eqn. 5.31 and the perturbation technique, so bridging the region where a theory is very difficult to develop. It

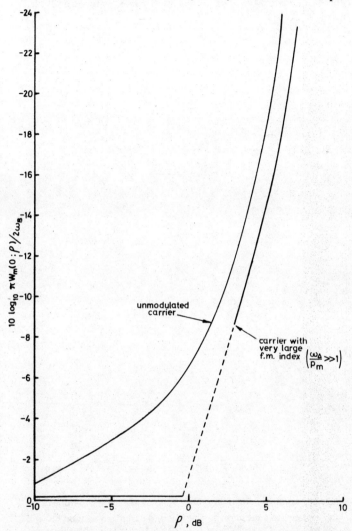

Fig. 5.4 Spectral density of the instantaneous frequency of a noise-modulated f.m. carrier plus Gaussian noise

Limiting curves (common to all baseband frequencies) for very large and very small f.m. indices

seems that $\psi_\mu(0)$ is the governing modulation parameter when $\rho < 1$, and two curves can be drawn (Fig. 5.4) that provide bounds within which the below threshold curves for all values of $\psi_\mu(0)$ will lie.

Fig. 5.5 shows a comparison of S/D ratios as predicted by the current theory and by theory given in Reference 10. (Shimbo's functions $R_{\theta_3'}$, $R_{\theta_5'}$ and $R_{\theta_6'}$ have been used.) The example refers to

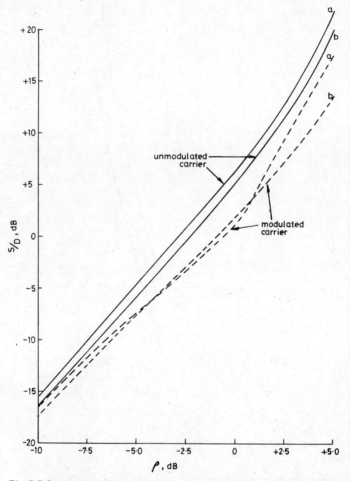

Fig. 5.5 Comparison of two theories in the region of low carrier-to-noise ratios

Curves labelled *a* are given by the theory described in Section 5.5 and Reference 16. Curves labelled *b* are derived from Shimbo's theory of Reference 10

$$\omega_\Delta/p_m = 3\cdot5 \qquad 2\omega_B/p_m = 16$$

$\omega_\Delta/p_m = 3\cdot5$ and $2\omega_B/p_m = 16$, and at the low values of carrier-to-noise ratio, for which the curves are drawn, the coherence factor $[1 - e^{-\rho}]^2$ is given, effectively, by ρ^2. It is seen that a ρ^2-law tends to be followed, and that the two different theoretical approaches are in pleasing agreement.

The curves on Fig. 5.3 probably find their greatest use in fading situations when $\psi_\mu(0)$ has a particular value and an averaged baseband interference level is to be calculated by using the probability distribution of the fading carrier amplitude. This amplitude is likely to obey a Rayleigh law or the flexible Nakagami m-distribution of eqn. 10.78.

5.6 Echo distortion, two-path fading, and adjacent channel interference

The subjects of the Section title have certain features in common, and, with echo distortion or two-path fading, the detector input is written

$$A \cos \left[\omega_0' t + \mu(t)\right] + rA \cos \left[\omega_0(t - \tau_0) + \mu(t - \tau_0)\right] \quad (5.32)$$

The single echo that accompanies the wanted signal has a delay of τ_0 and a relative amplitude r. Letting $\epsilon_1(t)$ be defined by

$$\epsilon_1(t) = \omega_0 \tau_0 + \mu(t) - \mu(t - \tau_0) \quad (5.33)$$

the instantaneous frequency of eqn. 5.32, as given by eqn. 3.4, is

$$\dot{\theta}(t) = \dot{\mu}(t) - \left[\frac{r^2 + r \cos \epsilon_1(t)}{1 + 2r \cos \epsilon_1(t) + r^2}\right] \cdot [\dot{\mu}(t) - \dot{\mu}(t - \tau_0)] (5.34)$$

With adjacent channel interference eqn. 5.32 is replaced by

$$A \cos \left[\omega_0 t + \mu(t)\right] + B(t) \cos \left[\overline{\omega_0 + \omega_D} t + \alpha(t)\right] \quad (5.35)$$

Here $B(t)$ is the envelope and $\alpha(t)$ is the phase of the interferer (the notation follows that used in eqn. 2.11) and ω_D is the carrier separation. Eqn. 5.35 applies after passage through the receiver filter of the interfered-with system. Let

$$\epsilon_2(t) = \omega_D t - \mu(t) + \alpha(t) \quad (5.36)$$

5.7 Undistorted output

When the relative amplitude r is less than unity, $[r^2 + r \cos \epsilon_1(t)] / [1 + 2r \cos \epsilon_1(t) + r^2]$ which appears in eqn. 5.34, can be expressed as $- \sum_{r=1}^{\infty} (-r)^n \cos [n\epsilon_1(t)]$. If $\mu(t)$, the phase modulation on the wanted carrier, is a Gaussian process, then, conditional on a value for $\omega_0 \tau_0$, the average value of $\cos [n\epsilon_1(t)]$ is given by

$$\langle \cos [n\epsilon_1(t)] \rangle = \exp -n^2 [\psi_\mu(0) - \psi_\mu(\tau_0)] \cos (n\omega_0\tau_0) \quad (5.37)$$

Then, with $\omega_0\tau_0$ fixed, the terms that refer to an undistorted version of $\dot{\mu}(t)$, when the spectral density of $\dot{\theta}(t)$ is calculated, are

$$\dot{\mu}(t) + [\dot{\mu}(t) - \dot{\mu}(t - \tau_0)] \Gamma \quad (5.38)$$

where

$$\Gamma = \sum_{n=1}^{\infty} (-r)^n \exp -n^2 [\psi_\mu(0) - \psi_\mu(\tau_0)] \cos (n\omega_0\tau_0) \quad (5.39)$$

If $W_m(\omega)$ is the spectral density of $\dot{\mu}(t)$, the power spectrum of $\dot{\theta}(t)$ then contains the term

$$\left[1 + 4\Gamma(1 + \Gamma) \sin^2 \left(\frac{\omega\tau_0}{2} \right) \right] W_m(\omega) \quad r < 1 \quad (5.40)$$

There are cases in which it is more fitting to take $\omega_0\tau_0$ (reduced modulo 2π) to be an angle which is uniformly distributed in $-\pi$ to $+\pi$. The value of Γ, when the extra average over $\omega_0\tau_0$ is taken, is then zero. For $r > 1$ we have

$$\frac{r^2 + r \cos \epsilon_1(t)}{1 + 2r \cos \epsilon_1(t) + r^2} = \sum_{n=0}^{\infty} \left(-\frac{1}{r} \right)^n \cos [n\epsilon_1(t)] \quad (5.41)$$

Then eqn. 5.40 is obtained again for the undistorted part of the output spectrum, but Γ is replaced by

$$- \sum_{n=0}^{\infty} \left(-\frac{1}{r} \right)^n \exp -n^2 [\psi_\mu(0) - \psi_\mu(\tau_0)] \cos (n\omega_0\tau_0) \quad r > 1$$

The square bracket of eqn. 5.40 is the coherence factor for two-path fading (or the single echo situation) and the expression eqn. 5.39 for Γ was given in Reference 17.

For large r the $n = 0$ term of eqn. 5.41 predominates ($\Gamma \approx -1$) and eqn. 5.38 is, effectively, $\dot{\mu}(t - \tau_0)$ so the echo can be said to have captured the receiver, although the detector output is merely delayed.

This capture effect is more commonly described in the adjacent channel interferer context to which eqn. 5.35 applies. The analysis is closely similar with r replaced by $[B(t)/A]$ and $\epsilon_1(t)$ by $\epsilon_2(t)$. The presence of $\alpha(t)$ in $\epsilon_2(t)$ usually means that $\epsilon_2(t)$ is regarded as an angle that is uniformly distributed in $-\pi$ to $+\pi$ so that $\langle \cos [n\epsilon_2(t)] \rangle = 0$ except for $n = 0$. Thus only the $n = 0$ term of eqn. 5.41 contributes ($\Gamma \equiv -1$) and the detector output is $\dot{\alpha}(t)$, the modulation on the unwanted signal.

It is seen that the capture effect can be accounted for by the $n = 0$ term of eqn. 5.41 irrespective of the statistical properties of

$\epsilon_1(t)$ or $\epsilon_2(t)$. It can be viewed in terms of a coherence factor which is unity when $r < 1$ but zero for $r > 1$. If the interferer amounts to narrow-band Gaussian noise, r is Rayleigh distributed and the average level of the undistorted output is then governed by $1 - e^{-\rho}$ ($P_r(r < 1)$, or the fraction of time the noise amplitude is less than the carrier amplitude). This is the coherence factor (voltage wise) that has been used in several places (eqns. 4.27, 4.28, 5.24 and 5.30).

The capture effect arises in digital transmissions also, and is referred to again in Sections 10.10, 10.12, and 10.17.

5.8 Distortion

The portions of the power spectrum of $\dot{\theta}(t)$ that refer to nonlinear distortion can be obtained straightforwardly but the resulting express-ions[17,18] are lengthy, especially for the case of multiple echoes such as may arise in the waveguide feeders of a microwave aerial system.[20]

A value of r slightly less than unity and an echo phase angle $\omega_0\tau_0$ close to an odd multiple of π are the conditions for deep fading (the echo nearly cancels the wanted signal) and it is interesting to see that the terms of Γ are then all positive, thus tending to maximise the coherence factor. As shown in Reference 17, enhancements of well over 10 dB are possible in the top channel when a 40 dB fade ($r = 0.99$) occurs on an 1800 channel f.m. f.d.m. system but nevertheless the n.p.r. can be as poor as +8 dB.

The working is simplified when $r \ll 1$ for then the distortion power is proportional to r^2 (effectively) and it is convenient to place $p_m\tau_0 = \theta_0$, i.e. $\theta_0 = 2\pi \times$ maximum modulating frequency $\times$ echo delay, and refer to $\theta_0 < 1$ as a short delay case and $\theta_0 > 10$ as a long delay case. At these two extremes it is possible to obtain simple expressions for the distortion-to-signal power ratio when $\omega_\Delta/p_m < 1$. With short delays the largest distortion contribution arises in the top channel (when no pre-emphasis is used) and

$$\frac{D}{S} = \frac{r^2}{4}\left(\frac{\omega_\Delta}{p_m}\right)^2 \cdot \theta_0^4 \tag{5.42}$$

With pre-emphasis of the type recommended by the CCIR (see eqn. 5.26) the middle baseband channels are most severely affected and the factor of 1/4 in eqn. 5.42 is replaced by 0.07725. For long delays, a formula of general applicability when $\omega_\Delta/p_m > 0.5$ is

$$\frac{D}{S} = r^2 \cdot \frac{1}{2\sqrt{\pi}\left(\dfrac{\omega_\Delta}{p_m}\right)^3} \exp{-\frac{1}{4}\left(\frac{p_m}{\omega_\Delta}\right)^2} \tag{5.43}$$

This applies to the top channel of a non-pre-emphasised system, and its experimental confirmation is reported in Section 8.4 of Reference 23. Intermediate cases where ω_Δ/p_m exceeds unity and $1 < \theta_0 < 10$ demand individual attention and information is provided on Fig. 5.6 and in Reference 18 and 19.

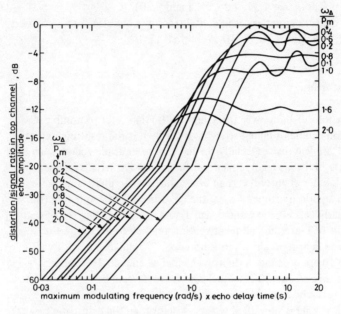

Fig. 5.6 Distortion in top channel due to a single echo

The echo is so phased that the curves show 'worst-case' distortion levels (Reference 18)

5.9 Adjacent channel interference

The composite envelope and phase $[\theta(t)]$ of eqn. 5.35 (assuming $[B(t)/A] < 1$) can be written

$$A\sqrt{1 + \left[\frac{B(t)}{A}\right]\cos \epsilon_2(t) + \left[\frac{B(t)}{A}\right]^2} =$$

$$A\left\{1 + \frac{1}{4}\left[\frac{B(t)}{A}\right]^2 + \frac{1}{64}\left[\frac{B(t)}{A}\right]^4 + \ldots\right\}$$

$$+ A\left[\frac{B(t)}{A}\right]\left\{1 - \frac{1}{8}\left[\frac{B(t)}{A}\right]^2 - \ldots\right\}\cos \epsilon_2(t)$$

$$-\frac{A}{4}\left[\frac{B(t)}{A}\right]^2\left\{1 - \frac{1}{4}\left[\frac{B(t)}{A}\right]^2 - \dots\right\}\cos 2\epsilon_2(t)$$

$$+ \dots \tag{5.44}$$

$$\theta(t) = \mu(t) + \tan^{-1}\left\{\frac{B(t)\sin\epsilon_2(t)}{A + B(t)\cos\epsilon_2(t)}\right\} =$$

$$\mu(t) - \sum_{n=1}^{\infty}\frac{[-B(t)/A]^n}{n}\sin[n\epsilon_2(t)] \tag{5.45}$$

The Fourier series for the envelope may be found in Appendix I of
Reference 28.

Perfect limiting and phase detection will provide $\theta(t)$ for the
receiver output but (as is explained more fully in Section 8.2) a
practical limiter will suffer to some extent from an amplitude-modula-
tion-to-phase-modulation transfer (a.m.-to-p.m. conversion) and
this means that to $\theta(t)$ will be added a copy of the envelope multiplied
by a factor k (known as the a.m.-to-p.m. conversion factor).

Assuming, temporarily, that this effect is ignored, the simplest case
of interest is that in which $[B(t)/A]$ is a constant (r, say), and both
$\alpha(t)$ and $\mu(t)$ are Gaussian processes. We then consider the case of one
f.m. f.d.m. signal suffering interference from another (independently
modulated), but with neither transmission modified by filtering
effects.

Then $\psi_\theta(\tau)$, the autocorrelation function of $\theta(t)$, is given by

$$\psi_\theta(\tau) = \psi_\mu(\tau) + \sum_{n=1}^{\infty}\frac{(r^2)^n}{2n^2}$$

$$\exp - n^2\left[\psi_\mu(0) - \psi_\mu(\tau) + \psi_\alpha(0) + \psi_\alpha(\tau)\right]\cos(n\omega_D\tau)$$

$$\tag{5.46}$$

On incorporating eqns. 4.7, 4.11 and 1.6, the D/S ratio in any baseband
channel (at p rad/s) of the interfered-with signal is given by

$$\frac{D}{S} = \frac{1}{2}\frac{(p_m - p_0)p^2}{\omega_\Delta^2 P(p)}\cdot\sum_{n=1}^{\infty}\frac{(r^2)^n}{n^2}$$

$$\left\{\frac{W_n(p + n\omega_D) + W_n(|p - n\omega_D|)}{\frac{1}{2}A^2}\right\} \tag{5.47}$$

where $W_n(q)$ is the power spectrum of the r.f. carrier $A\cos[\omega_0 t + n\{u(t) - \alpha(t)\}]$ and $P(p)$ is the pre-emphasis law applied to the wanted
baseband [$P(p)$ could be given by eqn. 5.26, for example].

Eqn. 5.47 is given in Reference 21. The $n = 1$ term has been widely used to assess the effects of adjacent channel interference,[21-25] and the spectrum $W_n(q)$ can also be expressed in terms of convolutions of the r.f. spectra of the wanted and unwanted transmissions (as is evident from eqn. 5.46). Note that eqn. 5.46 contains the terms

$$\frac{1}{2} \psi_\alpha(\tau) \cdot \sum_{n=1}^{\infty} (r^2)^n \exp{-n^2 [\psi_\mu(0) + \psi_\alpha(0)]} \cos{(n \omega_D \tau)}$$

which would refer to direct transfer of intelligence from the unwanted signal if $\cos{(n \omega_D \tau)}$ were exactly unity, as in the co-channel interference situation where $\omega_D = 0$. However, the attainable carrier stability is likely to mean that $\omega_D/(2\pi)$ exceeds 100 Hz which is recognised[26] as the frequency shift that seriously impairs the intelligibility of speech, and so intelligible crosstalk is unlikely to be experienced (see Appendix 8 of Reference 23).

The spectra shown on Figs. 4.1, 4.2 serve to evaluate eqn. 5.47 in many instances except perhaps near $p = n \omega_D$. This is because the curves refer to limiting spectra as $p_0 \rightarrow 0$ and so, in particular, no residual carrier components are present; the spectral levels in the immediate vicinity of the carrier may therefore need to be evaluated more exactly[28] before eqn. 5.47 is used.

5.10 D.A.C.I.

D.A.C.I. stands for 'direct adjacent channel interference' and this is another coherence factor effect whereby a direct transfer of intelligence from an unwanted signal is experienced even though the carrier separation ω_D is many times the baseband width of the wanted signal. It has been reported[29] that if the level of the interferer changes by 1 dB, d.a.c.i. changes (in the same direction) by 2 dB. With the wanted and unwanted signals added as in eqn. 5.35, and including the a.m.-to-p.m. effect, the output phase will be well approximated by

$$\theta(t) + \frac{k}{4} \left[\frac{B(t)}{A} \right]^2 \tag{5.48}$$

when $[B(t)/A] < 1$. The term added to $\theta(t)$ arises (Section 8.2) from the square bracket of eqn. 5.44, and harmonics of $\epsilon_2(t)$ (see eqn. 5.36) have been dropped because they will not contribute at the baseband frequencies when ω_D is sufficiently large.

The d.a.c.i. effect can be accounted for by including this extra term, and it comes about not only as a result of a.m.-to-p.m. conversion but because, when the interferer appears at the band edge of the receiver, the response has a time varying envelope $B(t)$.

While the effects of a particular filter can be investigated,[29] the net result (to a first approximation) is for the filter skirt to differentiate the interferer, so giving $B(t)/A$ the approximate form

$$\frac{B(t)}{A} \approx r\,[1 + c\dot{\nu}(t)] \qquad (5.49)$$

where c is a constant and $\dot{\nu}(t)$ is the frequency modulation applied to the undistorted interfering signal. Thus $[B(t)/A]^2$ contributes $r^2(2c)\,\dot{\nu}(t)$ and eqn. 5.48 contains

$$\mu(t) + \frac{k}{4}r^2 \cdot (2c)\cdot\dot{\nu}(t)$$

Being proportional to r^2, this exhibits the '2 dB for 1 dB law, and a 6 dB per octave slope across the baseband frequency range is also predicted when $\dot{\nu}(t)$ and $\dot{\mu}(t)$ both have flat spectral distributions. This behaviour was also revealed by the more rigorous treatment given in Reference 29.

5.11 References

1 GRADSHTEYN, I.S., and RYZHIK, I.M.: 'Tables of integrals, series and products' (Academic Press, 1965)

2 BLACHMAN, N.M.: 'FM reception and the zeros of narrow-band Gaussian noise', *IEEE Trans.*, 1964, **IT-10**, pp. 235–241

3 BLACHMAN, N.M.: 'Noise and its effect on communication' (McGraw-Hill, 1966)

4 COHN, J.: 'A new approach to FM threshold reception'. Proceedings of the National Electronics Conference, 1956, **12**, pp. 221–236

5 RICE, S.O.: 'Noise in FM receivers', *in* ROSENBLATT, M. (Ed.): Proceedings of the symposium on time-series analysis' (Wiley, 1963), pp. 395–422

6 YAVUZ, D., and HESS, D.T.: 'False clicks in FM detection', *IEEE Trans.*, 1970, **COM-18**, (6), pp. 751–756

7 RICE, S.O.: 'Mathematical analysis of random noise', *Bell Syst. Tech. J.*, 1944, **23**, pp. 282–332 and *ibid.*, 1945, **24**, pp. 46–157

8 ROBERTS, J.H.: 'F.M. click rates', *Electron. Lett.*, 1974, **10**, (2), pp. 16–17, and Errata, *ibid*, 1974, **10**, (10), p. 208

9 BLACHMAN, N.M., and ROBERTS, J.H.: 'F.M. click rates: a simple derivation', *Electron. Lett.*, 1974, **10**, (15), pp. 305–307

10 SHIMBO, O.: 'Threshold characteristics of FM signals demodulated by an FM discriminator', *IEEE Trans.*, 1969, **IT-15**, pp. 540–549

11 WANG, M.C., in LAWSON, J.L., and UHLENBECK, G.E. (Ed.): 'Threshold signals' (McGraw-Hill, 1950) chap. 13

12 STUMPERS, F.L.H.M.: 'Theory of frequency modulation noise', *Proc. IRE*, September 1948, pp. 1081–1092

13 RICE, S.O.: 'Statistical properties of a sine-wave plus random noise', *Bell Syst. Tech. J.*, 1948, **27**, p. 109–157

14 MEDHURST, R.G., and ROBERTS, J.H.: 'Evaluation of distortion in f.m. trunk radio systems by a Monte Carlo method', *Proc. IEE*, 1966, **113**, (4), pp. 570–580

15 TSEYTLIN, V.B.: 'Optimum pre-emphasis in multi-channel radio relay lines with frequency division multiplex and frequency modulation', *Telecommun. & Radio Eng.*, 1962, Pt. 1, No. 11, pp. 9–15

16 ROBERTS, J.H.: 'Effects of modulation on the threshold of an FM receiver', *Syst. Technol.* (Plessey Publication), September 1967, pp. 38–44

17 CLAYTON, F.M., and BACON, J.: 'Intermodulation distortion in f.m. f.d.m. trunk radio systems in 2-path fading situations', *Proc. IEE*, 1970, **117**, (2), pp. 359–368

18 MEDHURST, R.G.: 'Echo distortion in frequency modulation', *Electron & Radio Eng.*, 1959, **36**, (7), pp. 253–259

19 MEDHURST, R.G., and HODGINSON, M.: 'Intermodulation distortion due to fading in f.m. f.d.m. trunk radio systems', *Proc. IEE*, 1957, **104C**, pp. 475–480 (IEE Monograph 240R)

20 MEDHURST, R.G., and ROBERTS, J.H.: 'Multiple echo distortion in f.m. f.d.m. trunk radio systems', *IRE Trans.*, 1962, **CS-10**, (1), pp. 61–71

21 PRABHU, V.K., and ENLOE, L.H.: 'Interchannel interference considerations in angle modulated systems', *Bell Syst. Tech. J.*, 1969, **48**, pp. 2333–2358

22 MEDHURST, R.G., HICKS, E.M., and GROSSETT, W.: 'Distortion in frequency-division-multiplex f.m. systems due to an interfering carrier', *Proc. IEE*, 1958, **105B**, (5), pp. 282–292

23 HAMER, R.: 'Radio-frequency interference in multi-channel telephony f.m. radio systems', *Proc. IEE*, 1961, **108B**, pp. 75–89

24 MEDHURST, R.G., and ROBERTS, J.H.: 'Expected interference levels due to interactions between line-of-sight radio relay systems and broadband satellite systems', *Proc. IEE*, 1964, **111**, (3), pp. 519–523

25 BORODICH, S.Y.: 'Calculating the permissible magnitude of radio interference in multi-channel radio relay systems', *Telecommun. & Radio Eng. (Electrosvyaz)*, January, 1962, pp. 13–24

26 CRAIGLOW, R.L., and MARTIN, E.L.: 'Frequency control techniques for single sideband', *Proc. IRE* 1956, **44**, pp. 1697–1702

27 MEDHURST, R.G.: 'RF spectra and interfering carrier distortion in FM trunk radio systems with low modulation ratios', *IRE Trans.*, 1961, **CS-9**, (2), pp. 107–115

28 CORRINGTON, M.S.: 'Frequency modulation distortion caused by common and adjacent channel interference', *RCA Rev.*, 1946, **7**, (4), pp. 522–560

29 GOLDMAN, J.: 'A Volterra-series description of cross-talk interference in communications systems', *Bell Syst. Tech. J.*, 1973, **52**, (5), pp. 649–668

Chapter 6

Probability distribution of the instantaneous frequency

6.1 General result and its application to signal + noise

When digital data is conveyed by f.m. it is the probability distribution
of the instantaneous frequency, rather than the autocorrelation
function or power spectrum, that usually governs an assessment of
system performance.

Writing $V(t)$ for the sum of a narrow-band signal (filtered or
unfiltered) and narrow-band interference expressed as a combined
amplitude and phase modulated wave (as in eqn. 1.3)

$$V(t) = R(t)\cos\left[\omega_0 t + \theta(t)\right] \qquad (6.1)$$

this section calculates the distribution function of $\dot{\theta}(t)$. Accordingly,
consider the probability $[P_h(\omega)$, say] with which the following
inequality is satisfied:

$$\frac{\theta\left(t + \dfrac{h}{2}\right) - \theta\left(t - \dfrac{h}{2}\right)}{h} < \omega \qquad (6.2)$$

Then, as in previous working, h is to be reduced to zero and the aim is
to calculate $P_r(\dot{\theta} < \omega) = \lim_{h \to 0} P_h(\omega)$.

Eqn. 6.2 might be viewed as imprecise because it has not been stated
whether $\theta(t)$ is an absolute phase angle or a phase angle reduced
modulo 2π and, as has been seen, when noise is present, rapid phase
changes can occur even to the extent of forward or backward steps in
phase of 2π within a time typified by the reciprocal of the bandwidth
of eqn. 6.1. However, since h is to be reduced to zero, it may be safely
assumed that $\theta(t + h/2)$ and $\theta(t - h/2)$ lie on the same branch of
this many valued function and thus no ambiguity results.

Then $P_h(\omega) = \text{Prob}\left[\theta\left(t + \dfrac{h}{2}\right) - \theta\left(t - \dfrac{h}{2}\right) < \omega h \right]$

$$= \frac{1}{2}\left\langle \left[1 - \text{sgn}\left\{ -\omega h + \theta\left(t + \dfrac{h}{2}\right) - \theta\left(t - \dfrac{h}{2}\right)\right\}\right]\right\rangle \quad (6.3)$$

On using eqn. 2.17, therefore, we have the general result

$$P_r(\dot{\theta} < \omega) = \underset{h \to 0}{\text{Lim}}\ \frac{1}{2}\left[1 - \frac{1}{2\pi} \int\!\!\!\int_{-\infty}^{+\infty} \frac{\partial \Phi(u_1, u_2)}{\partial Z}\ \frac{du_1\, du_2}{u_1 u_2}\right] \quad (6.4)$$

where $\Phi(u_1, u_2)$ is the bivariate characteristic function of $V(t)$, Z is $-\omega h$.

By inserting the appropriate $\Phi(u_1, u_2)$ explicit results for $P_r(\dot{\theta} < \omega)$ can be obtained for any particular case, and the working will be given for the example of a general narrow-band signal accompanied by a narrow-band Gaussian noise. Then, for insertion in eqn. 6.4:

$$\Phi(u_1, u_2) = \left\langle J_0\left\{\sqrt{(u_1 R_1)^2 + (u_2 R_2)^2 + 2u_1 u_2 R_1 R_2 \cos[Z + \Delta(h)]}\right\}\right\rangle$$

$$\cdot \exp -\tfrac{1}{2}\left[\psi_N(0)(u_1^2 + u_2^2) + 2u_1 u_2 \psi_N(h) \cos Z\right] \quad (6.5)$$

Where $\qquad \Delta(h) = \theta_s(t + h/2) - \theta_s(t - h/2)$

$$R_1 = R_s(t - h/2), \quad R_2 = R_s(t + h/2)$$

This form has already been met in eqn. 2.10 and, when $R_1 = R_2 = A$, in eqn. 3.30 which was used in evaluating eqn. 3.26 and led to an expression for the expected number of zeros occurring per second. From a comparison of eqn. 6.4 and eqn. 2.18 it is evident that much of analysis required to obtain $P_r(\dot{\theta} < \omega)$ (all of the integration, in fact) has already been carried through, and $1 - 2P_h(\omega)$ is given by the right-hand side of eqn. 2.18 with $K_1 = K_2 = \psi_N(0)$ and

$$C = \frac{\psi_N(h)}{\psi_N(0)} = r_N(h).$$

On taking h down to zero (so that $R_1 = R_2 = R_s$, $\Delta(h) \to h\dot{\theta}_s$), and extracating the limit, we have

$$P_r(\dot{\theta} < \omega) = \left\langle \frac{1}{2}\left[1 - \sqrt{1 - \left(\frac{\beta}{\alpha}\right)^2}\cdot I_e\left(\frac{\beta}{\alpha}, \alpha\right) + \frac{\omega}{\sqrt{\omega^2 - r_N''(0)}}\ e^{-\alpha} I_0(\beta)\right]\right\rangle$$

$$(6.6)$$

where $\qquad \alpha = \dfrac{R_s^2}{4\psi_N(0)}\left[\dfrac{\omega^2 - r_N''(0) + (\dot{\theta}_s - \omega)^2 + \left(\dfrac{\dot{R}_s}{R_s}\right)^2}{\omega^2 - r_N''(0)}\right]$

$$\beta = \frac{R_s^2}{4\psi_N(0)} \sqrt{\frac{\left[\omega^2 - r_N''(0) - (\dot{\theta}_s - \omega)^2 - \left(\frac{\dot{R}_s}{R_s}\right)^2\right]^2 + 4\left(\frac{\dot{R}_s}{R_s}\right)^2 \left[\omega^2 - r_N''(0)\right]}{\omega^2 - r_N''(0)}}$$

It may be helpful to remark that, if the angle brackets are not implemented, the right-hand side of eqn. 6.6 gives $P_r(\dot{\theta} < \omega | \dot{\theta}_s > \omega)$ i.e. the probability, conditional on $\dot{\theta}_s$ (the instantaneous frequency of the signal to which the noise is added) exceeding ω, that the instantaneous frequency of signal plus noise lies below the threshold ω. Eqn. 6.6 can be expressed in terms of the Marcum Q function,[1] since

$$\sqrt{1 - \left(\frac{\beta}{\alpha}\right)^2} I_e\left(\frac{\beta}{\alpha}, \alpha\right) = Q\left[\frac{\sqrt{\alpha + \beta} + \sqrt{\alpha - \beta}}{\sqrt{2}}, \frac{\sqrt{\alpha + \beta} - \sqrt{\alpha - \beta}}{\sqrt{2}}\right]$$
$$- Q\left[\frac{\sqrt{\alpha + \beta} - \sqrt{\alpha - \beta}}{\sqrt{2}}, \frac{\sqrt{\alpha + \beta} + \sqrt{\alpha - \beta}}{\sqrt{2}}\right]$$

(6.7)

and

$$1 + e^{-\alpha} I_0(\beta) = Q\left[\frac{\sqrt{\alpha + \beta} - \sqrt{\alpha - \beta}}{\sqrt{2}}, \frac{\sqrt{\alpha + \beta} + \sqrt{\alpha - \beta}}{\sqrt{2}}\right]$$
$$+ Q\left[\frac{\sqrt{\alpha + \beta} + \sqrt{\alpha - \beta}}{\sqrt{2}}, \frac{\sqrt{\alpha + \beta} - \sqrt{\alpha - \beta}}{\sqrt{2}}\right]$$

(6.8)

Agreement then follows with the distribution derived in Reference 2 where results of greater generality are presented, since it is not assumed, as is done here, that the noise has a power spectrum that is symmetrical about ω_0 or some other r.f. frequency.

The literature also contains results for the probability density function $dP_r/d\omega$ (References 3 and 4). In the case of noise alone eqn. 6.6 gives

$$\frac{dP_r}{d\omega} = \frac{1}{2} \frac{-r_N''(0)}{\{\omega^2 - r_N''(0)\}^{3/2}}$$

(6.9)

and it follows that the instantaneous frequency of narrow-band Gaussian noise has an infinite variance.

6.2 Distribution of the instantaneous frequency of the sum of two independent narrow-band waves

Recalling earlier notation, $R_s(t)$ and $B(t)$ will be written for the envelopes, with $\theta_s(t)$ and $\alpha(t)$ for the phases, of the narrow-band waves that are added [$\alpha(t)$ contains the additive term $\omega_D t$ if it is wished to consider cases in which the nominal carrier frequencies are separated by ω_D rad/s].

Then using eqn. 2.11 in eqn. 6.4, the distribution of the instantaneous frequency of the sum of two independently modulated narrow-
band waves can be written (with the help of eqn. 3.27) as

$$P_r[\dot\theta < \omega] = \langle \frac{1}{2} \left[1 - \left\{ 0, \frac{1}{\pi}\cos^{-1}\left[\frac{L_+(\dot\alpha, \dot\theta_s) - 2\left(\frac{B}{R_s}\right)^2 (\dot\alpha - \omega)^2}{\sqrt{L_-^2(\dot\alpha, \dot\theta_s) + N^2}} \right] \right. \right.$$

$$\left. \left. \text{or } 1 \right\} \text{sgn}(\dot\alpha - \omega) \right] \rangle$$

$$+ \langle \frac{1}{2} \left[1 - \left\{ 0, \frac{1}{\pi}\cos^{-1}\left[\frac{L_+(\dot\theta_s, \dot\alpha) - 2\left(\frac{R_s}{B}\right)^2 (\dot\theta_s - \omega)^2}{\sqrt{L_-^2(\dot\theta_s, \dot\alpha) + M^2}} \right] \right. \right.$$

$$\left. \left. \text{or } 1 \right\} \text{sgn}(\dot\theta_s - \omega) \right] \rangle \qquad (6.10)$$

In the first term the alternatives are taken according as 1 lies below,
between or above the two values

$$\frac{L_+(\dot\alpha, \dot\theta_s) \pm \sqrt{L_-^2(\dot\alpha, \dot\theta_s) + N^2}}{2(\dot\alpha - \omega)^2 (B/R_s)^2}$$

and in the second according as 1 lies below between or above the two
values
$$\frac{L_+(\dot\theta_s, \dot\alpha) \pm \sqrt{L_-^2(\dot\theta_s, \dot\alpha) + M^2}}{2(\dot\theta_s - \omega)^2 \cdot (R_s/B)^2}$$

where
$$L_\pm(\dot\alpha, \dot\theta_s) = \left(\frac{\dot B}{B} - \frac{\dot R_s}{R_s}\right)^2 \pm (\dot\alpha - \omega)^2 + (\dot\theta_s - \omega)^2$$

$$M = 2\left[\frac{\dot R_s}{R_s} - \frac{\dot B}{B}\right](\dot\theta_s - \omega)$$

$$N = 2\left[\frac{\dot B}{B} - \frac{\dot R_s}{R_s}\right](\dot\alpha - \omega)$$

Eqn. 6.10 will be returned to when error probabilities in digital f.s.k.
systems are considered in Chapter 10.

6.3 Comparisons with a normal law

It is clear that $\dot\theta(t)$ is not a Gaussian process and since situations can be
met in which it is filtered, the resulting waveform has statistical

properties that are extremely difficult to determine. If, however, $\dot{\theta}(t)$ can be said to be nearly Gaussian under certain circumstances then the problem of dealing with the filtered version is greatly eased.

The discussion will be confined to the instantaneous frequency of the sum of a pure f.m. wave and narrow-band Gaussian noise and the distribution in question is then given at any time instant t [at which $M(t) = M$] by eqn. 6.6 with

$$\alpha = \frac{\rho}{2}\left[\frac{(M-\omega)^2}{\omega^2 - r_N''(0)} + 1\right]$$

$$\beta = \frac{\rho}{2}\left|1 - \frac{(M-\omega)^2}{\omega^2 - r_N''(0)}\right|$$

The following results will be needed (Appendix 1 of Reference 3):

$$I_e(0, \alpha) = 1 - e^{-\alpha} \qquad (6.11)$$

$$\sqrt{1 - \left(\frac{\beta}{\alpha}\right)^2}\, I_e\left(\frac{\beta}{\alpha}, \alpha\right) \approx 1 - \sqrt{\frac{\alpha+\beta}{2\beta}}\, \text{erfc}\,(\sqrt{\alpha-\beta})\ \ (\alpha > \beta > 3,\ \text{say}) \quad (6.12)$$

$$e^{-\alpha}I_0(\beta) \approx \frac{e^{-(\alpha-\beta)}}{\sqrt{2\pi\beta}} \quad (\beta > 3,\ \text{say}) \qquad (6.13)$$

Note, firstly, that when $\beta = 0$ the exact distribution for $\dot{\theta}(t)$ has the non-Gaussian form

$$P_r[\dot{\theta} < \omega] = \frac{1}{2}\left[1 + \frac{\omega}{\sqrt{\omega^2 - r_N''(0)}}\right]e^{-\rho} \qquad (6.14)$$

Supposing the carrier-to-noise ratio ρ to be such that if $[(M-\omega)^2]/[\omega^2 - r_N''(0)]$ lies either well above unity or well below unity, β is large enough for eqns. 6.12 and 6.13 to be used, then

$$P_r(\dot{\theta} < \omega) \approx \frac{1}{2}\left[\sqrt{\frac{\alpha+\beta}{2\beta}}\, \text{erfc}\,(\sqrt{\alpha-\beta}) + \frac{\omega}{\sqrt{\omega^2 - r_N''(0)}}\, \frac{e^{-(\alpha-\beta)}}{\sqrt{2\pi\beta}}\right]$$
$$(6.15)$$

If $\alpha - \beta$ is also large a further stage of approximation provides[*]

$$P_r(\dot{\theta} < \omega) \approx \frac{1}{2}\frac{e^{-(\alpha-\beta)}}{\sqrt{\pi(\alpha-\beta)}}\left\{\sqrt{\frac{\alpha+\beta}{2\beta}} + \frac{\omega}{\sqrt{\omega^2 - r_N''(0)}}\sqrt{\frac{\alpha-\beta}{2\beta}}\right\}$$
$$(6.16)$$

Now $\alpha - \beta$ is given by $\qquad \rho \qquad$ if $\qquad \dfrac{(M-\omega)^2}{\omega^2 - r_N''(0)} > 1$

and by $\dfrac{\rho(M-\omega)^2}{\omega^2 - r_N''(0)}$ if $\dfrac{(M-\omega)^2}{\omega^2 - r_N''(0)} < 1$

---

[*] The $\omega = 0$ case is stated using different notation in Reference 5

and in the former case a distribution rather like eqn. 6.14 is obtained, while, in the latter, the leading exponential in eqn. 6.16 has an argument that depends on the threshold value ω. Then

$$P_r(\dot\theta < \omega) \approx \frac{\exp - \left[\dfrac{\rho(M-\omega)^2}{\omega^2 - r_N''(0)} \right]}{2\sqrt{\dfrac{\pi\rho(M-\omega)^2}{\omega^2 - r_N''(0)}}}$$

$$\cdot \frac{1}{\sqrt{1 - \dfrac{(M-\omega)^2}{\omega^2 - r_N''(0)}}} \left\{ 1 + \frac{\omega}{\sqrt{\omega^2 - r_N''(0)}} \sqrt{\frac{(M-\omega)^2}{\omega^2 - r_N''(0)}} \right\}$$

(6.17)

It is now helpful to recall that for large ρ (see eqn. 5.19)

$$\theta(t) \approx \mu(t) + \frac{I_s \cos\mu(t) - I_c \sin\mu(t)}{A}$$ (6.18)

and, as has been shown in Section 5.3, so far as the spectral distribution of $\dot\theta(t)$ at modulating frequencies is concerned

$$\dot\theta(t) \approx \dot\mu(t) + \frac{\dot I_s}{A}$$ (6.19)

Using this, the probability that $\dot\mu(t) = M$ is negative, for example, is given by $\dfrac{1}{2}\left[1 - \mathrm{erf}\left(\sqrt{\dfrac{\rho M^2}{-r_N''(0)}} \right) \right]$ which, for large argument, is well

approximated by $\dfrac{1}{2}\sqrt{\dfrac{-r_N''(0)}{\pi\rho M^2}}\, e^{-[\rho M^2/-r_N''(0)]}$, and this is seen to be

the leading term of eqn. 6.17 when $\omega = 0$. Likewise, when ω is not zero, it is easy to find that the probability that $(M + \dot I_s/A)/(1 + I_c/A)$ is less than ω is given, to a like order of approximation, by

$$\frac{1}{2\sqrt{\dfrac{\pi\rho(M-\omega)^2}{\omega^2 - r_N''(0)}}} \exp - \left[\frac{\rho(M-\omega)^2}{\omega^2 - r_N''(0)} \right]$$

which is the leading term of eqn. 6.17. Provided that this term dominates, therefore, the conclusion reached is that $\dot\theta(t)$ can be replaced by the simpler forms discussed above, and, in particular, eqn. 6.19 which is easy to modify to account for subsequent filtering, can be used when interest lies purely in whether the sampled filter output is positive or negative. The conditions under which these simplifications arise may be summarised in the inequality

$$\frac{1}{\rho} < \frac{(M - \omega)^2}{\omega^2 - r_N''(0)} < 1 \qquad (6.20)$$

6.4 References

1   SCHWARZ, M., BENNETT, W.R., and STEIN, S.: 'Communication systems and techniques' (Mc-Graw-Hill, 1966)
2   SALZ, J., and STEIN, S.: 'Distribution of instantaneous frequency for signal plus noise', *IEEE Trans.*, 1964, **IT-10**, (4), pp. 272–274
3   RICE, S.O.: 'Statistical properties of a sine wave plus random noise', *Bell Syst. Tech. J.* 1948, **27,** pp. 109–157
4   GATKIN, N.C., GERANIN, V.A., KARNOVSKIY, M.I., KRANSY, L.G., and CHERNEY, N.I.: 'Probability density of phase derivative of the sum of a modulated signal and Gaussian noise', *Radio Eng. & Electron. Phys.*, 1965, (8), pp. 1223–1229
5   MAZO, J.E., and SALZ, J.: 'Probability of error for quadratic detectors', *Bell Syst. Tech. J.* 1965, **44,** pp. 2165–2186

Chapter 7

Filtering and then demodulating an analogue f.m. wave

7.1 Instantaneous phase and frequency of the filter output

The filter in question will be assumed to be a bandpass passive network having, as in earlier sections, the equivalent lowpass impulse response function $g(t)$. Use of the equivalent lowpass filter in narrow-band situations where filter distortions are of interest is a well recognised technique, and is discussed in Sections II and III of Reference 1, for example.

In the current notation, $P(t)$ and $Q(t)$ the in-phase and quadrature components of the filter output [supposing the input to be $A \cos \{\omega_0 t + \mu(t)\}$] are then given by

$$P(t) + jQ(t) = A \int_{-\infty}^{+\infty} g(x) e^{j\mu(t-x)} dx$$

where

$$g(t) = \frac{1}{2\pi} \int_{-\infty}^{+\infty} H(j\omega) e^{j\omega t} d\omega$$

(7.1)

and $H(j\omega)$ (ω measured from ω_0) is the transfer characteristic of the equivalent lowpass filter. When the bandpass filter is realisable, $g(t)$ will be non-anticipative and the lower limit shown in eqn. 7.1 can then be replaced by zero. Initially, for ease of presentation, the function $g(t)$ will be taken to be real, thus implying that the bandpass filter has an amplitude characteristic that is symmetrical about ω_0 and a phase characteristic that is antisymmetrical. Then, the in-phase and quadrature components are given by

$$P(t) = A \int_{-\infty}^{+\infty} g(x) \cos \mu(t-x) dx$$

$$Q(t) = A \int_{-\infty}^{+\infty} g(x) \sin \mu(t-x) dx$$

(7.2)

Throughout this chapter an idealised receiver consisting of a filter-demodulator pair will be assumed so that the carrier wave before filtering will be called the receiver input and the output will be the instantaneous frequency of the filtered wave as measured by a perfect frequency detector.

When noise accompanies the carrier, the autocorrelation function of the instantaneous frequency $\dot{\theta}(t)$ is given by eqn. 3.71 and interest now centres on the leading terms [those not involving $\psi_N'(\tau)$ and $\psi_N''(\tau)$] as these provide both the undistorted and the distorted versions of the modulation $\dot{\mu}(t)$. The term distortion is to be qualified here, however, because the combined effect of filter and additive noise at the receiver input means that in $\dot{\theta}(t)$ the modulation does not suffer a pure distortion but is additionally affected in a nonlinear manner by the noise, as is evidenced by the presence of the exponential factor $\exp\left[-F_N(0)\right]$ in eqn. 3-68 which defines the coefficients $a_m(l)$ and $b_m(l)$.

In the majority of cases the filter is used to remove noise from the system and so the combined effect of any residual noise and of the bandwidth restriction caused by filtering should be accounted for. This was done for the linearly-filtered component in Section 4.5 of Chapter 4, but to cater for the kind of nonlinear interaction referred to above is difficult and is best handled by simulation methods (Section 7.7). It appears, however, that in most practical situations a satisfactory assessment of performance can be gained from separate considerations of the outcome of passing the modulated carrier and the noise through the filter-demodulator chain and we therefore agree to drop the noise in investigating the distortion levels introduced into $\dot{\theta}(t)$ by filtering. Then, as eqn. 3.71 is an autocorrelation function for which the averaging has been performed conditional on some arbitrary form for the signal to which the noise has been added, it must collapse to the defining form

$$R(\tau) = \langle \left[\frac{P(t)\dot{Q}(t) - Q(t)\dot{P}(t)}{P^2(t) + Q^2(t)}\right] .$$

$$\left[\frac{P(t+\tau)\dot{Q}(t+\tau) - Q(t+\tau)\dot{P}(t+\tau)}{P^2(t+\tau) + Q^2(t+\tau)}\right] \rangle \qquad (7.3)$$

However, eqn. 3.71 reduces, initially, to its first seven terms but these are difficult to handle, and the expression will receive only an occasional mention in the following. Absence of noise causes the coefficients $a_m(l)$ and $b_m(l)$ to become more simply related [the notation now follows that used in 3.68] and we have

$$a_m(l) = \cos(m\Delta)I_m(l)$$
$$b_m(l) = -\sin(m\Delta)I_m(l)$$
(7.4)

where
$$I_m(l) = \frac{1}{\pi}\int_{-\pi}^{\pi}\frac{J_l\left[\sqrt{(r_1x)^2+(r_2y)^2+2r_1r_2xy\cos\beta}\right]}{\left[\sqrt{(r_1x)^2+(r_2y)^2+2r_1r_2xy\cos\beta}\right]l}\cos m\beta\, d\beta$$

and
$$\tan\Delta = \frac{\iint_{-\infty}^{+\infty}g(x)g(y)\sin[\mu(t+\tau-x)-\mu(t-y)]dxdy}{\iint_{-\infty}^{+\infty}g(x)g(y)\cos[\mu(t+\tau-x)-\mu(t-y)]dxdy}$$

A formidable problem is proposed by observance of the angled averaging brackets in eqn. 7.3 since eight variables are involved that may be mutually correlated. One simplification to be exploited comes from recognising that in many practical cases the filter can be allowed to cause only a slight perturbation of the phase of the unfiltered wave (together with an equally small amplitude modulation component) certainly a mechanism such as that producing f.m. clicks is absent. The phase, which is given by

$$\tan^{-1}\left[\frac{Q(t)}{P(t)}\right]$$

can therefore be assumed to lie in the range $-\pi$ to $+\pi$ or to be the same as the phase angle reduced modulo 2π. Consequently, it is easier, where possible, to work in terms of phase rather than frequency (the spectral distributions of phase and frequency are then related through multiplying the former one by ω^2) and in place of eqn. 7.3 we consider

$$R_\theta(\tau) = \left\langle \tan^{-1}\left[\frac{Q(t)}{P(t)}\right]\tan^{-1}\left[\frac{Q(t+\tau)}{P(t+\tau)}\right]\right\rangle$$
(7.5)

Now a function of four variables, rather than eight, has to be averaged but this is still a difficult task.

For future reference we keep before us the expressions for phase and frequency that are obtained when eqns. 7.2 are incorporated:

$$\theta(t) = \tan^{-1}\left(\frac{\int_{-\infty}^{+\infty}g(x)\sin\mu(t-x)dx}{\int_{-\infty}^{+\infty}g(x)\cos\mu(t-x)dx}\right)$$
$$= \mu(t) + \tan^{-1}\left(\frac{\int_{-\infty}^{+\infty}g(x)\sin[\mu(t-x)-\mu(t)]dx}{\int_{-\infty}^{+\infty}g(x)\cos[\mu(t-x)-\mu(t)]dx}\right)$$
(7.6)

$$\dot\theta(t) = \frac{\iint_{-\infty}^{+\infty}g(x)g(y)M(t-x)\cos[\mu(t-x)-\mu(t-y)]dxdy}{\iint_{-\infty}^{\infty}g(x)g(y)\cos[\mu(t-x)-\mu(t-y)]dxdy}$$
(7.7)

and for definiteness it will be assumed that $\mu(t)$ and therefore $M(t) = \dot{\mu}(t)$ are Gaussian processes with spectral distributions confined to the angular frequency range p_0 to p_m, with $\langle M(t)^2 \rangle = \omega_\Delta^2$.

7.2 Approximation for small phase deviations

The values given to p_0, p_m and ω_Δ determine $G(\omega)$, the power spectrum of the filtered wave, and, before progressing further, it is helpful to recall (see eqn. 4.8) that the spectrum contains a residual carrier component with an amplitude proportional to $\exp\left[-\frac{1}{2}\psi_\mu(0)\right]$, where $\psi_\mu(0)$ is the mean square value of the phase modulation $(\psi_\mu(0) = \langle \mu^2(t) \rangle)$. If $\psi_\mu(0)$ is small, therefore, this carrier has an amplitude that is comparable to that of the unmodulated carrier, the sideband structure falls away very rapidly, and the spectral power is almost totally confined to a band such as $\omega_0 - 2p_m$ to $\omega_0 + 2p_m$. With a small phase deviation the approximations $\sin \mu \approx \mu - \frac{1}{6}\mu^3$ and $\cos \mu \approx 1 - \frac{1}{2}\mu^2$ are usually acceptable and the second of these, in particular, means that the in-phase component both before and after filtering has an average value that is close to its maximum value.

Referring to eqn. 7.6 therefore, in such circumstances the cosine in the denominator of the inverse tangent can be replaced by unity and the approximation

$$\theta(t) = \mu(t) + \int_{-\infty}^{+\infty} g(x) \sin\left[\mu(t-x) - \mu(t)\right] dx \qquad (7.8)$$

is likely to be acceptable. The integral here will be referred to as the phase error. The autocorrelation function of the phase error may be calculated using the theory outlined for a sine nonlinearity in Section 2.5, and it is given by

$$\iint_{-\infty}^{+\infty} g(x)g(y) \exp - \left[2\psi_\mu(0) - \psi_\mu(x) - \psi_\mu(y)\right] \sinh\left[\psi_\mu(\tau + x - y)\right.$$

$$\left. - \psi_\mu(\tau + x) - \psi_\mu(\tau - y) + \psi_\mu(\tau)\right] dx\, dy \qquad (7.9)$$

where $\psi_\mu(\tau)$ is the autocorrelation function of $\mu(t)$. If the first term in the series expansion of the hyperbolic sine is subtracted out, the remaining terms refer to distortion,[2] and Shimbo and Loo[3] have described a sampling (digital) method of evaluating the Fourier transform of the double integral. Their results are discussed later. (Section 7.11)

7.3 Large r.m.s. phase deviation

When the applied phase deviation is large, the spectrum contains a
residual carrier that is very small but, of course, the f.m. wave still has
a constant envelope. In these circumstances it will be assumed that the
filter bandwidth is sufficiently large for the envelope variations that it
introduces to be ignored. The squared envelope of the filtered wave is
given by $P^2(t) + Q^2(t)$ and it is seen that this expression is a
denominator in eqn. 3.4. On averaging $P^2 + Q^2$ we find

$$\langle P^2(t) + Q^2(t) \rangle = A^2 \iint_{-\infty}^{+\infty} g(x)g(y) \exp -[\psi_\mu(0) - \psi_\mu(x-y)] \, dxdy$$

and this double integral can be transformed (using eqn. 4.7) into

$$A^2 \int_{-\infty}^{+\infty} |H(j\omega)|^2 \left\{ \frac{G(\omega)}{\frac{1}{2}A^2} \right\} d\omega \qquad (7.10)$$

Thus, if the filter removes only a small amount of the spectral power,
the mean squared envelope will closely approximate the maximum level
of A^2 and then the integral in eqn. 7.10 can be used to gain a feel for
the situations that are compatible with the following approximation to
eqn. 7.7.

$$\dot{\theta}(t) = \iint_{-\infty}^{+\infty} g(x)g(y)M(t-x)\cos[\mu(t-x) - \mu(t-y)]dxdy \qquad (7.11)$$

However, the statistic 7.10 turns out to be a plausible but rather
pessimistic criterion of success, and it does not carry enough information to predict with full confidence when the approximation eqn. 7.11
will be successful. Rather, success depends on the type of filter under
examination and the conclusion is that, the steeper the filter skirts, the
better the accuracy realised in calculating the spectrum of $\dot{\theta}(t)$ over the
baseband range, even though the integral in eqn. 7.10 may approach
one half. This evidently reflects the frequency content of the envelope
ripples; when the filter skirts are steep, the oscillations are such that the
frequency components of the squared reciprocal envelope lie well
beyond the baseband range.

The right-hand side of eqn. 7.11 is not a perfect derivative and so the
simplification of working in terms of phase is not available but, as is
shown later, the linear and third-order distortion contributions can be
extracted without difficulty.

Note that ignoring envelope variations is equivalent to supposing
that the discriminator output $(Q\dot{P} - P\dot{Q})/(P^2 + Q^2)$ is multiplied by
$P^2 + Q^2$. In future, therefore, the approximation eqn. 7.11 will be
referred to as multiplication by the square of the envelope.

A direct calculation of the autocorrelation function of $\dot{\theta}(t)$, as given by eqn. 7.11, is shown later (it gives eqn. 7.21) but $Q\dot{P} - P\dot{Q}$ will be seen to be P_1 of eqn. 3.70 and, consequently, this autocorrelation function may also be obtained from the $P_1 P_3$ term of eqn. 3.71 (then the integrals $I_m(l)$ appearing in eqn. 7.4 become independent of time because r_1 and r_2 of eqn. 3.66 are each assumed to equal A).

Approximations like eqn. 7.8 are open to objection on various grounds and may break down for one filter type but not another. The underlying difficulty of replacing $\theta(t)$ or $\dot{\theta}(t)$ by some other waveform $X(t)$, say, that is easier to manipulate, is satisfying the proper criterion by which $X(t)$ should be chosen. In the present case $X(t)$ is required to have a spectral density which is closely equal to that of $\theta(t)$ or $\dot{\theta}(t)$ over the frequency range p_0 to p_m. Outside this range the quality of the approximation is generally of no concern, but our requirement is not necessarily met by choosing $X(t)$ to share with $\theta(t)$ or $\dot{\theta}(t)$ the leading terms in a power-series development, or the same mean square value, for example, and it is replacements of this kind that are easiest to find.

7.4 Volterra-series approach

In recent years expansions of the following kind have found favour

$$\tan^{-1} \frac{Q(t)}{P(t)} = \int_{-\infty}^{+\infty} g(x)\mu(t-x)dx$$

$$- \frac{1}{6}\left\{ \left(\int_{-\infty}^{+\infty} g(x)\mu^3(t-x)dx \right. \right.$$

$$- 3\int_{-\infty}^{+\infty} g(x)\mu(t-x)dx \int_{-\infty}^{+\infty} g(x)\mu^2(t-x)dx$$

$$+ 2\left[\int_{-\infty}^{+\infty} g(x)\mu(t-x)dx \right]^3 \right\} + \dots \qquad (7.12)$$

This is the particular case of

$$\tan^{-1}\left[\frac{Q(t)}{P(t)} \right] = \int_{-\infty}^{+\infty} g_1(x_1)\mu(t-x_1)dx_1$$

$$+ \frac{1}{3!}\iiint_{-\infty}^{+\infty} g_3(x_1, x_2, x_3)\prod_{l=1}^{3}\mu(t-x_l)dx_1 dx_2 dx_3 \qquad (7.13)$$

$$+ \frac{1}{5!}\iiiint\!\!\int_{-\infty}^{+\infty} g_5(x_1, x_2, x_3, x_4, x_5)\prod_{l=1}^{5}\mu(t-x_l)dx_1 \dots dx_5$$

$$+ \dots$$

which is known as a Volterra series.[4] The functions g_1, g_3, g_5 etc. are called kernels and their identification has been the subject of a number of papers in recent years dealing with the application of Volterra series to general problems that involve nonlinear systems with memory.[5-7]

A volterra series for the envelope, corresponding to eqn. 7.12 is

$$\sqrt{P^2(t) + Q^2(t)} = 1 - \frac{1}{4} \iint_{-\infty}^{+\infty} g(x)g(y) \left[\mu(t-x) - \mu(t-y)\right]^2 dx dy$$

$$+ \frac{1}{48} \iint_{-\infty}^{+\infty} g(x)g(y) \left[\mu(t-x) - \mu(t-y)\right]^4 dx dy$$

$$- \frac{1}{32} \left[\iint_{-\infty}^{+\infty} g(x)g(y) \left[\mu(t-x) - \mu(t-y)\right]^2 dx dy \right]^2 + \dots$$

(7.14)

only even orders of distortion with a d.c. term appear when $g(t)$ is real.

Eqn. 7.12 is seen to be an expansion of the left-hand side into terms of weight one and three in $\mu(t)$, with later terms being of weight five, seven etc. (terms of even weight do not appear when $g(t)$ is real). The first term is $\mu(t)$ filtered by the low-pass equivalent network but the second term, although it is of weight three, will make a contribution to the linearly-filtered version of $\mu(t)$ when the averaging (or self-correlating) indicated in eqn. 7.5 is carried out. Likewise, this second term will not represent the complete third-order distortion component until contributions from further terms in eqn. 7.12 are included. The situation corresponds, in eqns. 2.34 of Section 2.5, to knowing only a_1 and a_3 so that the coefficients B_1 and B_3, which are seen to involve a_5, a_7 etc. are not completely specified.

In fact, when the kernels on the right-hand side of a Volterra development obey $g_n(x_1, x_2, \dots x_n) = a_n \delta(x_1) \dots \delta(x_n) n!$, the case of the zero-memory nonlinearity $\Sigma a_n \left[\mu(t)\right]^n$, as discussed above eqn. 2.34, is retrieved, and this offers a useful way of checking complicated results.[5]

It is highly desirable for $R_\theta(\tau)$ of eqn. 7.5 to be written as a Volterra series or, even better, for the corresponding spectral density $W_\theta(\omega)$ (obtained through eqn. 1.6) to be so expressed with the role of $\mu(t)$ in eqn. 7.13 being taken over by $W_\mu(\omega)$, the spectral density of $\mu(t)$, and with the kernels being functions of $H(j\omega)$, the transfer characteristic of the filter. However, to achieve this end, there seems no alternative at present to adopting the Volterra series of eqn. 7.12, multiplying out and separately averaging each of the terms that result from eqn. 7.5, collecting together the coherently adding contributions, and then performing the final Fourier transform that gives the required spectral density.

The quintuple integral that appears as the third term in eqn. 7.13 is a clear warning of the gigantic algebraic difficulties that are encountered if this process is attempted even with as few as three terms on the right-hand side of eqn. 7.13, and it has been the achievement of Mircea[7,8] to identify the general forms of the convolution-type integrals that appear in the resulting Volterra series for $W_\theta(\omega)$. If higher orders of distortion than third are accounted for in the series, the triple and quintuple etc. integrals to be evaluated present yet another problem, in that the ranges of the multiple integrations have to be identified. This is not a trivial exercise since $W_\mu(\omega)$, the spectral distribution of $\mu(t)$, is non-zero only over the angular frequency range p_0 to p_m, say, and so, above and/or below certain critical values that depend on the integration variable that is to be considered next, the integrals become zero.[1,9,10]

Only the simplest, and therefore most tractable, path through this morass of complication will be taken here, this being when eqn. 7.13 is confined to the two terms shown explicitly in eqn. 7.12. These, it may be noticed, can be written

$$L(t) - \frac{1}{6}\int_{-\infty}^{+\infty} g(x)[\mu(t-x) - L(t)]^3 \, dx \qquad (7.15)$$

where

$$L(t) = \int_{-\infty}^{+\infty} g(y)\mu(t-y)dy$$

This more compact form eases the analysis somewhat and it is convenient to define $G_3(\omega_1, \omega_2, \omega_3)$ as follows:

$$
\begin{aligned}
G_3(\omega_1, \omega_2, \omega_3) = {} & H[j(\omega_1 + \omega_2 + \omega_3)] \\
& - H(j\omega_1)H[j(\omega_2 + \omega_3)] \\
& - H(j\omega_2)H[j(\omega_1 + \omega_3)] \\
& - H(j\omega_3)H[j(\omega_1 + \omega_2)] \\
& + 2H(j\omega_1)H(j\omega_2)H(j\omega_3) \qquad (7.16)
\end{aligned}
$$

Thus far the (Mircea-Sinnreich) series for $W_\theta(\omega)$ is

$$W_\theta(\omega) = W_\mu(\omega)\left| H(j\omega) - \frac{1}{4}\int_{-\infty}^{+\infty} W_\mu(x)G_3(\omega, x, -x)dx \right|^2$$

$$+ \frac{1}{24}\iint_{-\infty}^{+\infty} W_\mu(x)W_\mu(y)W_\mu(\omega-x-y)|G_3(x, y, \omega-x-y)|^2 dx\, dy$$

$$= W_1(\omega) + W_3(\omega) \qquad (7.17)$$

Note that $W_\theta(\omega)$ and $W_\mu(\omega)$ are power spectra defined for $\omega > 0$; they are therefore one-sided as opposed to the two sided spectra which are sometimes used.[5,10] In the integrals of eqn. 7.17, however, $W_\mu(x)$ is to be taken as equalling $W_\mu(-x)$ as this admits of the compact form in which the result can be written.

When no assumptions are made regarding the low-pass equivalent filter amplitude and phase characteristics a second-order distortion term must be added to the right of eqn. 7.17. The terms already shown appear with the following alterations

$$H(j\omega) \quad \text{is replaced by} \quad \frac{H(j\omega) + H^*(-j\omega)}{2}$$

$$G_3(\omega_1, \omega_2, \omega_3) \quad \text{is replaced by}$$

$$\frac{G_3(\omega_1, \omega_2, \omega_3) + G_3^*(-\omega_1, -\omega_2, -\omega_3)}{2}$$

and the term to be added (to the same order of approximation) is

$$\frac{1}{4}\int_{-\infty}^{+\infty} W_\mu(x) W_\mu(\omega - x) \left| \frac{H(j\omega) - H(jx)H[j(\omega-x)] - H^*(-j\omega) + H^*(-jx)H^*[j(x-\omega)]}{2} \right|^2 dx$$

$$(7.18)$$

where the star denotes complex conjugate.

Perhaps the most common case requiring the inclusion of this extra term is when mistuning has occurred and the filter characteristic fails to have the intended symmetry and antisymmetry about ω_0 (Reference 12), but other situations also arise.[13]

The distortion-to-signal ratio is obtained from eqn. 7.17 by dividing the second, and any further terms that are included, by the first term, and, in principle, the Volterra-series approach offers a way of calculating D/S to any desired accuracy. However, owing to the enormous increase in the work required to handle even one additional term in eqn. 7.12 it is usually the case that eqn. 7.17 has to suffice, whereupon

$$\frac{D}{S} = \frac{W_3(\omega)}{W_1(\omega)} \qquad (7.19)$$

As mentioned above, later terms in the Volterra series contribute to the third-order distortion and from the power-series nature of the expansion it might be anticipated that these later terms will increase in importance if the r.m.s. value of $\mu(t)$ increases.

Now, for a flat f.m. spectrum, the mean square phase deviation is given by

$$\psi_\mu(0) = \int_{p_0}^{p_m} W_\mu(\omega)d\omega = \int_{p_0}^{p_m} \frac{\omega_\Delta^2}{(p_m - p_0)\omega^2} d\omega = \left(\frac{\omega_\Delta}{p_m}\right)^2 \left(\frac{p_m}{p_0}\right) \quad (7.20)$$

and so, when, as is commonly the case, p_m greatly exceeds p_0, it is suggested that ω_Δ/p_m must be correspondingly small if the Volterra-series approach is to prove acceptable. However, judging from the available theoretical and experimental evidence,[*] it seems that the overriding requirement is that ω_Δ/p_m does not exceed 0·5 or so, even though p_m/p_0 may be such that $\psi_\mu(0)$ cannot be regarded as small.

7.5 Multiplication by square of envelope as a means of calculating distortion

$\omega_\Delta/p_m \leqslant 0·5$ is a rather restricted range (in satellite systems the f.m. index can have a value such as 2 or 3) and an alternative approach has to be developed for the large f.m. index cases.

As the leading nonlinear term in $\tan^{-1}\{Q(t)/P(t)\}$ is the cubic one, the distortion may, in general, be regarded as being entirely of third-order type if the filter bandwidth is sufficiently large, and, if the disturbance to the envelope is ignored, the approximation shown in eqn. 7.11 is appropriate. The autocorrelation function of eqn. 7.11 can be formed straightforwardly (the derivation of eqn. 2.33 shows the method) and is given by

$$R_1(\tau) = \iiiint_{-\infty}^{+\infty} g(x)g(y)g(u)g(v)\psi_M(\tau + x - u)$$

$$. \exp - [2\psi_\mu(0) - \psi_\mu(x - y)$$

$$- \psi_\mu(u - v)] . \cosh[\psi_\mu(\tau + x - v)$$

$$+ \psi_\mu(\tau + y - u) - \psi_\mu(\tau + y - v)$$

$$- \psi_\mu(\tau + x - u)] . dx\,dy\,du\,dv \quad (7.21)$$

Then, replacing the cosh by the first two terms in its series expansion, $S(\omega)$ the spectral density of the sum of the linear and third-order contributions can be expressed conveniently through the introduction of the function $E(a, b)$ defined as follows

[*] See Figs. 7.4, 7.12 and 7.13, for example.

$$E(a, b) = \int_{-\infty}^{+\infty} \left\{ \frac{G(q)}{\frac{1}{2}A^2} \right\} H[j(q + a)]H[j(b - q)] \, dq \qquad (7.22)$$

where $G(q)$, as before, is the power spectrum of the unfiltered wave.

Then $\qquad\qquad\qquad S(\omega) = S_1(\omega) + S_3(\omega)$

Where $\qquad\qquad\quad S_1(\omega) = W_M(\omega)|E(0, \omega)|^2 \qquad\qquad (7.23)$

$$S_3(\omega) = \frac{1}{8}\iint_{-\infty}^{+\infty} W_\mu(x)W_\mu(y)W_M(\omega - x - y)|E(0, \omega)$$

$$+ E(x + y, \omega - x - y) - E(x, \omega - x)$$

$$- E(y, \omega - y)|^2 \, dxdy \qquad (7.24)$$

and the distortion-to-signal ratio is given by

$$\frac{D}{S} = \frac{S_3(\omega)}{S_1(\omega)} \qquad (7.25)$$

Recalling eqn. 7.17, $S(\omega)$ is the counterpart of $W_\theta(\omega)$ as provided by the Volterra series approach, and in the integrals of eqn. 7.24 $W_\mu(x)$ is defined to equal $W_\mu(-x)$, and also $W_M(x) \equiv W_M(-x)$. The power factor by which the useful signal is depressed at frequency ω is given by $|E(0, \omega)|^2$ and this coherence factor will be seen to agree with eqn. 4.27 which was also obtained by disregarding envelope variations (the term $[1 - e^{-\rho}]^2$ appears in eqn. 4.27 because there noise is included).

While the double integral for $S_3(\omega)$ given in eqn. 7.24 is somewhat similar to the double integral appearing in eqn. 7.17, the very important difference to be noted is that $E(a, b)$ shows an explicit dependance on the spectrum $G(q)$ while $G_3(x, y, \omega - x - y)$ (see eqn. 7.16) does not and is only a function of the filter transfer characteristic. Consequently D/S ratios calculated through eqn. 7.25 display a differing dependence on the f.m. index (and therefore the r.f. spectrum) to D/S ratios calculated from eqn. 7.19.

If a 12 dB per octave slope is apparent when n.p.r. measurements (as the ordinate) are plotted against small values of the f.m. index, the inference is that third-order distortion predominates. Likewise, a 24 dB per octave slope is indicative of fifth-order distortion. Usually, however, these slopes are not maintained and the curve flattens out as the f.m. index increases (see Fig. 7.4 and Figs. 7.12 to 7.14).

Using the Volterra series shown in eqn. 7.17, the D/S ratio will have an external factor of $(\omega_\Delta/p_m)^4$ and the 12 dB per octave slope will follow, but unless other Volterra terms are included this is the sole dependence on ω_Δ/p_m. It is clear, however, that as ω_Δ/p_m is

increased so the r.f. spectrum of the filtered wave will change its shape
and this behaviour can be accounted for when the multiplication by
squared envelope approach is adopted and eqn. 7.24 is used.

For large f.m. indices it is well known that a useful approximation is
realised by equating the spectrum $G(\omega)$ (when suitably normalised) to
the probability density function of the frequency modulation,[17, 18]
so, in the present case

$$G(\omega) \approx \frac{A^2}{2} \frac{1}{\sqrt{2\pi\omega_\Delta^2}} \exp -\frac{1}{2}\left(\frac{\omega}{\omega_\Delta}\right)^2 \tag{7.26}$$

This form can be used in eqn. 7.22 when ω_Δ/p_m exceeds unity and,
interestingly, it proves to be acceptable also when small deviation cases
are investigated and results are compared with the Volterra-series
approach. Such comparisons are discussed in Section 7.11.

7.6 Quasi-stationary approximation

Recall eqn. 7.1 and suppose that $g(x)$ is such that only small values of x
are significant so $\mu(t - x)$ can be replaced by $\mu(t) - x\dot{\mu}(t)$ when
performing the integration. Of course, later terms $(x^2/2!)\ddot{\mu}(t) - (x^3/3!)$
$\dddot{\mu}(t) + \ldots$ are present also but these will not be included, the
assumption being that $g(x)$ is so sharply peaked at the origin that
$\mu(t - x)$ can be replaced by only two terms. Then

$$P(t) + jQ(t) = A\int_{-\infty}^{+\infty} g(x) e^{j[\mu(t) - x\dot{\mu}(t)]} dx$$
$$= A e^{j\mu(t)} H[j\dot{\mu}(t)] \tag{7.27}$$

Writing $H(j\omega) = |H(j\omega)| e^{j\phi(\omega)}$

where $\phi(\omega)$ is the phase characteristic of the low-pass equivalent filter,
this result shows that the steady-state response of the filter to
$A \cos[\omega_0 t + \mu(t)]$ is given by

$$|H[j\dot{\mu}(t)]| \cos[\omega_0 t + \mu(t) + \phi[\dot{\mu}(t)]] \tag{7.28}$$

On demodulation, the phase, therefore, is

$$\theta_q(t) = \mu(t) + \phi[\dot{\mu}(t)] \tag{7.29}$$

and it is seen that the amplitude characteristic of the filter is not
involved.

The steps leading to eqn. 7.28 constitute the quasi-stationary
approximation and the r.h.s. of eqn. 7.27 is the leading term in a

series originally derived by Carson and Fry,[19] and Van der Pol.[20] Much discussion and several exchanges of correspondence[21] have taken place regarding the precise conditions under which this series converges, and when it is adequate to use eqn. 7.29.

Rather than review the literature in this area we choose to compare the outcome of using the quasi-stationary approximation with measurements that are now available and with the results of other theoretical approaches such as those described earlier.

The expression for $\theta_q(t)$ is seen to involve a nonlinear zero memory transformation of the frequency modulation $\dot{\mu}(t)$ [we now place $\dot{\mu}(t) = M(t)$ and suppose $\mu(t)$ and therefore $M(t)$ to be Gaussian processes] and the form is precisely that discussed in eqn. 2.27 of Section 2.5. $R_q(\tau)$ the autocorrelation function of $\theta_q(t)$ is therefore given by a series like 2.34 and in the present instance

$$R_q(\tau) = \psi_\mu(\tau) + \frac{\psi_M(\tau)}{\omega_\Delta^2} I_1^2(\omega_\Delta)$$
$$+ \sum_{m=1}^{\infty} \frac{1}{(2m+1)!} \left[\frac{\psi_M(\tau)}{\omega_\Delta^2} \right]^{2m+1} I_{2m+1}^2(\omega_\Delta) \quad (7.30)$$

where
$$I_{2m+1}(\omega_\Delta) = \frac{1}{\sqrt{2\pi}} \int_{-\infty}^{+\infty} \phi(x\omega_\Delta) e^{-\frac{x^2}{2}} He_{2m+1}(x) dx \quad (7.31)$$

$He_m(x)$ is a Hermite polynomial: $He_0(x) = 1, He_1(x) = x$

$$He_n(x) = xHe_{n-1}(x) - (n-1)He_{n-2}(x)$$

The summation refers to 3rd, 5th, 7th etc. orders of distortion of $M(t)$ because the assumption has been made that $\phi(\omega) = -\phi(-\omega)$, and taking the Fourier cosine transform in order to determine the corresponding power spectrum, the distortion-to-signal ratio $(D/S)_q$ in the case of flat f.m., is given by

$$\left(\frac{D}{S} \right)_q = \frac{\left(\frac{\omega}{\omega_\Delta} \right)^2 \sum_{m=1}^{\infty} \left[\frac{I_{2m+1}(\omega_\Delta)}{2^m(2m)!} \right]^2 \frac{1}{(2m+1)} \sum_{r=0}^{2m+1} (-1)^r \binom{2m+1}{r} \left[2m+1-2r-\frac{\omega}{p_m} \right]^{2m}}{1 + \left[\frac{\omega}{\omega_\Delta} I_1(\omega_\Delta) \right]^2}$$
$$(7.32)$$

where the summation over r terminates when $2m + 1 - 2r - \omega/p_m$ becomes negative.[22] If, for ease of presentation, attention is confined to third order distortion

$$\left(\frac{D}{S}\right)_q = \frac{\left[\frac{\omega}{\omega_\Delta} I_3(\omega_\Delta)\right]^2}{1 + \left[\frac{\omega}{\omega_\Delta} I_1(\omega_\Delta)\right]^2} \frac{1}{24} \left[3 - \left(\frac{\omega}{p_m}\right)^2\right] \qquad (7.33)$$

A peculiarity of the quasi-stationary approximation, evidenced by the factor $1 + [(\omega/\omega_\Delta)I_1(\omega_\Delta)]^2$ appearing in the denominator of eqn. 7.32, is that the coherence factor exceeds unity. Thus, upon demodulation, the spectral components of the wanted signal are always amplified rather than being depressed, as a result of filtering. This result, which is counter to intuition, is not of great consequence, however, as, when the quasi-stationary approach is successful, it appears that $(\omega/\omega_\Delta)I_1(\omega_\Delta)$ is then much less than unity at all baseband frequencies. It may be recalled that a coherence factor that can exceed unity by a large margin arose in the case of echo distortion discussed in Section 5.8 but the distortion then too was very large.

The quasi-stationary approach is taken further in Section 7.13.

7.7 Monte Carlo method

The general availability of powerful high-speed computers soon made it apparent that many of the tedious analytical operations that are needed to examine the performance of communication systems using nonlinear elements or filtering could be relegated to the machine. With filtering, for example, the case of harmonic distortion of a single-tone modulation can, in principle, be computed as exactly as required by modifying each sideband of the spectrum (the amplitudes being given by Bessel functions of the first kind) according to the transfer characteristic of the filter, and the distorted frequency modulation recovered by Fourier analysis.[24] When the modulation contains more than one tone such a procedure is still applicable but the number of operations to be done is much greater.

On first sight, therefore, when the modulation is of a complicated kind, such as a noise test signal, this direct approach would seem to be out of the question, but the situation does have one redeeming feature. It is legitimate to represent the noise band by tones whose frequencies are equally spaced[16,25] and thus the r.f. spectrum can only contain sidebands spaced from the carrier by multiples of this basic frequency step. Consequently, if the tones simulating the noise band modulation are specified in amplitude and phase (the amplitudes being determined by the r.m.s. frequency deviation and by the pre-emphasis law, if any, that is used, and the phases being chosen pseudo randomly), then evaluation of the sideband amplitudes and phases can be performed by Fourier analysing the expression for the modulated wave. As with single-tone modulation, modifications can then be made to the sideband array in conformity with the transmission medium between transmitter and receiver and the distorted frequency modulation recovered by a further stage of Fourier analysis. The Fast-Fourier transform enables the switch from the time domain to the frequency domain (or vice versa) to be done with great ease and the whole exercise is ultimately restricted in accuracy only by machine capacity and the cost of each run.

The Monte Carlo approach has a feature in common with the noise-test set arrangement of the laboratory in that, by omitting one or two tones in the baseband model, the distortion falling into the gap so made can be calculated following filtering and/or the addition of noise, and subsequent demodulation. The coherence factor is not included unless special steps are taken and the usual procedure is to calculate this separately and apply it to the final results if its size is appreciable.

Both the modulation and any external thermal noise are modelled by summing pseudo-randomly phased tones equally stepped in frequency across the pertinent bandwidths, and then with a particular choice of phase angles a value for the distortion-to-signal ratio is calculated. A fresh choice of phase angles is then made and a second result for D/S obtained. This process is repeated a number of times and the answers are averaged to give a final estimate.

As with all exercises of this kind, a law of diminishing returns is obeyed regarding the extra accuracy to be achieved through increasing the number of runs, and as runs can be lengthy, a balance between useful accuracy and cost must be struck. Typically, four runs of the program when averaged give an accuracy of about ± 2·5 dB when the gap consists of two tones.

Fig 7.1 (taken from Reference 25 where some further discussion of the expected error is given) shows the probaaility of exceeding a specified departure from the true mean value, plotted against M which is the product of the number of program cycles and the number of tones in a gap. The phase modulation is written

$$\mu(t) = \sum_{n=1}^{N} a_n \cos [n\omega_a t + \alpha_n] \qquad (7.34)$$

so that the corresponding frequency modulation is

$$M(t) = -\omega_a \sum_{n=1} na_n \sin [n\omega_a t + \alpha_n] \qquad (7.35)$$

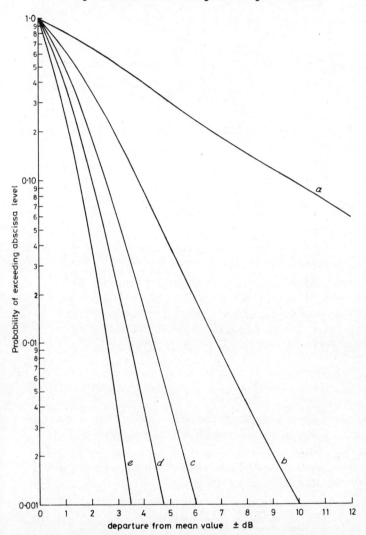

Fig. 7.1 Distribution of the expected error in $\frac{D}{S}$ as given by Monte-Carlo computations

M = product of the number of program cycles and the number of tones in a gap

$a\ M = 1.\ b\ M = 4.\ c\ M = 8.\ d\ M = 12.\ e\ M = 20.$

Here α_n are the set of pseudo-random phase angles, ω_a is the frequency step so that $N\omega_a$ is the highest modulating frequency p_m, and N is the number of tones used. The mean square frequency deviation ω_Δ^2 is then given by

$$\omega_\Delta^2 = \frac{1}{2}\sum_{n=1}^{N}(na_n\omega_a)^2 \tag{7.36}$$

and, similarly, the mean square phase deviation $\psi_\mu(0)$ is

$$\psi_\mu(0) = \frac{1}{2}\sum_{n=1}^{N}a_n^2$$

For flat f.m. na_n is constant for all n (the common value being c, say) and using eqn. 7.36

$$\omega_\Delta^2 = \frac{N}{2}(c\omega_a)^2 \tag{7.37}$$

$$\psi_\mu(0) = \frac{1}{2}c^2\left(1 + \frac{1}{2^2} + \frac{1}{3^2} + \ldots + \frac{1}{N^2}\right)$$

$$\approx \frac{(c\pi)^2}{12} \quad \text{for large } N \tag{7.38}$$

In pre-emphasised cases the a_n are shaped appropriately. With a representation for $\mu(t)$ such as eqn. 7.34, the in-phase and quadrature components of the carrier can be developed as follows:

$$P(t) = \cos\mu(t) = \sum_{n=0}^{kN}\{C_n^c\cos(n\omega_a t) + S_n^c\sin(n\omega_a t)\} \tag{7.39}$$

$$Q(t) = \sin\mu(t) = \sum_{n=0}^{kN}\{C_n^S\cos(n\omega_a t) + S_n^S\sin(n\omega_a t)\} \tag{7.40}$$

where the C_n and S_n are determined by Fourier analysis, and k is chosen so that $-kN\omega_a$ to $+kN\omega_a$ is the band that is occupied by the significant frequency components of the carrier. Like forms for $\dot{P}(t)$ and $\dot{Q}(t)$ can be obtained by directly differentiating eqns. 7.39 and 7.40. The modulated carrier becomes

$$\frac{1}{2}\sum_{n=0}^{kN}(C_n^c + S_n^s)\cos[\overline{\omega_0 + n\omega_a}t]$$

$$+ \frac{1}{2}\sum_{n=0}^{kN}(S_n^c - C_n^s)\sin[\overline{\omega_0 + n\omega_a}t]$$

$$+ \frac{1}{2}\sum_{n=0}^{kN}(C_n^c - S_n^s)\cos[\overline{\omega_0 - n\omega_a}t] \tag{7.41}$$

$$- \frac{1}{2}\sum_{n=0}^{kN}(C_n^s + S_n^c)\sin[\overline{\omega_0 - n\omega_a}t]$$

and if this wave is filtered by a network that multiplies the amplitudes of the sidebands at $\pm n\omega_a$ by $A_{\pm n}$, and changes their phase by $\phi_{\pm n}$, then the output wave is given by

$$\frac{1}{2}\sum_{n=0}^{kN}(C_n^c + S_n^s)A_{+n}\cos\{(\omega_0 + n\omega_a)t + \phi_{+n}\}$$

$$+\frac{1}{2}\sum_{n=0}^{kN}(S_n^c - C_n^s)A_{+n}\sin\{(\omega_0 + n\omega_a)t + \phi_{+n}\}$$

$$+\frac{1}{2}\sum_{n=0}^{kN}(C_n^c - S_n^s)A_{-n}\cos\{(\omega_0 - n\omega_a t) + \phi_{-n}\} \qquad (7.42)$$

$$-\frac{1}{2}\sum_{n=0}^{kN}(C_n^s + S_n^c)A_{-n}\sin\{(\omega_0 - n\omega_a)t + \phi_{-n}\}$$

By collecting together the coefficients of $\cos\omega_0 t$ and $\sin\omega_0 t$ this expression provides in in-phase and quadrature components $[P_F(t)$ and $Q_F(t)$, say] of the filtered wave. Direct differentiation of these forms gives $\dot{P}_F(t)$ and $\dot{Q}_F(t)$ and so the combination

$$\frac{P_F(t)\dot{Q}_F(t) - Q_F(t)\dot{P}_F(t)}{P_F^2(t) + Q_F^2(t)} \qquad (7.43)$$

which gives the instantaneous frequency of the filtered wave, can be formed and Fourier analysed to examine the frequency components (these are once again spaced at intervals of ω_a) lying in the baseband range.

Note that combinations other than eqn. 7.43 can be treated with equal ease and so the effects of imperfect limiting, no limiting at all, or multiplication by the square of the envelope in which the denominator of eqn. 7.43 is replaced by a constant, can be investigated by simple program changes.

The algebraic formulation given above provides the basis for writing a computer program to perform the necessary steps and through exploiting the Fast Fourier transform algorithm and routines for random number generation very efficient programs can be developed.

In the current section the Monte Carlo approach is being discussed as an alternative way of assessing the effects of filtering an f.m. wave but thermal noise can be accommodated in the program in a straight-forward manner and so a brief discussion of this feature will be included here.

7.8 Inclusion of additive thermal noise

Before any nonlinear operations take place in the receiver, the carrier
and its accompanying noise can be treated separately (and, indeed,
should be so treated from the point of view of program efficiency),
and then to eqn. 7.42 is added

$$n(t) = \sum_{m=-kN}^{+kN} b_m \cos\left[(\omega_0 + m\omega_a)t + \beta_m\right] \qquad (7.44)$$

where the β_m are pseudo-random phase angles chosen independently of
the α_n used in eqn. 7.34. The noise power (as measured in bandwidth
$2kN\omega_a$ at the filter output) is given by

$$\frac{1}{2} \sum_{m=-kN}^{kN} b_m^2$$

and by appropriate scaling at this stage, several noise levels or C/N
ratios can be dealt with simultaneously. The b_m therefore follow the
voltage transfer characteristic of the filter and it is clear that $P_F(t)$,
$Q_F(t)$, $\dot{P}_F(t)$ and $\dot{Q}_F(t)$ receive additive modifications whereupon the
Fourier analysis of the instantaneous frequency follows as before.[25]

Subject to the inherent statistical error of the Monte Carlo approach,
therefore, the combined effects of filtering and thermal noise can be
investigated but, as will be discussed next, restrictions on the r.m.s.
frequency deviation and on the number of tones N used to model the
baseband, must be recognised.

7.9 Size of N

For adequate simulation of the noise-band modulation the statistical
properties of the assembly of tones with quasi-random phases should
be close to those of random noise and this indicates that N should be
as large as possible. It is found in some applications of noise
modelling that as few as ten or a dozen such tones are enough, but in
the current context N fixes the ratio of the highest to the lowest
modulating frequency [values for this ratio such as 17·5 (a 240
channel f.m. f.m.d. system) or 26 (an 1800 channel f.m. f.d.m system)
are met in practice], and it is also required that the removal of pairs of
tones to simulate measuring slots should cause a negligible change in
the statistical properties of the baseband model.

Fig 7.2 shows the instantaneous level distributions for 10, 20, 50 and 100 randomly phased tones, together with the limiting Gaussian curve. It is seen that 100 tones provide a distribution which is close to the limit, and even for 50 tones the departure is not very great.

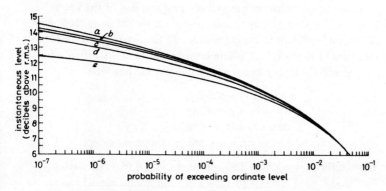

Fig. 7.2 Distribution of the sum of various numbers of incommensurate equi-amplitude sinusoids
a Gaussian limit. *b* 100 tones. *c* 50 tones. *d* 20 tones. *e* 10 tones

Now, from the expression for the modulated carrier given in eqn. 7.41, the number of sidebands to be modified in amplitude and phase is $2kN + 1$, and, if a carrier with a large f.m. index is of interest, then $2k$ could easily be as large as 16 (such a figure is suggested by curve *a* on Fig 4.1, for example, if all the spectral energy outside the band $\pm 8p_m$ were to be regarded as negligible). It is clear, therefore, that with both k and N large, there can be a danger of exceeding the storage capacity of the machine.

The example cited above referred to $\omega_\Delta/p_m = 2$ and this is by no means the largest f.m. index that could be of interest, but retaining this example and assuming that the r.f. power spectrum follows the Gaussian law of the modulation (as in eqn. 7.26) the probaability that the instantaneous frequency lies outside $\pm 8p_m$ will be the same as the probability that the instantaneous frequency lies beyond four times the r.m.s. frequency (since $\omega_\Delta/p_m = 2$), that is, $6{\cdot}27 \times 10^{-5}$, and this probaability is plotted for an ordinate value of 12 dB on the Gaussian limiting curve of Fig. 7.2.

Thus, if so few tones are employed that a level such as the 12 dB used above is exceeded with a probability that differs appreciably from $6{\cdot}27 \times 10^{-5}$, it cannot be expected that an r.f. spectrum with correctly distributed tails will be generated by the Monte Carlo program. Fig. 7.2

amply demonstrates that in such cases N should exceed 50 by a large
margin although the situation changes dramatically if a level such as
8 dB above r.m.s. is examined. Then it would appear that as few as ten
tones (as used in Reference 26) are adequate, but in view of the
important part played by the low-frequency end of the phase
modulating spectrum (being inversely proportional to the square of
frequency) it seems likely that accuracy will be lost in predicting the
distortion levels low in the baseband.* 97 tones were used for the
baseband in Reference 25 where several sources of distortion were
treated and these may be summarised under the headings:

> Quadratic group delay
> Narrow bandpass filtering
> Frequency selective fading
> Additive r.f. noise and the threshold effect

The results referred to an 1800 channel f.m. f.d.m. system having a
baseband range (316 kHz to 8204 kHz) and multi-channel r.m.s.
frequency deviation (1065 kHz) that comply with CCIR specifications.
These modulation parameters give $\omega_\Delta/p_m = 0.13$, and the program was
also used to determine the shape of the r.f. spectrum.

Several similar Monte Carlo approaches have been reported in the
literature.[26–28] These treat other distortion mechanisms such as
a.m.-to-p.m. conversion (Section 8.2).

Besides being capable of modelling a practical situation in fine detail,
the Monte Carlo method offers a valuable means of checking the
validity of approximate ways of calculating f.m. distortions. The f.m.
first-order approximation theory which is discussed in Chapter 8, is a
case in point.

7.10 Two filter types

While there are a limitless variety of filters that can be investigated
using the methods of the previous sections, two types will be picked
out for special attention.

Firstly the truncating or band-limiting filter will be considered.
This has a unity transfer characteristic over the frequency band
$\omega_0 - p_l$ to $\omega_0 + p_l$ (with a zero phase characteristic) and is zero
elsewhere. Strictly, such a filter is unrealisable but it is often closely

---

* The p_0 of a particular case can be complied with by reducing the first few a_ns
to zero in eqn. 7.34.

approximated to and it has been adopted in a number of investigations aimed at finding the bandwidth outside which even complete removal of the spectral components can be tolerated.

Secondly, we shall consider a single-pole bandpass filter. This type has gained importance due to the stability that is realised when it is used in the loop of frequency-modulation receivers that employ frequency feedback (the f.m.f.b. receiver discussed in Section 9.4).

The two kinds of filter to be examined each have their areas of practical application therefore, but, more than this, they represent extremes in the rates of decay of $g(t)$, the impulse response functions of their lowpass equivalent forms:

For the truncating filter

$$H(j\omega) = 1 \quad \text{for} \quad -p_l < \omega < p_l$$

So

$$g(t) = \frac{p_l}{\pi} \cdot \left(\frac{\sin p_l t}{p_l t} \right) \tag{7.45}$$

For the single-pole filter

$$H(j\omega) = \frac{1}{1 + j\left(\dfrac{\omega}{\alpha p_m}\right)}$$

and

$$g(t) = \alpha p_m \cdot e^{-\alpha p_m t} \qquad t > 0 \tag{7.46}$$

$$= 0 \qquad\qquad\qquad \text{otherwise}$$

here $2\alpha p_m$ (where α is a numerical factor) is the 3 dB bandwidth of the filter.

While eqn. 7.46 exhibits the fastest decay to zero of all filters, the successive peaks of eqn. 7.45 represent the slowest decay and in this sense all other filters lie somewhere between these two extremes.

7.11 Truncating filter

The first approximation that has been proposed is that shown in eqn. 7.8 and it is appropriate when the r.m.s. phase deviation is small. The first term contributing to distortion is the cubic member from $\sin[\mu(t-x) - \mu(t)]$, so

$$\theta(t) \approx \mu(t) - \frac{1}{6} \int_{-\infty}^{+\infty} g(x) [\mu(t-x) - \mu(t)]^3 dx \tag{7.47}$$

Now recall the Volterra-series result given in eqn. 7.15. If $g(x)$ refers to the truncating filter of eqn. 7.45 and $p_l > p_m$ (as will always be assumed to be the case here), it is seen that $L(t) = \mu(t)$, so eqns 7.15 and 7.47 are identical. This, then, is an example in which two theories have been brought into alignment through the particular choice of filter.

The distortion-to-signal power ratio in the highest baseband channel when $p_m < p_l < 2p_m$ is then given by

$$\frac{D}{S} = \frac{1}{8 W_\mu(p_m)} \int_{p_l - p_m}^{p_m} \int_{p_l - p_m}^{r} W_\mu(q) W_\mu(r) W_\mu(p_m + q - r) dq \, dr \tag{7.48}$$

This result is obtained by sorting out the ranges over which non-zero contributions to the integration arise and the upper limit for the q integration is seen to be r. This is a simple example of the situation referred to earlier in which the integration has to be halted at certain critical points in order to traverse correctly the ranges over which the integrand is non-zero. If $2p_m < p_l < 3p_m$ so that the restriction $p_l < 2p_m$ is not observed then the quintic term from $\sin [\mu(t - x) - \mu(t)]$ is the first distortion contributor and eqn. 7.48 has to be replaced by a quadruple integral.

If a constant spectral density is assumed for the phase modulation (as an approximation to a pre-emphasised baseband, for example) then

$$W_\mu(\omega) = K \quad \text{for} \quad 0 \leqslant \omega < p_m$$

$$= 0 \text{ otherwise}$$

and for the mean square frequency deviation to equal ω_Δ^2

$$Kp_m = 3 \left(\frac{\omega_\Delta}{p_m} \right)^2$$

Then eqn. 7.48 gives

$$\frac{D}{S} = \frac{9}{16} \left(\frac{\omega_\Delta}{p_m} \right)^4 \left[2 - \frac{p_l}{p_m} \right]^2 \quad p_m < p_l < 2p_m \tag{7.49}$$

The integration for flat f.m. is much more involved and comes out in terms of rational functions, logarithms, and Spence integrals. The result was given by Medhurst and with $p_l/p_m = k$ it can be written

$$\frac{D}{S} = \left(\frac{\omega_\Delta}{p_m} \right)^4 F(k) \tag{7.50}$$

where $F^{\frac{1}{2}}(k)$ is shown in Fig. 7.3.

These formulae assume the coherence factor to be unity and values of k in the range 1·6 to 1·9, say, (suggested by Carson's rule) are likely to be of most interest. In view of eqn. 7.49 it is intructive to compare $F^{\frac{1}{2}}(k)$ with $\frac{3}{4}[2 - k]$ whereupon it is quickly found that, for $1·6 < k < 1·9$ eqns. 7.49 and 7.50 predict comparable distortion levels. Thus, differences in baseband spectral distribution can result in little change in D/S. Further examples of this behaviour will be found when

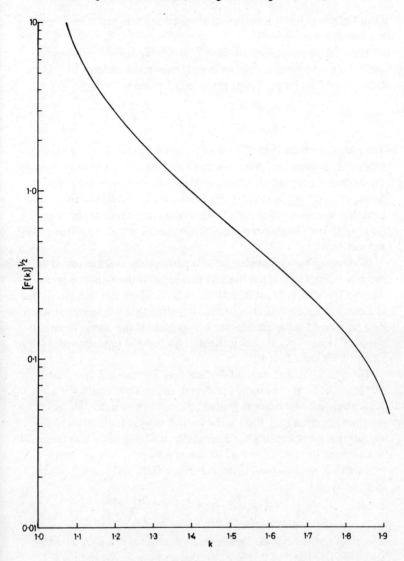

Fig. 7.3 Variation with k of the function $[F(k)]^{\frac{1}{2}}$

The D/S power ratio in top channel when the distortion is introduced by a truncating filter of bandwidth $2p_l$, is given by

$$\frac{D}{S} = \left(\frac{\omega_\Delta}{p_m}\right)^4 F(k) \quad \text{where} \quad k = \frac{p_l}{p_m}$$

Reproduced from *Proc. IRE*, 1956, **44** (2), p. 189

filter distortion levels from pre-emphasised and non-pre-emphasised basebands are compared.

Eqn. 7.49 was obtained by Rice[29] who extends the Volterra-series analysis in the case of a flat spectrum for the phase modulation. The extension to $2p_m < p_l < 3p_m$ gives, in top channel

$$\frac{D}{S} = \frac{5}{96}\left[\frac{3}{2}\left(\frac{\omega_\Delta}{p_m}\right)^2\left(3 - \frac{p_l}{p_m}\right)\right]^4 \qquad (7.51)$$

The distortion is entirely of fifth-order but the corresponding extension of eqn. 7.50 is not available owing to the difficulty of carrying through the necessary integration. However, it may be anticipated that for $5/2p_m < p_l < 3p_m$, eqn. 7.51 can serve also for the case of flat f.m. provided fifth-order distortion is the major contributor so that the $(\omega_\Delta/p_m)^8$ law (24 dB per octave) is obeyed when D/S is plotted against the f.m. index.

The role of the coherence factor is particularly well illustrated by the truncating filter. It has been mentioned that the formulae given above assume unity for this factor, and on recalling (see eqn. 4.29) that the simplest theoretical estimate for it is $|H(j\omega)|^2$, it is seen that when $p_l > p_m$ a unity coherence factor is again used if the simple theory is adopted. (If $p_l < p_m$ then this theory says that the upper baseband channels are annihilated.)

Now, in the digital method described by Shimbo and Loo,[3] the factor $|H(j\omega)|^2$ is universally employed, and so their results for a truncating filter are never degraded by a coherence factor. Moreover, in a number of cases they show curves which suggest that, on increasing the deviation but keeping the bandwidth fixed, the distortion levels will become less (see their Fig. 10, for example). A very different picture emerges, however, if the coherence factor $|E(0, \omega)|^2$, which is given by

$$\left[\frac{1}{2}\ \text{erf}\left(\frac{p_l}{\omega_\Delta\sqrt{2}}\right) + \frac{1}{2}\ \text{erf}\left(\frac{p_l - \omega}{\omega_\Delta\sqrt{2}}\right)\right]^2 \qquad (7.52)$$

is applied to their curves. This form for the factor complies with the spectrum $G(q)$ having the Gaussian shape of eqn. 7.26, and Fig 7.4 shows a comparison with results derived from a computer program written to evaluate eqns. 7.24 and 7.25 with a Gaussian spectrum, and so provide values for D/S in the case of multiplication by the square of the envelope. The frequency modulation has a flat spectrum, so

$$W_\mu(\omega) = \frac{\omega_\Delta^2}{(p_m - p_0)\omega^2} \qquad p_0 \leqslant \omega \leqslant p_m \qquad (7.53)$$

and from an investigation of several values of p_0/p_m it became apparent that D/S is virtually independent of this ratio provided it is given a value typical of those met in practice $(0.01 < p_0/p_m < 0.1$, say).

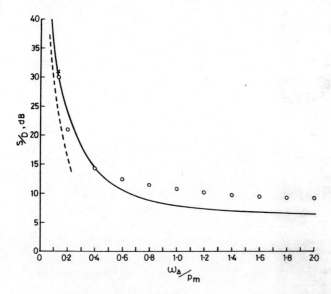

Fig. 7.4 Variation of S/D in top channel with increasing f.m. index for a fixed-bandwidth truncating filter

$$\frac{p_l}{p_m} = \frac{\text{semi-bandwidth of truncating i.f. filter}}{\text{maximum modulating frequency}} = 1.17$$

$- - -$ theory of Medhurst (flat f.m., eqn. 7.50)
∘ ∘ ∘ ∘ theory of Shimbo and Loo (flat f.m., Fig. 10 of Reference 3) modified by a coherence factor (see eqn. 7.52)
———— multiplication by square of envelope (flat f.m.)
   X   Monte Carlo (Reference 3)[*]
[*]Courtesy Institute of Electrical and Electronic Engineers Inc.

On Fig. 7.4 the expected flattening out is exhibited as the deviation increases, while all theories tend to follow a 12 dB per octave slope when the f.m. index is small. In this region the Medhurst (Volterra) points give the highest accuracy (until the flattening out occurs) as they follow from a proper expansion of the instantaneous phase. The agreement between the Monte Carlo point at $\omega_\Delta/p_m = 0.13$ and multiplication by the square of the envelope is thought to be slightly fortuitous.

While two different approximations have been used to calculate the nonlinear distortion contributions (the approaches taken are shown by eqns. 7.8 and 7.11) it is seen that, when a common coherence factor is used to calculate D/S, comparable levels are obtained with a disagreement of about 2·5 dB in the flattened-out region.

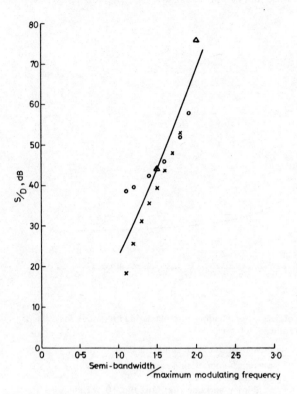

Fig. 7.5 Variation of S/D in top channel with truncating filter bandwidth for a fixed value of f.m. index
$(\omega_\Delta/p_m = 0.13)$
X X X X theory of Medhurst (flat f.m., eqn. 7.50)
○ ○ ○ ○ ○ theory of Rice (flat p.m., Reference 29)[*]
△ △ △ △ △ Monte Carlo points of Anuff and Liou with 5 dB pre-emphasis of the top channel (Reference 27)[†]
———— multiplication by square of envelope (flat f.m.)
[*] Courtesy *Bell System Technical Journal*
[†] Courtesy Institute of Electrical and Electronic Engineers Inc.

The factor $\exp - [2\psi_\mu(0) - \psi_\mu(x) - \psi_\mu(y)]$ appearing in eqn. 7.9 can be directly related to the r.f. spectrum through eqn. 4.7 and so in the theory of Shimbo and Loo the shape of the spectrum enters the working in much the same way as it enters eqn. 7.21 (the role of this exponential factor was reviewed in Reference 12). In low deviation cases the spectral shape is not of great importance and so the simplification of using the Gaussian spectrum of eqn. 7.26 for both small and large f.m. indices can be exploited when eqn. 7.22 is to be evaluated.

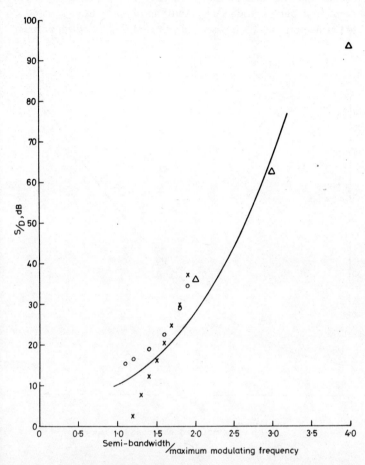

Fig. 7.6 Variation of *S/D* in top channel with truncating filter bandwidth for a fixed value of f.m. index
($\omega_\Delta/p_m = 0.5$)
X X X X theory of Medhurst (flat f.m. eqn. 7.50)
o o o o o theory of Rice (flat p.m., Reference 29)[*]
△ △ △ △ △ Monte Carlo points of Anuff and Liou (Reference 27)[†] with 5 dB pre-emphasis of the top channel
——— multiplication by square of envelope (flat f.m.)
[*] Courtesy *Bell System Technical Journal*
[†] Courtesy Institute of Electrical and Electronic Engineers Inc.

Fig 7.5 shows a low deviation case in which $\omega_\Delta/p_m = 0.13$ (this corresponds to an 1800 channel f.m. f.d.m. terrestrial system that complies with CCIR recommendations regarding the upper and lower baseband frequencies and test-tone deviation). Two points are shown that come from curves produced by Anuff and Liou[27] using a Monte Carlo approach. Their baseband was modelled by 50 tones and

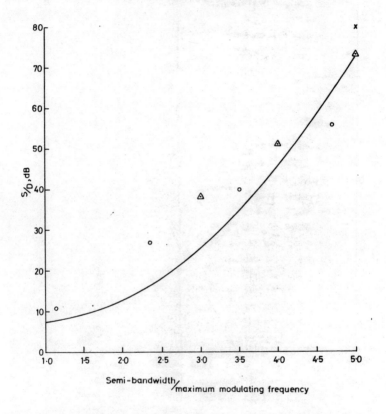

Fig. 7.7 Variation of *S/D* in top channel with truncating filter bandwidth for a fixed value of f.m. index
($\omega_\Delta/p_m = 1$)
o o o o theory of Shimbo and Loo (flat f.m., Reference 3)*
△ △ △ △ Monte Carlo points of Anuff and Liou with 5 dB pre-emphasis of the top channel (Reference 27) *
   X   Monte Carlo point of Ruthroff (flat f.m., Reference 26)†
———— multiplication by square of envelope (flat f.m.)
* Courtesy Institute of Electrical and Electronic Engineers Inc.
† Courtesy *Bell System Technical Journal*

ten trials were averaged so providing a 90% confidence interval of about
2·5 dB. A pre-emphasis law that enhances the topmost channel by 5 dB
and attenuates the lowest channel by 6·5 dB was assumed.

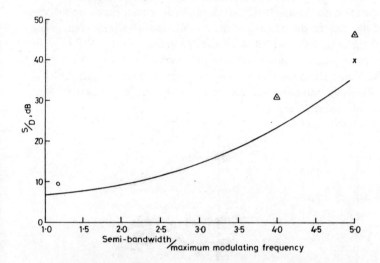

Fig. 7.8 Variation of *S/D* in top channel with truncating filter bandwidth for a
fixed value of the f.m. index
$(\omega_\Delta/p_m = 1\cdot5)$
o o o o theory of Shimbo and Loo (flat f.m. Reference 3)[*]
△ △ △ △ Monte Carlo points of Anuff and Liou with 5 dB pre-emphasis
of the top channel (Reference 27)[*]
  X   Monte Carlo point of Ruthroff (flat f.m., Reference 26)[†]
——— Multiplication by square of envelope (flat f.m.)
[*] Courtesy Institute of Electrical and Electronic Engineers
[†] Courtesy *Bell System Technical Journal*

7.12 Truncating filter: the region $\omega_\Delta/p_m \geqslant 0\cdot5$

Figs 7.6 to 7.10 present curves for $\omega_\Delta/p_m = 0\cdot5$, $1\cdot0$, $1\cdot5$, $2\cdot0$ and $3\cdot0$
with points superimposed from other sources in the literature. The
results all refer to the top channel position in the baseband and the
widest scatter of points occurs when $\omega_\Delta/p_m = 1\cdot0$ and the f.m. index
can be regarded as neither large or small. Stricter compliance with the
theory would then be achieved by using points read from the curve for
$\omega_\Delta/p_m = 1\cdot0$ on Fig. 4.1 to specify $G(\omega)$.

It would appear that all theoretical treatments predict that the
topmost channel receives the largest distortion contribution and the
pre-emphasis law assumed by Anuff and Liou is seen to suggest

(especially for the larger f.m. indices) that the improvement over the non-pre-emphasized case is approximately the amount by which the top channel is enhanced, i.e. 5 dB. This outcome is not too surprising when it is recognized that the distortion is the result of a nonlinear operation on the baseband that does not depend critically on the shape of the spectral distribution of the modulation. The linear component, on the other hand, which forms the denominator of the D/S ratio, has a one-to-one relationship with the pre-emphasis law assumed. (For all the Monte Carlo results shown on our figures, the coherence factor is effectively unity and was, presumably, taken to be precisely unity in References 26 and 27).

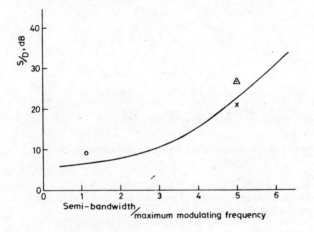

Fig. 7.9 Variation of S/D in top-channel with truncating filter bandwidth for a fixed value of the f.m. index
$(\omega_\Delta/p_m = 2\cdot0)$
o   theory of Shimbo and Loo (flat f.m., Reference 3)[+]
△   Monte Carlo point of Anuff and Liou with 5 dB pre-emphasis of the top channel (Reference 27)[*]
X   Monte Carlo point of Ruthroff (flat f.m., Reference 26)[†]
————— multiplication by square of envelope (flat f.m.)
[*] Courtesy Institute of Electrical and Electronic Engineers Inc.
[†] Courtesy *Bell System Technical Journal*

At the centre point of the baseband the pre-emphasis adopted by Anuff and Liou[27] enhances the signal level by $1\cdot3$ dB and Fig. 7.11 shows a comparison of their results with the multiplication by square of the envelope technique. The circles refer to the nearest full curves and the sensitivity to the value of ω_Δ/p_m is fully apparent.

At very low baseband frequencies the distortion levels are usually extremely small and therefore of little practical interest. If there is a

requirement to calculate them accurately then approximate approaches
of the type detailed above can be hazardous (errors of over 20 dB are
likely to be incurred) and a Monte Carlo method is probably the most
fruitful approach.

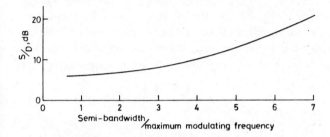

F ig. 7.10 Variation of *S/D* in top-channel with truncating filter bandwidth for a
fixed value of the f.m. index
$(\omega_\Delta/p_m = 3.0)$
——— multiplication by square of envelope (flat f.m.)

Ruthroff shows results obtained from a Monte Carlo exercise with
large f.m. indices (Fig.3 of Reference 26) in which more distortion falls
at $p/p_m = 0.1$ than at $p/p_m = 1.0$. This unusual behaviour was
obtained for a baseband consisting of only ten tones and so it does not
reflect the situation when a closer model of the usual f.d.m. modulation
is used, although Ruthroff's top-channel results have been accepted
when the truncating bandwidth is not too wide, and these have been
shown here on Figs. 7.7, 7.8 and 7.9.

It is felt that the information contained in Figs 7.5 to 7.10 gives a
useful indication of the interplay between distortion and bandwidth
restriction and the curves may be used to produce modified versions of
Carson's rule for assessing necessary bandwidth.[27]

The Volterra-series approach is fitting when the f.m. index is small
but large indices are perhaps best handled by Monte Carlo or
multiplication by squared envelope methods. It may be mentioned that
in the case of the truncating filter no theoretical methods other than
Shimbo and Loo's digital approach or the more compact multiplication
by squared envelope results, shown here, appear to be available for
treating the large f.m. indices cases. The success of the latter may seem
surprising especially when it is recalled that merely the quadratic term
from the hyperbolic cosine in eqn. 7.21 has been used. This corresponds
to accepting only the first term of the series that is obtained for the
autocorrelation function of the distortion following a stage of approximation such as eqn. 7.8 or eqn. 7.11.

Usually this first term refers to all contributions that arise to the third-order type distortion spectrum (corresponding to the fourth term in the development of eqn. 2.37) and, as will now be shown, a like situation holds in a quasi-stationary analysis in which the $m = 1$ term from eqn. 7.32 provides sufficient accuracy in many cases. Clearly a development in powers of ω_Δ/p_m is not being relied on when ω_Δ/p_m exceeds unity, as in Figs 7.8 to 7.10. The conclusion to be drawn is that, at least to frequencies in the upper half of the baseband, little or no contribution arises from the terms beyond the first in the series for the autocorrelation function of the distortion even though ω_Δ/p_m may be quite large.

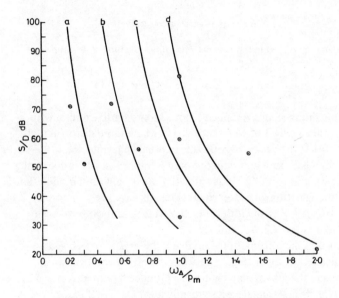

Fig. 7.11 Variation of *S/D* at midpoint of the baseband with increasing f.m. index for a fixed-bandwidth truncating filter

$$\frac{\text{semi-bandwidth of truncating filter}}{\text{maximum modulating frequency}} = \begin{matrix} 2 \text{ for curve } a \\ 3 \text{ for curve } b \\ 4 \text{ for curve } c \\ 5 \text{ for curve } d \end{matrix}$$

∘ ∘ ∘ ∘ Monte Carlo points of Anuff and Liou with 1·3 dB of emphasis at the midpoint of the baseband (Reference 27)[*]
——— multiplication by square envelope (flat f.m.)
[*] Courtesy Institute of Electrical and Electronic Engineers Inc.

7.13 Single-pole filter

As the single-pole filter has the impulsive response function that falls away to zero most rapidly, it would seem to be the filter best suited to the quasi-stationary approach described in Section 7.6.

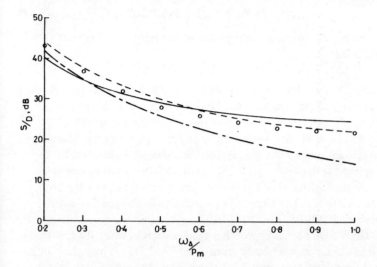

Fig. 7.12 Variation of *S/D* in top channel with increasing f.m. index for a fixed-bandwidth single-pole i.f. filter ($\alpha = 1\cdot223$), and flat f.m.

$$2\alpha = \frac{\text{3 dB filter bandwidth}}{\text{maximum modulating frequency}} = 2\cdot446$$

——— quasi-stationary theory (eqn. 7.33)
− − − curve drawn through Monte Carlo results. From Ruthroff for 50 tones (Reference 26)[*]
o o o o Bodtmann measurement data[*]
−·−·− theory of Bedrosian and Rice (Reference 1)[†]
[*]Courtesy *Bell System Technical Journal*
[†] Courtesy Institute of Electrical and Electronics Engineers Inc.

Interest will be confined to the expression for $(D/S)_q$ given by eqn. 7.33 and then two Integrals $I_1(\omega_\Delta)$ and $I_3(\omega_\Delta)$ have to be evaluated.

$$I_1(\omega_\Delta) = \frac{1}{\sqrt{2\pi}}\int_{-\infty}^{+\infty} \phi(x\omega_\Delta)xe^{-x^2/2}dx \qquad (7.54)$$

where $\phi(\omega)$ is the phase characteristic of the single-pole network, i.e. $\phi(\omega) = \tan^{-1}[\omega/(\alpha p_m)]$. We then have

$$I_1(\omega_\Delta) = \sqrt{\frac{\pi}{2}}\left\{1 - \text{erf}\left(\frac{d}{\sqrt{2}}\right)\right\}e^{d^2/2} \qquad (7.55)$$

where $$d = \frac{\alpha p_m}{\omega_\Delta}$$

and $$I_3(\omega_\Delta) = (1 + d^2)I_1(\omega_\Delta) - d \qquad (7.56)$$

Incidentally, the integrals $I_m(\omega_\Delta)$ obey the following recurrence relationship[12]

$$I_{m+2}(\omega_\Delta) = -dI_{m+1}(\omega_\Delta) + mI_m(\omega_\Delta) \qquad (7.57)$$

The even-order integrals are superfluous to present requirements and originate from

$$I_2(\omega_\Delta) = 1 - dI_1(\omega_\Delta)$$

The particular value $\alpha = 1\cdot223$ will be taken as a first example because a set of measurements for a flat f.m. spectrum, and complying with this bandwidth factor, have been shown by a number of authors.[11,12,26] A comparison of results is presented in Fig. 7.12 where the flattening out is again apparent as the deviation increases. It is seen that the simple quasi-stationary theory of eqn. 7.33 follows the general trend of the measurements while the Monte Carlo computations of Ruthroff have a close fit. (The Monte Carlo agreement is also good at other baseband positions.[26])

The Volterra-series approach is again successful when the f.m. index is small, and the paper by Bedrosian and Rice[1] from which the plotted levels have been extracted is devoted entirely to applying the Mircea/Volterra theory,* taken as far as the cubic term, to the single-pole filter.

Fig. 7.13 shows the situation when $\alpha = 2$ and three baseband positions (or r.b.f. values†) have been examined by both theoretical and measurement procedures. The measured levels were shown in Reference 12 during a discussion of the region of applicability of the Volterra-series method, and it was there pointed out by S.O. Rice how well the quasi-stationary approach follows the measurements made for $\alpha = 1\cdot223$. Fig. 7.13 shows this also to be the case when $\alpha = 2$ except at the lower end of the baseband where the theory of Bedrosian and Rice crosses the measurements and where more terms in the quasi-stationary series eqn. 7.32 could perhaps improve the agreement.

For a channel near the top of the baseband it is seen that the Volterra approach falls away from the measured values when ω_Δ/p_m exceeds $0\cdot5$ and for $\omega_\Delta/p_m = 1\cdot4$, which features in an example quoted by the authors of Reference 1, the discrepancy is about 10 dB.

* While the theory given in this paper is not directly referred to as the Mircea/Volterra-series approach, comparison with References 8 and 10 reveals the equivalence

† r.b.f. = relative baseband frequency

An obvious requirement to increase the plausibility of replacing $\mu(t-x)$ by $\mu(t) - x\dot{\mu}(t)$ in eqn. 7.1 is that the filter bandwidth should greatly exceed modulation parameters such as ω_Δ or p_m (Reference 21). This implies that the parameter d should be large, whereupon

$$
\left.
\begin{aligned}
I_1(\omega_\Delta) &\approx \frac{1}{d} - \frac{1}{d^3} + \dots \\[2mm]
I_3(\omega_\Delta) &\approx \frac{2}{d^3} + \frac{3}{d^5} + \dots
\end{aligned}
\right\}
\tag{7.58}
$$

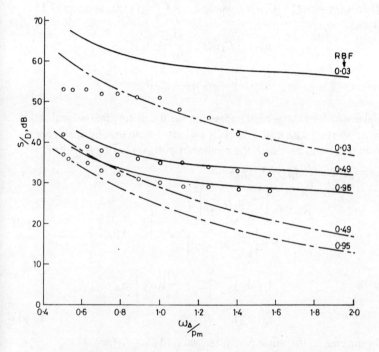

Fig. 7.13 Variation of *S/D* in various channels with increasing f.m. index for a fixed-bandwidth single-pole i.f. filter ($\alpha = 2\cdot0$), and flat f.m.

$$2\alpha = \frac{3\,\text{dB Filter bandwidth}}{\text{maximum modulating frequency}} = 4\cdot0$$

——— quasi-stationary theory (eqn. 7.33)
∘ ∘ ∘ ∘ measurement data (Reference 12)[*]
— · — · theory of Bedrosian and Rice (Reference 1)[*]
RBF = relative baseband frequency
[*] Courtesy Institute of Electrical and Electronic Engineers Inc.

and we have the top-channel approximation

$$\left(\frac{D}{S}\right)_q \approx \frac{1}{3\alpha^6}\left(\frac{\omega_\Delta}{p_m}\right)^4 \cdot \frac{1}{[1+(1/\alpha)^2]}, \quad d \gg 1 \qquad (7.59)$$

Eqn. 7.59 has been referred to as the small-and-slow deviation approximation[1,12] and, as in the case of the Volterra approach that starts form eqn. 7.12, the result is proportional to the fourth power of the f.m. index.

It is of interest therefore to retrieve eqn. 7.12 and examine the distortion levels it predicts when the quasi-stationary view is adopted. Then $L(t) = \mu(t) - C_1\dot\mu(t)$, where $C_1 = \int_{-\infty}^{+\infty} xg(x)dx$, and eqn. 7.15 gives

$$\mu(t) - C_1\dot\mu(t) + \frac{D_1}{6}[\dot\mu(t)]^3$$

where $$D_1 = \int_{-\infty}^{+\infty} g(x)[x - C_1]^3\, dx$$

Having derived the general expression for the distortion-to-signal ratio when starting with eqn. 7.29, it is evident that an exactly analogous situation holds here with the nonlinearity $\phi(\dot\mu(t))$ having the form $-C_1\dot\mu(t) + \frac{D_1}{6}[\dot\mu(t)]^3$. Thus

$$\frac{D}{S} = \frac{\left[\frac{\omega}{\omega_\Delta}\mathfrak{I}_3(\omega_\Delta)\right]^2}{1+\left[\frac{\omega}{\omega_\Delta}\mathfrak{I}_1(\omega_\Delta)\right]^2} \cdot \frac{1}{24}\left[3-\left(\frac{\omega}{p_m}\right)^2\right] \qquad (7.60)$$

with $$\mathfrak{I}_1(\omega_\Delta) = \left[C_1 - \frac{D_1}{2}\omega_\Delta^2\right]\omega_\Delta$$

$$\mathfrak{I}_3(\omega_\Delta) = D_1\omega_\Delta^3 \qquad (7.61)$$

In the case of the single-pole filter, we find $C_1 = 1/(\alpha p_m)$, $D_1 = 2/(\alpha p_m)^3$ and thus when $d = (\alpha p_m/\omega_\Delta)$ is large, $\mathfrak{I}_1$ and $\mathfrak{I}_3$ agree with the leading terms in I_1 and I_3 of eqn. 7.58, and so, in the limit of large d, the quasi-stationary result eqn. 7.33 and the Mircea/ Volterra result eqn. 7.60 predict the same levels of third-order distortion.

Eqn. 7.60 is a general result, however, and it can be applied (with unknown accuracy) to any filter for which C_1 and D_1 have finite non-zero values. They can be expressed in terms of derivatives of the lowpass filter transfer characteristic as follows

$$C_1 = jH'(0) \quad \text{where} \quad H'(0) = \left.\frac{\partial H(j\omega)}{\partial \omega}\right|_{\omega=0}$$

$$D_1 = -j\{[3 - H(0)][H'(0)]^3 - 3H'(0)H''(0) + H'''(0)\} \quad (7.62)$$

Also, this approach can be extended to cover cases in which the filter amplitude and phase characteristics are not even and odd, respectively, in their departure from the centre frequency,[12] and then a second-order distortion term is to be included (this term corresponds to the single integral that was to be added to eqn. 7.17 in similar circumstances).

Returning to eqn. 7.30, the roles that the coefficients $I_1(\omega_\Delta)$ and

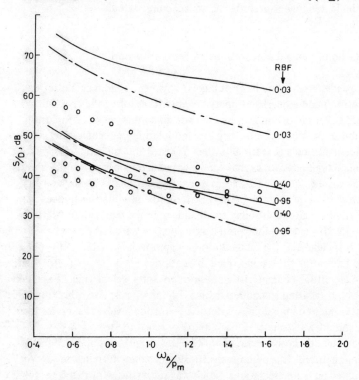

Fig. 7.14 Variation of *S/D* in various channels with increasing f.m. index for a fixed-bandwidth single-pole i.f. filter ($\alpha = 3\cdot0$), and flat f.m.

$$2\alpha = \frac{3 \text{ dB filter bandwidth}}{\text{maximum modulating frequency}} = 6\cdot0$$

——— quasi-stationary theory (eqn. 7.33)
o o o o measurement data (Reference 12)*
—·—·— theory of Bedrosian and Rice (Reference 1)*
RBF = relative baseband frequency
* Courtesy Institute of Electrical and Electronic Engineers Inc.

$I_3(\omega_\Delta)$ play is now more apparent. When eqn. 7.29 is accepted, $I_3(\omega_\Delta)$ accounts for all contributions to the third-order type distortion that arise from the nonlinearity $\phi\,[\dot{\mu}(t)]$; $I_3(\omega_\Delta)$ is proportional to ω_Δ^3 when d is large but it can become proportional to the r.m.s. deviation for intermediate values of d. The situation in the case of the Mircea/ Volterra approach corresponds to the nonlinearity being confined to a cubic law because the cumbersome nature of the higher-degree terms debars their inclusion. Thus only when this cubic term is the dominant contributor to the distortion can the Mircea/Volterra approach be accepted, and it is incapable of predicting the weaker dependence on ω_Δ that is evident from Figs 7.12 and 7.14 unless excessively complicated higher-order terms are accommodated.

7.14 Some general observations on filter distortion

The agreement in the limit of large d between the Mircea/Volterra approach and a quasi-stationary viewpoint regarding the level of third-order distortion is contained within a more general conclusion deduced by Mircea.[8] For very low modulating frequencies the agreement holds true for all orders of distortion and, supposedly, for general linear networks that can be expanded in a Taylor series about the centre frequency (ω_0) as is a requirement of the Carson and Fry – Van der Pol quasi-static theory. Strictly, the modulation frequencies should be made vanishingly small and so, in the light of our previous results, this is to be interpreted as $\omega_\Delta/p_m \to 0$ so that $d \to \infty$.

It is clear that the quasi-stationary approach is void if it is applied to the truncating filter considered in Section 7.11, because $\phi(\omega) \equiv 0$ and the amplitude characteristic does not enter the calculations. Expansion of the truncating characteristic in a Taylor series is also not permissible but it might be possible to infer the distortion levels it generates from examining a sequence of filters that approach the truncating characteristic in some way, although this would not appear to have been reported. It is perhaps significant that the multiplication by the squared envelope technique which was successful with this filter tends to badly over estimate the distortion in the case of a single-pole network while the digital method of Shimbo and Loo shows a similar, if not so poor, behaviour.

The intermediate frequency filters used in most microwave radio relay systems have sharply falling skirts to provide protection against adjacent channel interference and so have considerable resemblance, so far as their amplitude characteristics are concerned, to the truncating

filter. One such filter was adopted in Reference 25 to illustrate the use
of the Monte Carlo program, and this filter had a 3 dB bandwidth of
36 MHz with a 20 dB bandwidth of 52 MHz. The Monte Carlo exercise
was applied to an 1800 channel f.m. f.d.m. system for which
$\omega_\Delta/p_m = 0.13$ and $p_m/2\pi = 8.204$ MHz. The average of six program
cycles gave $S/D = 73.6$ dB in the top channel for the distortion level
generated purely by the amplitude characteristic. With such a filter, the
3 dB bandwidth and the noise bandwidth are highly comparable, and,
from Fig. 7.5, a very similar level of distortion is read for an abscissa
value of $18/8.204 = 2.19$, thus suggesting that likening the amplitude
response to that of a truncating network is not unreasonable in this
case. When the S/D ratio is as large as 73.6 dB, it is usually permissible
to separately add the distortion that comes from the amplitude and
phase characteristics. Distortion generated by phase characteristics
receives further consideration in Section 8.1 of Chapter 8.

Figs. 7.5 to 7.10 are intended to cater for the truncating filter which
is seen to require an analytical approach that differs from that used on
more smoothly varying characteristics.

For general networks the quasi-stationary approach is attractive as
the D/S ratio can be expressed as the series eqn. 7.32 with coefficients
that are readily amenable to calculation, and, for flat f.m., simple
limiting forms can be obtained for the contributions from the
successive orders of distortion. The outstanding questions to be settled,
however, are: under what conditions is sufficient accuracy provided by
accepting just the first distortion term, how does this accuracy vary
with the baseband position, and, while the single-pole filter seems to be
best suited to this style of analysis, how well do other practical filters
conform to the theory?

Such questions have received a good deal of attention in the
past[15,21] with emphasis placed on the single tone modulation case, but
it seems fair to say that no concisely formulated recipe for success can
be laid down, although a large value for $\alpha p_m/\omega_\Delta$, or some closely
similar requirement, is agreed to be necessary.

This ratio can be large by virtue of a wide filter bandwidth ($\alpha \gg 1$)
so that, even though the f.m. index is large, the filter only significantly
affects components of the carrier that are remote from the centre
frequency. It is then felt that the impulse response of the filter will
be sharply peaked, so lending support to the approximation $\mu(t - x) \simeq
\mu(t) - x\dot{\mu}(t)$ on which a quasi-stationary approach depends. Equally,
the ratio can be large owing to the f.m. index being small and this
situation is most benign to theoretical treatment since, as our curves
show, the quasi-static approach and other methods of attack are usually

in fair agreement as to the low levels of distortion that then arise. The Mircea-Volterra approach is the preferred computational method here, although the filter transfer characteristic has to be substituted into double integrals (and perhaps single integrals too) of the complicated kind shown in eqn. 7.17. Present day computing aids can make the evaluation of these integrals a routine matter and results for the case of the single-pole filter are given in graphical form in Reference 1.

With such computing facilities available perhaps the best way to gain insight is to run a few cycles of a Monte Carlo program. These will probably not provide the full accuracy that is required but an indication of whether the quasi-stationary theory is being obeyed can be rapidly acquired so that relatively simple formulae such as eqn. 7.59 or 7.60 that reveal the trade-off between bandwidths, distortion levels, baseband frequencies and deviations, can be used with confidence.

The results of applying the various theoretical approaches to a wide variety of linear networks are to be found in the literature (see, in particular References 8, 11, 25 to 29). The most satisfactory situations are those in which theory is shown to compare favourably with Monte Carlo computations or measurements, but this is not always done, and the reader interested in further information on distortion due to filtering is referred to the quoted sources with this observation in mind.

This topic continues to promote interest, as is evidenced by a recent paper of Foschini,[30] but it seems unlikely that a general method of attack will be discovered that can handle with equal success all the cases that are met in practice.

The distortion mechanism depends on both the filter characteristics and the modulation parameters in a highly nonlinear fashion and compliance with the averaging brackets that appear in eqns. 7.3, 7.5 or 3.71 is the central problem. Some approximate ways of coping with it, and their success when compared to a Monte Carlo exercise, have been illustrated here. Another approach, aimed at dealing with network characteristics that may be specified empirically, is described next.

7.15 References

1 BEDROSIAN, E., and RICE, S.O.: 'Distortion and cross-talk in linearly filtered, angle modulated signals', *Proc. IEEE,* 1968, **56,** pp. 2–13

2 BENNETT, W.R., CURTIS, H.E., and RICE, S.O.: 'Interchannel interference in FM and PM systems under noise loading conditions', *Bell Syst. Tech. J.,* 1955, **34,** (3), pp. 601–636

3 SHIMBO, O., and LOO, C.: 'Digital computation of FM distortion due to linear networks', IEEE International Conference on Communications, Philadelphia, 1968, pp. 482–486

4 DEUTSCH, R.: 'Non-linear transformations of random processes' (Prentice Hall Applied Mathematics Series, 1962)

5 BEDROSIAN, E., and RICE, S.O.: 'The output properties of Volterra systems (non-linear systems with memory) driven by harmonic and Gaussian inputs', *Proc. IEEE*, 1971, 59, (12), pp. 1688–1707

6 MOJOLI, L.: 'Analysis of angle modulated transmission systems and identification of their Volterra series', *Alta Freq.*, 1972, XLI, pp. 252–262 (82E-92E)

7 MIRCEA, A., and SINNREICH, H.: 'Distortion noise in frequency-dependent nonlinear networks', *Proc. IEE* 1969, 116, (10), pp. 1644–1648

8 MIRCEA, A.: 'Harmonic distortion and intermodulation noise in linear FM transmission systems, *Rev. Roum. Sci. Tech. Electrotech. & Energ.*, 1967, 12, (3), pp. 359–371

9 STOJANOVIC, I.S., and STOJANOVIC Z.D.: 'Determination of integration limits in calculating distortion noise power', *Proc. IEE*, 1967, 114, (9) pp. 1206–1208

10 MIRCEA, A.: 'FM intermodulation noise theory', *Proc. IEEE*, 1966, 54, pp. 1463–1465

11 RAINAL, A.J.: 'Computing distortion in analog FM communication systems', *Bell Syst. Tech. J.* 1973, 52, pp. 627–648

12 ROBERTS, J.H., BEDROSIAN, E., and RICE, S.O.: 'FM distortion: a comparison of theory and measurement', *Proc IEEE* 1969, 57, (4), pp. 728–732

13 BEDROSIAN, E.: 'Transionospheric propagation of FM signals' *IEEE Trans.*, 1970, COM-18, pp. 102–109

14 MEDHURST, R.G.: 'RF spectra of waves frequency modulated with white noise', *Proc IEE*, 1960, 107C, pp. 314–323 (IEE Monograph 380E)

15 BORODIN, S.V.: 'Applicability of the quasi-stationary approximation for calculating non-linear cross-talk in multi-channel link systems', *Telecommun. & Radio Eng.*, 1966, (9), pp. 1–7

16 SLACK, M.: 'The probability distributions of sinusoidal oscillations combined in random phase', *J. IEE*, 1946, 93, pt. III, pp. 76–86

17 BLACHMAN, N.M., and McALPINE, G.A.: 'The spectrum of a high-index FM waveform: Woodward's theorem revisited', *IEEE Trans.*, 1969, COM-17, (2), pp. 201–208

18 SLEPIAN, D.: 'An expansion of FM spectra', *IEEE Trans.*, 1971, COM-19, pp. 223–225

19 CARSON, J.R., and FRY, T.C.: 'Variable frequency electric circuit theory with application to the theory of FM' *Bell Syst. Tech. J.* 1937, 16, pp. 513–540

20 VAN DER POL, B.: 'The fundamental principles of frequency modulation', *Proc. IEE* 1946, 93, (Pt. III), pp. 153–158

21 ROWE, H.: 'Signals and noise in communication systems' (Van Nostrand, 1965)

22 MEDHURST, R.G., and ROBERTS, J.H.: 'Evaluation of the integral $2/\pi \int_0^\infty (\sin x/x)^n \cos bx dx$, *Math. Comput.*, 1965, 19, (89), pp. 113–117

23 CLAYTON, F.M., and BACON, J.M.: 'Intermodulation distortion in f.m. f.d.m. trunk-radio systems in 2-path fading situations', *Proc. IEE*, 1970, 117, (2), pp. 359–368

24 MEDHURST, R.G.: 'Harmonic distortion of frequency-modulated waves by linear networks', *Proc. IEE* 1954, 101, Pt. III pp. 171–181

25 MEDHURST, R.G., and ROBERTS, J.H.: 'Evaluation of distortion in f.m. trunk radio systems by a Monte Carlo method', *Proc. IEE*, 1966, **113**, (4), pp. 570–580

26 RUTHROFF, C.L.: 'Computation of FM distortion in linear networks for band limited periodic signals', *Bell Syst. Tech. J.*, 1968, **47**, pp. 1043–1062

27 ANUFF, A., and LIOU, M.L.: 'A note on necessary bandwidth in FM systems' *Proc. IEEE*, 1971, **59**, pp. 1522–1523

28 GRIERSON, J.K., and McGEE, W.F.: 'The digital simulation of an FDM-FM system', N.E. Technical Memorandum TM 8162-7-67, 1967

29 RICE, S.O.: 'Distortion produced by band limitation of an FM wave', *Bell Syst. Tech. J.*, 1973, **52**, pp. 605–626

30 FOSCHINI, G.: 'Demodulating analytically modulated signals after propagation over certain channels', *SIAM Appl. Math.* 1975, **28**, (2), pp. 282–289

F.M. first-order approximation and a treatment of discriminator distortion, limiting, and a.m. to p.m. conversion

8.1 Nature of the approximation

The preceding Chapter has made plain the complexity in calculating the distortion of the instantaneous frequency caused by amplitude and phase characteristics that are nonlinear with frequency and so far no imperfections in the operation of system amplifiers, limiters, or discriminators have been taken into account. Any potential defects are of central importance to the design of high-quality radio relay systems because the end-to-end intermodulation and noise specifications mean that linking components, in particular the i.f. amplifiers used in repeater stages, must meet extremely tight requirements of linearity. Thus, it is highly desirable that some relatively straightforward method of assessment be developed even though it be approximate.

A general situation will be considered in which the modulated r.f. or i.f. carrier is first passed into a linear network (typically a filter of the mixer) and subsequently is amplified or limited. Let the circuitry of the former stage have a transfer characteristic $Y(j(\omega_0 + \omega))$ that is specified as follows

$$Y[j(\omega_0 + \omega)] = A(\omega_0 + \omega)e^{j\phi(\omega_0 + \omega)} =$$

$$\sum_{n=0}^{\infty} b_n \omega^n + j \sum_{n=1}^{\infty} a_n \omega^n \text{ with } b_0 = 1 \qquad (8.1)$$

Here, ω is measured from the centre frequency ω_0, a_n and b_n are coefficients in series expansions (in powers of ω) of the real and imaginary parts of the transfer function, and $A(\omega_0 + \omega)$ and $\phi(\omega_0 + \omega)$ are the corresponding amplitude and phase characteristics.

Using eqn. 7.1, the output wave $v_0(t)$ can be expressed as

$$v_0(t) = Re\left[\{P(t) + jQ(t)\}e^{j\omega_0 t}\right]$$

This will be rewritten as follows

$$v_0(t) = Re\left\{e^{\alpha(t)+j\beta(t)} e^{j[\omega_0 t + \mu(t)]}\right\} \qquad (8.2)$$

and here

$$e^{\alpha(t)+j\beta(t)} = \sum_{n=0}^{\infty} (b_n + ja_n)(j)^n \int_{-\infty}^{+\infty} e^{j[\mu(t-x)-\mu(t)]} \delta^{(n)}(x)\, dx$$

$$= 1 + \sum_{n=1}^{\infty} (b_n + ja_n)(-j)^n \left[(XX^{(n)} + YY^{(n)})\right.$$

$$\left. - j(YX^{(n)} - XY^{(n)})\right] \qquad (8.3)$$

where $X = \cos\mu(t)$, $Y = \sin\mu(t)$ $X^{(n)} = d^n x(t)/dt^n$ etc., and $\delta^{(n)}(x)$ is the nth derivative of the Dirac delta function.

When $v_0(t)$ is expressed as in eqn. 8.2, $\mu(t) + \beta(t)$ is the complete phase [$\beta(t)$ is the phase error] and the tacit assumption has been made that the group delay by which the output wave will lag the input wave is either of no concern or has been compensated for. Thus, it is customary when applying the present theory to make b_n and a_n refer to the real and imaginary parts of the network so equalised that it has no linear phase term (then a_1 is zero).

Ideally $\beta(t)$ would be broken into two parts, the first consisting of terms that do not refer to distortion of $\mu(t)$, and the second made up of terms (incoherent with the first set) that do, so $\beta(t) = \beta_1(t) + \beta_2(t)$. Then $\beta_1(t)$ contributes only to the coherence factor and the aim is to find an approximate expression for $\beta_2(t)$.

In view of the remarks made earlier regarding low-distortion requirements, it is clear that the perturbation represented by $e^{\alpha(t)+j\beta(t)}$ must be very small and so the approximation

$$e^{\alpha(t)+j\beta(t)} \approx 1 + \alpha(t) + j\beta(t) \qquad (8.4)$$

is appropriate. This is the f.m. first-order approximation. Using eqn. 8.3, the phase error $\beta(t) = \beta_1(t) + \beta_2(t)$ is then given by

$$\beta(t) = b_2(YX^{(II)} - XY^{(II)}) + b_3(XX^{(III)} + YY^{(III)})$$

$$- b_4(YX^{(IV)} - XY^{(IV)}) - \dots$$

$$- a_2(XX^{(II)} + YY^{(II)}) + a_3(YX^{(III)} - XY^{(III)}) + a_4(XX^{(IV)} + YY^{(IV)}) - \dots$$

$$(8.5)$$

while the amplitude modulation is given by

$$1 + \alpha(t) = 1 - b_1(YX^{(I)} - XY^{(I)}) - b_2(XX^{(II)} + YY^{(II)})$$

$$+ b_3(YX^{(III)} - XY^{(III)}) + b_4(XX^{(IV)} + YY^{(IV)}) + \dots$$

$$-a_2(YX^{(\text{II})} - XY^{(\text{II})}) - a_3(XX^{(\text{III})} + YY^{(\text{III})})$$
$$+ a_4(YX^{(\text{IV})} - XY^{(\text{IV})}) + \ldots \quad (8.6)$$

With $\dot{\mu}(t) = M(t) = M$, so that $M^{(n)} = \mu^{(n+1)}$ we have

$$[XX^{(n)} + YY^{(n)}] = \sum_{r=1}^{n-1} \binom{n-1}{r} M^{(n-r-1)}[YX^{(r)} - XY^{(r)}]$$

$$[YX^{(n)} - XY^{(n)}] = -\sum_{r=1}^{n-1} \binom{n-1}{r} M^{(n-r-1)}[XX^{(r)} + YY^{(r)}] \quad (8.7)$$

and these can be used to extend the explicit forms given in Table 8.1.

Table 8.1 nth order functions of the frequency modulation arising in the f.m. first-order theory

n	$YX^{(n)} - XY^{(n)}$	$XX^{(n)} + YY^{(n)}$
0	0	1
1	$-M$	0
2	$-M^{(\text{I})}$	$-M^2$
3	$-M^{(\text{II})} + M^3$	$-3M \cdot M^{(\text{I})}$
4	$-M^{(\text{III})} + 6M^{(\text{I})}M^2$	$-4MM^{(\text{II})} - 3(M^{(\text{I})})^2 + M^4$
5	$-M^{(\text{IV})} + 10M^2 M^{(\text{II})}$	$-5MM^{(\text{III})} - 10M^{(\text{I})}M^{(\text{II})}$
	$+ 15M(M^{(\text{I})})^2 - M^5$	$+ 10M^3 M^{(\text{I})}$

M can be any type of frequency modulation and so Table 8.1 can be used to investigate harmonic distortion as well as intermodulation distortion. Measurements of differential phase and gain constitute a widely-used method of probing the passband of a microwave link to identify the a_n and b_n. $M(t)$ is then the sum of a low-level high frequency sinusoid and a high-level low frequency sinusoid.

From the table it is seen that the first distorting term in $\beta(t)$ is the one in b_3 and a term like $b_4 M^{(\text{III})}$ which arises from $-b_4 (YX^{(\text{IV})} - XY^{(\text{IV})})$ is a member of $\beta_1(t)$, while $-b_4 \cdot 6M^{(\text{I})}M^2$ which is also present contributes to both $\beta_1(t)$ and $\beta_2(t)$. The respective power contributions to $\beta_1(t)$ and $\beta_2(t)$ can be separated out by noting that $6M^{(\text{I})}M^2 = 2d(M^3)/dt$ and, when M is a band of Gaussian noise, the corresponding autocorrelation function using

$$\left\langle \frac{dM^3}{dt}(t) \cdot \frac{dM^3}{dt}(r+\tau) \right\rangle = -\frac{\partial^2}{\partial \tau^2} \langle M^3(t) \cdot M^3(t+\tau) \rangle$$

is

$$-4\frac{\partial^2}{\partial \tau^2}[9\psi_M^2(0)\,\psi_M(\tau) + 6\psi_M^3(\tau)] =$$

$$-36\psi_M(0)\,\psi_M''(\tau) - 72\{\psi_M^2(\tau)\,\psi_M''(\tau) + 2\psi_M(\tau)[\psi_M'(\tau)]^2\} \quad (8.8)$$

These results follow from eqn. 2.34 of Chapter 2. Thus, the terms in the curly bracket refer to third-order intermodulation distortion, while the first term is non-distorting and therefore belongs to $\beta_1(t)$. The f.m. first-order theory identifies the distortion $\beta_2(t)$ with those terms that refer to distortion in eqn. 8.5 which is linear in the coefficients a_n and b_n, a second-order theory would include forms that are quadratic in the a_n and b_n.

These theories do not usually attempt to evaluate explicitly the coherence factor* (it is assumed to be unity), and continuing with the example shown in eqn. 8.8, the distortion-to-signal ratio (following from eqns. 1.6 and 2.36) on assuming a flat spectral distribution for $M(t)$, is given by

$$\frac{D}{S} = p_m^4 \cdot \omega_\Delta^4 \cdot b_4^2 \; 18 \left(\frac{p}{p_m}\right)^4 \left[1 - \frac{1}{3}\left(\frac{p}{p_m}\right)^2\right] \quad p_0 \leqslant p \leqslant p_m \quad (8.9)$$

To reiterate, eqn. 8.9 is the D/S expression given by first-order theory in the case of a fourth-degree amplitude characteristic. The distortion is of third order and only the term $-b_4(YX^{(IV)} - XY^{(IV)})$ from eqn. 8.5 has been considered. If one or more of the terms with a_n is included, then Table 8.1 shows that an even order of distortion is generated and so D/S receives a direct addition to the right-hand side of eqn. 8.9 (distortions arising from real and imaginary part nonlinearities add on a power basis in a first-order theory). However, if the terms b_6, b_8 etc. are brought in, D/S must be modified by including contributions in $b_4 b_6$ (this may be negative) b_6^2, $b_6 \cdot b_8$ etc. and the third-order contribution will accordingly be changed and higher odd-order distortions introduced.

Magnusson[1] has made the necessary analysis that produces formulae like eqn. 8.9 for the simultaneous appearance of all coefficients in eqn. 8.1 up to b_8 and a_7 (extending the areas covered in References 2 and 3). The formulae and tables given by Magnusson are reproduced here (using the current notation), these cover the cases of flat f.m. and a baseband pre-emphasised according to the CCIR law (eqn. 5.26) while allowing ten baseband positions to be examined.

Use of the tables can be illustrated by again supposing that a fourth-degree amplitude characteristic is of interest, i.e. b_4 only. Opposite the

---

*In cases where the relative phasing of the frequency components of the modulation is important (system performance is measured by waveform preservation rather than n.p.r.) an evaluation of the coherence factor is necessary

$n = 3$ column of Table 8.2, we find $p_m^4 \omega_\Delta^4 b_4^2 \beta_{1,3}$, and $\beta_{1,3}$ is shown*
in Table 8.5. In the top channel, $\beta_{1,3} = 12$ is in agreement with
$18[1 - 1/3]$ as given by eqn. 8.9 for the case of flat f.m., while the
entry under 12, i.e. 5·45, shows that pre-emphasis improves the
situation in the ratio 12:5·45, or 3·43 dB.

The band over which the power series expansions hold is not
uniquely defined, but it can be anticipated that the fit need be good
only for frequencies to which the input carrier makes a significant
contribution, and the 3 dB, 6 dB, or Carson bandwidths may be
equally plausible contenders. Clear-cut definitions of what is meant
by a 'good fit' and a 'significant contribution' are very difficult to
formulate, being so dependent on particular cases, and this is a penalty
in precision that is paid by resorting to power series in the search for a
flexible theory. However, as the formulae are simple, it is not a difficult
task to examine their sensitivity to changes in the coefficient values.

On recalling the notation of Chapter 7, and assuming a real
impulse response $g(t)$, it is seen that the f.m. first-order approximation
gives

$$\beta(t) = \int_{-\infty}^{+\infty} g(x) \sin \left[\mu(t-x) - \mu(t)\right] dx \qquad (8.10)$$

$$1 + \alpha(t) = \int_{-\infty}^{+\infty} g(x) \cos \left[\mu(t-x) - \mu(t)\right] dx \qquad (8.11)$$

and taking the first of these is sometimes referred to as a first-order
approach[4] As was shown in Section 7.11 of Chapter 7, eqn. 8.10 can
give results in precise agreement with the Mircea/Volterra method so
far as third-order distortion is concerned, although higher-order distortions (which, hopefully, make much smaller contributions in many
instances) are unlikely to enjoy such exact agreement.

In summary, from a finite number of the a_n and b_n coefficients
obtained by fitting to measured or postulated characteristics, distortion
levels can be estimated by substitution into simple formulae like the
one shown in eqn. 8.9, or by consulting Magnusson's tables.

The approach can be readily extended to give a treatment of
amplitude modulation-to-phase modulation conversion or discriminator
distortion and the next section deals with the former topic.

*The second subscript of β indicates the intermodulation order

8.2 A.M. to p.m. conversion

All present day saturating devices that can be used to effect an amplify-
ing or limiting action on a narrow-band signal have the property of
converting any amplitude modulation present into a phase modulation.
The operation of the device can be described as follows. If the input,
after passage through preceding circuitry (specified by eqn. 8.1), is

$$R(t) \cos \left[\omega_0 t + \theta(t) \right] \tag{8.12}$$

then the output (following the removal of frequencies in the region of
$3\omega_0, 5\omega_0$ etc.) can be written

$$F\{R(t)\} \cos \left[\omega_0 t + \theta(t) + f\{R(t)\} \right] \tag{8.13}$$

where $F\{R(t)\}$ and $f\{R(t)\}$ are single-valued odd and even functions of
their arguments. Quite simple forms for $F\{R(t)\}$ and $f\{R(t)\}$ can be
used to model the operation of a travelling wave tube (TWT) for
example,[5] and a quadratic $f[R(t)]$ is commonly assumed[6] while
Reference 7 offers a theory that retains generality.

It is variation of the electrical length of the TWT with r.f. input
level that is the basic cause of a.m.-to-p.m. conversion, and, when
the first-order f.m. theory is used, we have $R(t) = 1 + \alpha(t)$, $\theta(t) =
\mu(t) + \beta(t)$, so eqn. 8.12 becomes

$$[1 + \alpha(t)] \cos \left[\omega_0 t + \mu(t) + \beta(t) \right] \tag{8.14}$$

With regard to the output wave, a quadratic form for $f[1 + \alpha(t)]$
provides a predominantly linear term in $\alpha(t)$ so that to the existing
phase modulation $\mu(t) + \beta(t)$ is added a copy of $\alpha(t)$ with a suitable
multiplying factor. It has become accepted practice to express this
factor (k) in degrees of phase shift per decibel of amplitude modulation
and then a typical form for eqn. 8.13 is

$$[1 + \lambda\alpha(t)] \cos \left[\omega_0 t + \mu(t) + \beta(t) + 0{\cdot}1516\,k\alpha(t) \right] \tag{8.15}$$

λ may be termed the compression factor (in application to a hard limiter
it would be very small) and k is the a.m.-to-p.m. conversion factor in
degrees/dB. Typically, k is a fraction of a degree per decibel for a good
limiter and $3°$ or $4°$ per dB for a TWT. With $\beta(t)$ and $\alpha(t)$ given by
eqns. 8.5 and 8.6, it is clear that $\beta(t) + 0{\cdot}1516\,k\alpha(t)$ can be expressed
similarly, as

$$\beta(t) + 0{\cdot}1516\,k\alpha(t) = -0{\cdot}1516\,k b_1 (YX^{(\mathrm{I})} - XY^{(\mathrm{I})})$$

$$+ (b_2 - 0{\cdot}1516\,k a_2)[YX^{(\mathrm{II})} - XY^{(\mathrm{II})}]$$

$$+ (b_3 - 0\cdot1516ka_3)[XX^{(\text{III})} + YY^{(\text{III})}]$$
$$- (a_2 + 0.1516kb_2)[XX^{(\text{II})} + YY^{(\text{II})}]$$
$$+ (a_3 + 0\cdot1516kb_3)[YX^{(\text{III})} - XY^{(\text{III})}]$$
$$- \ldots \ldots \tag{8.16}$$

Thus, Magnusson's tables can again be used to determine how large k may become before a distortion specification is exceeded. An exercise of this kind is illustrated by Fig. 8.1 where the compression factor has been taken as zero so that perfect amplitude limiting has been realised.

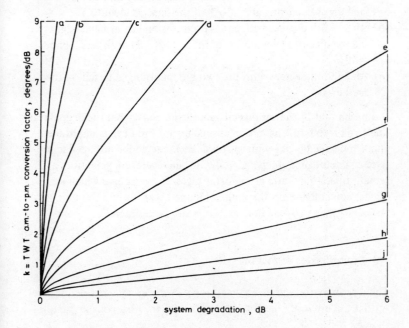

Fig. 8.1 Degradation in system *S/D* in top channel due to a.m. to p.m. conversion

1800 Channel system with CCIR pre-emphasis
The TWT has an a.m.–p.m. conversion factor of k degrees/dB and the circuitry preceding the tube has the following nonlinear characteristics:

a 3rd degree amplitude
b 4th degree phase
c 5th degree amplitude
d 6th degree phase
e 6th degree amplitude
f 5th degree phase

Curves *g, h, j* are double humped amplitude characteristics described in the text (Section 8.2)

The curves refer to an 1800 channel f.m. f.d.m. system that employs CCIR pre-emphasis and show the system degradation in top channel. By system degradation is meant the ratio (expressed in decibels) of the total phase distortion to the distortion arising in absence of a.m.-to-p.m. conversion, with particular nonlinear characteristics for the circuitry preceding the TWT.

Curves are shown for amplitude and phase characteristics of 3rd, 4th, 5th and 6th degrees and also for three forms of double-humped amplitude characteristic. The latter are made up as follows:

(a) 2nd and 4th degrees with equal transmission loss at the band edges and the band centre. (This constitutes a Tchebychev design: the humps occurring at $\pm 1/\sqrt{2}$ of the semi-bandwidth.)

(b) 4th and 6th degrees with equal transmission loss at band edges and band centre (the humps occur at $\pm \sqrt{(2/3)}$ of the semi-bandwidth.)

(c) 4th and 6th degrees with the two humps arranged to fall on the band edges.

It appears that of the various characteristics considered the degradation due to a.m. to p.m. conversion is smallest for 3rd-degree amplitude and 4th-degree phase (cubic group delay). The double humped amplitude characterisitcs are associated with the severest degradation, and we remark that a quadratic group delay gives rise to a curve which is almost coincident with the double-humped case for humps falling at the band-edges ($\pm 16 \cdot 5$ Mhz), and so is also undesirable.

8.3 Discriminator distortion

The discriminator will be assumed to be preceded by a perfect limiter so that the input is a narrow-band signal $V(t)$, with a constant amplitude K.

$$V(t) = K \sin [\omega_0 t + \theta(t)]$$

Ideally, the output is $\dot{\theta}(t)$ (or $\omega_0 + \dot{\theta}(t)$) and there are two principles of operation whereby this output is usually obtained.

The first is a zero counting method which implements the theory outlined in Section 3.1 (see eqns. 3.5 to 3.7 in particular). The second recognises that if $V(t)$ is differentiated we obtain

$$\dot{V}(t) = K [\omega_0 + \dot{\theta}(t)] \cos [\omega_0 t + \theta(t)] \qquad (8.17)$$

so that subsequent envelope detection provides $|\omega_0 + \dot{\theta}(t)|$ and hence $\dot{\theta}(t)$ (assuming $\omega_0 + \dot{\theta}(t)$ is rarely negative).

A method of calculating the spectral density of the envelope of a wave such as eqn. 8.17 has already been presented in Section 2.6 (see eqn. 2.39) but the bivariate characteristic function $\Phi(u_1, u_2)$ which is required in the double integration cannot be expressed in a simple way when, as we now assume, the discriminator does not operate perfectly. The zero counting method is also difficult due, mainly, to it being hard to assess the consequences of taking plausible steps to simplify the analysis.

However, the f.m. first-order theory, with a_n and b_n of eqn. 8.1 referring to the real and imaginary parts of the discriminator characteristic, provides an expression for the envelope. When the input is $A \sin [\omega_0 t + \mu(t)]$ the square of this envelope, $e^{2\alpha(t)}$, is given, with no approximation, by multiplying the right-hand side of eqn. 8.3 by its complex conjugate. Before the multiplication is done, however, note that to realise differentiation the discriminator has an amplitude characteristic that deviates from linearity as little as possible (again, the range of linearity need only correspond to the band over which the carrier has significant components) and B_1, as used below in eqn. 8.18, is the slope of a perfectly linear amplitude characteristic. Thus, B_1 can be regarded as being much larger than coefficients d_2, d_3 etc. which refer to a departure from a linear law, and the phase characteristic is ascribed small coefficients c_2, c_3 etc. to represent its nonlinearity. Through equating the discriminator characteristic

$$[1 + B_1 \omega + d_2 \omega^2 + d_3 \omega^3 + \ldots] \exp j [c_2 \omega^2 + c_3 \omega^3 + \ldots]$$

to   (8.18)

$$1 + b_1 \omega + b_2 \omega^2 + \ldots + j (a_2 \omega^2 + a_3 \omega^3 + \ldots)$$

our real and imaginary part coefficients are given by

$$b_1 = B_1$$
$$b_r = d_r \qquad\qquad r = 2, 3, \ldots$$
$$a_2 = c_2$$
$$a_r = c_r + B_1 c_{r-1} \qquad r = 3, 4, \ldots \qquad (8.19)$$

(cross product terms between the c_n and d_n being dropped). It might be supposed that a $\pi/2$ phase shift should be included to account for the sine becoming a cosine by differentiation but any constant addition to the phase $\mu(t)$ [or to the phase error $\beta(t)$] does not affect the envelope.

Writing Z for the terms involving a_2, b_2, a_3, b_3 etc. on the right-hand side of eqn. 8.3:

$$e^{2\alpha(t)} = [1 + B_1 M]^2 + 2(1 + B_1 M) \, Re \, \{Z\} + ZZ^* \quad (8.20)$$

where Z^* is the conjugate of Z and $Re\{Z\}$ is the real part of Z. So

$$e^{\alpha(t)} = [1 + B_1 M] \left\{ 1 + \frac{2Re\{Z\}}{1 + B_1 M} + \frac{ZZ^*}{(1 + B_1 M)^2} \right\}^{1/2}$$

$$\approx 1 + B_1 M + Re \, (Z) \quad (8.21)$$

This is the approximation to the envelope that is given by the first-order theory, and, recognising that $Re\{Z\}$ consists of the terms in $a_2, b_2, a_3,$ b_3 etc. on the right-hand side of eqn. 8.6

$$e^{\alpha(t)} \approx 1 + B_1 M - b_2 (XX^{(\text{II})} + YY^{(\text{II})}) + b_3 (YX^{(\text{III})} - XY^{(\text{III})}) + \ldots$$

$$- a_2 \, (YX^{(\text{II})} - XY^{(\text{II})}) - a_3 (XX^{(\text{III})} + YY^{(\text{III})}) + \ldots$$

$$(8.22)^\dagger$$

Inspecting eqns. 8.22 and 8.5 it is seen that by swapping the a_n and b_n we can change an expression for $e^{\alpha(t)}$ to an expression for $\beta(t)$. Now, Magnusson's tables refer to the distortion generated by the phase error $\beta(t)$ and the entries give the ratio of the spectral density of the inter-modulation contribution to the spectral density of $\mu(t)$ at ten baseband frequencies. In the present context it is not $\mu(t)$ that is involved but $B_1 M(t)$ (the desired output from the discriminator) and so the required D/S ratios can also be read from Magnusson's tables if two rules are applied:

 (i) for a_n read b_n and vice versa
(ii) divide by $(p/p_m)^2 \, [B_1 p_m]^2$

If it is more convenient to work with the coefficients c_n and d_n for the nonlinearities of the amplitude and phase characteristics, then use eqn. 8.19. As an illustration, consider the distortion-to-signal ratio for a discriminator with the characteristic

$$1 + B_1 \omega + b_2 \omega^2 + j \, (a_2 \omega^2 + a_6 \omega^6)$$

When the coefficients of the nonlinear terms in this expression are looked up in Table 8.2, using rule i, we find

b_2 gives the second-order term $\quad p_m^2 \omega_\Delta^2 \alpha_1 b_2^2$
a_2 gives no contribution
a_6 gives the third-order term $\quad \{\beta_4 p_m^4 + \beta_5 p_m^2 \omega_\Delta^2 + \beta_6 \omega_\Delta^4\} a_6^6$
and the fifth-order term $\quad p_m^4 \omega_\Delta^8 \beta_1 a_6^2$

$\dagger g(t)$ of eqn. 7.1 will be complex for a discriminator, and eqn. 7.14 then contains extra terms that give rise to the odd-order contributors in eqn. 8.22

Thus, applying rule ii, the required expression for D/S is

$$\frac{D}{S} = \frac{p_m^2 \omega_\Delta^2 b_2^2 \alpha_{1,2} + a_6^2 \{\beta_{4,3} p_m^4 + \beta_{5,3} p_m^2 \omega_\Delta^2 + \beta_{6,3} \omega_\Delta^4\} + p_m^4 \omega_\Delta^8 a_6^2 \beta_{1,5}}{(p/p_m)^2 [B_1 p_m]^2}$$

$$(8.23)$$

where the αs and βs are obtained from Tables 8.4, 8.5 and 8.9, the second subscript indicating the intermodulation order of the coefficient. At the midpoint of the baseband $p/p_m = 1/2$ for example, $\alpha_{1,2} = 0 \cdot 375$,

$$\beta_{4,3} = 2 \cdot 57, \quad \beta_{5,3} = 44 \cdot 4, \quad \beta_{6,3} = 232, \quad \text{and} \quad \beta_{1,5} = 37 \cdot 9$$

when the baseband is not pre-emphasised.

Mention should be made here of another type of frequency detector that is commonly used, namely the delay line discriminator. With an input $A \cos [\omega_0 t + \mu(t)]$ this device can provide an output proportional to $\sin [\mu(t) - \mu(t - \tau)]$ which, for sufficiently small τ, approximates to $\tau \dot{\mu}(t)$. τ has therefore to be chosen so that this approximation is met satisfactorily (a corresponding n.p.r. is usually specified) and the following top channel formula can be used to assess τ:

$$\frac{D}{S} = \frac{1}{12} \left(\frac{\omega_\Delta}{p_m} \right)^4 (p_m \tau)^4 \quad \text{(no pre-emphasis: } S/D > 30 \text{ dB)}$$

Also, $\omega_0 \tau$ is to be an odd multiple of $\pi/2$, and ω_0 can be adjusted appropriately by mixing down from r.f.

8.4 Some observations on first-order theory

A peculiarity of the first-order theory is that the coefficient b_2 of the quadratic departure from unity of the real part of the transfer characteristic, does not give rise to distortion. This suggests that the role played by b_2 in a second-order theory should be investigated and this exercise reveals that $- 1/6 \, b_2^2$ is associated with precisely the same distortion components as is b_4 in the first-order theory. A voltage addition can therefore be effected and the theory applied as before but with $(b_4 - 1/6 \, b_2^2)$ replacing b_4.

By deliberately arranging for b_2 to equal $\sqrt{6b_4}$ a complete cancellation of third-order distortion can occur, therefore, and no doubt other carefully manufactured cases could be identified that call for theories of successively higher order to be produced in order to unearth the distorting terms. These are rather artificial examples, however, and of greater concern should be the accuracy provided by the theory in the situations most often encountered in practice. A useful variety of frequency characteristics are covered in References 8 and 9 where the latter paper arose as a result of doubt being thrown on the general validity of the first-order theory.

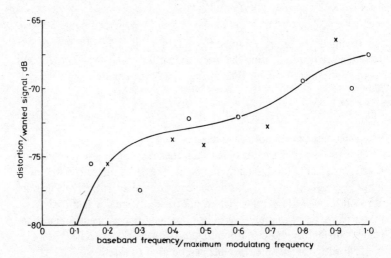

Fig. 8.2 Distortion introduced across the baseband of a pre-emphasised 1800 channel system by a typical bandpass filter with group-delay equalisation. Comparison of Monte Carlo results and first-order theory

The bandpass filter has the following transfer characteristic:

$$\text{amplitude} = 1 - 0.0005840 \left(\frac{\omega}{p_m}\right)^8 \text{ (voltage-ratio)}$$

$$\text{phase} = -0.0031196 \left(\frac{\omega}{p_m}\right)^2 - 0.01235 \left(\frac{\omega}{p_m}\right)^3$$
$$+ 0.005725 \left(\frac{\omega}{p_m}\right)^5 \text{ (rad)}$$

——— first-order theory
X X X first computer run (average of 6 program cycles)
o o o second computer run (average of 6 program cycles)

The case of an 1800 channel system with pre-emphasis of the form recommended by the CCIR was investigated by the Monte Carlo approach and a comparison made with the predictions of the first-order theory as read from Magnusson's tables. Fig. 8.2 has been reproduced from Reference 9 and is a typical illustration of the agreement obtained. The usefulness of the first-order theory as a tool for system design is evident and another example showing its success in predicting the distortion introduced by a cubic phase characteristic (quadratic group delay) may be found in Reference 8.

The Monte Carlo approach has been of great value in confirming the validity of a theory that has been used, rather on trust, for many years (although some experimental evidence for its acceptability was provided in Reference 10.). It should be noted that the theory has been corroborated mainly for low-deviation cases (that is, $\omega_\Delta/p_m < 1$, the circled and crossed points on Figs. 7.5 and 7.6 come from the first-order approximation when taken in the form of eqn. 8.10). Most of the large capacity terrestrial f.m. f.d.m. systems currently engineered fall into the low deviation category and so are well suited to treatment with the first-order theory, but this is not usually the case with satellite systems and the Monte Carlo technique is then likely to be the best method of attack.

The reader is reminded that coefficient a_1 is made zero, and attention is drawn to the different kinds of approximations that are involved in applying this theory. Firstly, some error is nearly always incurred by fitting the filter or discriminator characteristic with a finite number of the a_ns and b_ns. This leads to a nonlinearly related error in the calculated distortion level.

Again, the theory is formulated in terms of real and imaginary parts but it may be more convenient to work in terms of amplitude and phase characteristics (this is the case with the discriminator). Then the a_n and b_n are obtained from relationships like those shown in eqn. 8.19 but by dropping cross product terms (see below eqn. 8.19) another source of error is introduced. While errors of all these kinds may be present, this does not detract from the usefulness of the first-order theory because they usually turn out to be acceptably small when care is taken and due regard given to the ranges over which the original power-series fit is made.

Table 8.2   General Form of Contributions to Intermodulation Noise/Signal Power Ratio

Intermodulation order n	Resistance characteristic *	Reactance characteristic
2	$p_m^4 \omega_\Delta \{b_3^2 \beta_1 + b_3 b_5 [\beta_2 p_m^2 + \beta_3 \omega_\Delta^2] + b_5^2 [\beta_4 p_m^4 + \beta_5 p_m^2 \omega_\Delta^2$ $+ \beta_6 \omega_\Delta^4] + b_3 b_7 [\beta_7 p_m^4 + \beta_8 p_m^2 \omega_\Delta^2 + \beta_9 \omega_\Delta^4] + b_5 b_7 [\beta_{10} p_m^6$ $+ \beta_{11} p_m^4 \omega_\Delta^2 + \beta_{12} p_m^2 \omega_\Delta^4 + \beta_{13} \omega_\Delta^6] + b_7^2 [\beta_{14} p_m^8 + \beta_{15} p_m^6 \omega_\Delta^2$ $+ \beta_{16} p_m^4 \omega_\Delta^4 + \beta_{17} p_m^2 \omega_\Delta^6 + \beta_{18} \omega_\Delta^8]\}$	$p_m^2 \omega_\Delta^2 \{a_2^2 \alpha_1 + a_2 a_4 [\alpha_2 p_m^2 + \alpha_3 \omega_\Delta^2] + a_4^2 [\alpha_4 p_m^4 + \alpha_5 p_m^2 \omega_\Delta^2$ $+ \alpha_6 \omega_\Delta^4] + a_2 a_6 [\alpha_7 p_m^4 + \alpha_8 p_m^2 \omega_\Delta^2 + \alpha_9 \omega_\Delta^4] + a_4 a_6 [\alpha_{10} p_m^6$ $+ c_{11} p_m^4 \omega_\Delta^2 + \alpha_{12} p_m^2 \omega_\Delta^4 + \alpha_{13} \omega_\Delta^6] + a_6^2 [\alpha_{14} p_m^8 + \alpha_{15} p_m^6 \omega_\Delta^2$ $+ \alpha_{16} p_m^4 \omega_\Delta^4 + \alpha_{17} p_m^2 \omega_\Delta^6 + \alpha_{18} \omega_\Delta^8]\}$
3	$p_m^4 \omega_\Delta^4 \{b_4^2 \beta_1 + b_4 b_6 [\beta_2 p_m^2 + \beta_3 \omega_\Delta^2] + b_6^2 [\beta_4 p_m^4 + \beta_5 p_m^2 \omega_\Delta^2$ $+ \beta_6 \omega_\Delta^4] + b_4 b_8 [\beta_7 p_m^4 + \beta_8 p_m^2 \omega_\Delta^2 + \beta_9 \omega_\Delta^4] + b_6 b_8 [\beta_{10} p_m^6$ $+ \beta_{11} p_m^4 \omega_\Delta^2 + \beta_{12} p_m^2 \omega_\Delta^4 + \beta_{13} \omega_\Delta^6] + b_8^2 [\beta_{14} p_m^8 + \beta_{15} p_m^6 \omega_\Delta^2$ $+ \beta_{16} p_m^4 \omega_\Delta^4 + \beta_{17} p_m^2 \omega_\Delta^6 + \beta_{18} \omega_\Delta^8]\}$	$p_m^2 \omega_\Delta^4 \{a_3^2 \alpha_1 + a_3 a_5 [\alpha_2 p_m^2 + \alpha_3 \omega_\Delta^2] + a_5^2 [\alpha_4 p_m^4 + \alpha_5 p_m^2 \omega_\Delta^2$ $+ \alpha_6 \omega_\Delta^4] + a_3 a_7 [\alpha_7 p_m^4 + \alpha_8 p_m^2 \omega_\Delta^2 + \alpha_9 \omega_\Delta^4] + a_5 a_7 [\alpha_{10} p_m^6$ $+ \alpha_{11} p_m^4 \omega_\Delta^2 + \alpha_{12} p_m^2 \omega_\Delta^4 + \alpha_{13} \omega_\Delta^6] + a_7^2 [\alpha_{14} p_m^8 + \alpha_{15} p_m^6 \omega_\Delta^2$ $+ \alpha_{16} p_m^4 \omega_\Delta^4 + \alpha_{17} p_m^2 \omega_\Delta^6 + \alpha_{18} \omega_\Delta^8]\}$

4	$p_m^4 \omega_\Delta^6 \{ b_5^2 \beta_1 + b_5 b_7 [\beta_2 p_m^2 + \beta_3 \omega_\Delta^2] + b_7^2 [\beta_4 p_m^4 + \beta_5 p_m^2 \omega_\Delta^2]$ $+ \beta_6 \omega_\Delta^4] \}$	$p_m^2 \omega_\Delta^6 \{ a_4^2 \alpha_1 + a_4 a_6 [\alpha_2 p_m^2 + \alpha_3 \omega_\Delta^2] + a_6^2 [\alpha_4 p_m^4 + \alpha_5 p_m^2 \omega_\Delta^2]$ $+ \alpha_6 \omega_\Delta^4] \}$
5	$p_m^4 \omega_\Delta^8 \{ b_6^2 \beta_1 + b_6 b_8 [\beta_2 p_m^2 + \beta_3 \omega_\Delta^2] + b_8^2 [\beta_4 p_m^4 + \beta_5 p_m^2 \omega_\Delta^2]$ $+ \beta_6 \omega_\Delta^4] \}$	$p_m^2 \omega_\Delta^8 \{ a_5^2 \alpha_1 + a_5 a_7 [\alpha_2 p_m^2 + \alpha_3 \omega_\Delta^2] + a_7^2 [\alpha_4 p_m^4 + \alpha_5 p_m^2 \omega_\Delta^2]$ $+ \alpha_6 \omega_\Delta^4] \}$
6	$p_m^4 \omega_\Delta^{10} b_7^2 \beta_1$	$p_m^2 \omega_\Delta^{10} a_6^2 \alpha_1$
7	$p_m^4 \omega_\Delta^{12} b_8^2 \beta_1$	$p_m^2 \omega_\Delta^{12} a_7^2 \alpha_1$

Table 8.3   Coefficient Values for $n = 2$, Reactance Characteristic

P/p_m	0·1	0·2	0·3	0·4	0·5	0·6	0·7	0·8	0·9	1·0
β_1	0·000428 *0·00120*	0·00648 *0·0139*	0·0310 *0·0488*	0·0922 *0·105*	0·211 *0·174*	0·408 *0·247*	0·702 *0·323*	1·11 *0·405*	1·62 *0·502*	2·25 *0·637*
β_2	0·000439 *0·00238*	0·00648 *0·0251*	0·0318 *0·0823*	0·102 *0·171*	0·264 *0·286*	0·590 *0·429*	1·19 *0·612*	2·21 *0·862*	3·83 *1·23*	6·25 *1·80*
β_3	0·00855 *0·0240*	0·130 *0·277*	0·620 *0·975*	1·84 *2·10*	4·22 *3·48*	8·16 *4·95*	14·0 *6·47*	22·1 *8·09*	32·5 *10·0*	45·0 *12·7*
β_4	0·000199 *0·00138*	0·00267 *0·0133*	0·0122 *0·0408*	0·0378 *0·0808*	0·0989 *0·132*	0·237 *0·202*	0·535 *0·306*	1·14 *0·473*	2·30 *0·760*	4·38 *1·28*
β_5	0·00439 *0·0238*	0·0648 *0·251*	0·318 *0·823*	1·02 *1·71*	2·64 *2·86*	5·90 *4·29*	11·9 *6·12*	22·1 *8·62*	38·3 *12·3*	62·5 *18·0*
β_6	0·0428 *0·120*	0·648 *1·39*	3·10 *4·88*	9·22 *10·5*	21·1 *17·4*	40·8 *24·7*	70·2 *32·3*	111 *40·5*	162 *50·2*	225 *63·7*
β_7	0·000334 *0·00232*	0·00449 *0·0224*	0·0205 *0·0685*	0·0634 *0·136*	0·166 *0·222*	0·398 *0·339*	0·899 *0·514*	1·92 *0·795*	3·86 *1·28*	7·35 *2·15*
β_8	0·0192 *0·0993*	0·287 *1·03*	1·39 *3·49*	4·30 *7·39*	10·5 *12·3*	21·9 *17·9*	41·4 *24·5*	72·3 *32·7*	118 *43·9*	184 *60·8*
β_9	0·0898 *0·252*	1·36 *2·91*	6·51 *10·2*	19·4 *22·0*	44·3 *36·5*	85·7 *52·0*	147 *67·9*	232 *85·0*	341 *106*	473 *134*
β_{10}	0·000362 *0·00287*	0·00446 *0·0254*	0·0189 *0·0728*	0·0558 *0·138*	0·143 *0·221*	0·353 *0·341*	0·857 *0·537*	2·04 *0·899*	4·71 *1·61*	10·4 *3·08*

β_{11}	0·0168 / *0·124*	0·233 / *1·24*	1·09 / *3·88*	3·42 / *7·84*	8·89 / *13·0*	20·8 / *19·6*	45·3 / *29·0*	92·9 / *43·4*	180 / *66·8*	330 / *108*
β_{12}	0·238 / *1·18*	3·55 / *12·9*	17·3 / *43·6*	53·8 / *91·9*	132 / *153*	281 / *224*	539 / *310*	955 / *418*	1590 / *568*	2490 / *797*
β_{13}	0·898 / *2·52*	13·6 / *29·1*	65·1 / *102*	194 / *220*	443 / *365*	857 / *520*	1470 / *679*	2320 / *850*	3410 / *1060*	4730 / *1340*
β_{14}	0·000179 / *0·00154*	0·00203 / *0·0126*	0·00810 / *0·0339*	0·0228 / *0·0615*	0·0571 / *0·0969*	0·142 / *0·150*	0·361 / *0·245*	0·943 / *0·439*	2·46 / *0·866*	6·20 / *1·87*
β_{15}	0·0115 / *0·102*	0·146 / *0·939*	0·636 / *2·77*	1·91 / *5·35*	4·95 / *8·67*	12·1 / *13·3*	28·5 / *20·6*	65·3 / *33·2*	144 / *56·9*	304 / *104*
β_{16}	0·289 / *2·15*	4·12 / *22·3*	19·5 / *72·3*	60·9 / *149*	154 / *247*	346 / *368*	717 / *526*	1400 / *751*	2580 / *1100*	4540 / *1680*
β_{17}	2·02 / *9·79*	30·2 / *108*	146 / *367*	452 / *776*	1100 / *1290*	2300 / *1880*	4340 / *2580*	7590 / *3430*	12400 / *4610*	19300 / *6380*
β_{18}	4·71 / *13·2*	71·4 / *153*	342 / *538*	1020 / *1160*	2330 / *1920*	4500 / *2730*	7740 / *3560*	12200 / *4460*	17900 / *5540*	4800 / *27030*

Table 8.4   Coefficient Values for n = 3, Resistance Characteristic

P/p_m	0·1	0·2	0·3	0·4	0·5	0·6	0·7	0·8	0·9	1·0
α_1	0·0190 / 0·0532	0·0720 / 0·154	0·153 / 0·241	0·256 / 0·291	0·375 / 0·309	0·504 / 0·305	0·637 / 0·293	0·768 / 0·281	0·891 / 0·276	1·00 / 0·283
α_2	0·0121 / 0·0646	0·0490 / 0·179	0·122 / 0·287	0·253 / 0·379	0·469 / 0·460	0·800 / 0·537	1·27 / 0·620	1·90 / 0·719	2·71 / 0·850	3·67 / 1·05
α_3	0·228 / 0·639	0·864 / 1·85	1·84 / 2·89	3·07 / 3·50	4·50 / 3·71	6·05 / 3·67	7·64 / 3·52	9·22 / 3·37	10·7 / 3·31	12·0 / 3·40
α_4	0·00330 / 0·0227	0·0125 / 0·0602	0·0314 / 0·0964	0·0716 / 0·134	0·157 / 0·180	0·328 / 0·244	0·645 / 0·333	1·19 / 0·463	2·06 / 0·658	3·37 / 0·967
α_5	0·0726 / 0·387	0·294 / 1·08	0·731 / 1·72	1·52 / 2·27	2·81 / 2·76	4·80 / 3·22	7·63 / 3·72	11·4 / 4·31	16·2 / 5·10	22·0 / 6·28
α_6	0·684 / 1·92	2·59 / 5·54	5·51 / 8·67	9·22 / 10·5	13·5 / 11·1	18·1 / 11·0	22·9 / 10·6	27·6 / 10·1	32·1 / 9·93	36·0 / 10·2
α_7	0·00666 / 0·0458	0·0256 / 0·123	0·0633 / 0·198	0·137 / 0·268	0·279 / 0·341	0·539 / 0·426	0·990 / 0·537	1·73 / 0·696	2·88 / 0·937	4·57 / 1·32
α_8	0·371 / 1·79	1·45 / 5·08	3·36 / 8·04	6·35 / 10·2	10·8 / 11·7	17·0 / 12·8	25·4 / 13·8	36·2 / 15·1	49·5 / 17·0	65·0 / 20·1
α_9	1·71 / 4·79	6·48 / 13·9	13·8 / 21·7	23·0 / 26·2	33·8 / 27·8	45·4 / 27·5	57·3 / 26·4	69·1 / 25·3	80·2 / 24·8	90·0 / 25·5
α_{10}	0·00436 / 0·0343	0·0159 / 0·0882	0·0391 / 0·142	0·0899 / 0·202	0·206 / 0·283	0·467 / 0·402	1·04 / 0·593	2·20 / 0·911	4·42 / 1·46	8·42 / 2·46

α_{11}	0·199 *1·46*	0·774 *3·94*	1·93 *6·30*	4·24 *8·56*	8·73 *11·0*	17·1 *14·0*	31·6 *18·0*	55·6 *23·6*	92·6 *31·9*	147 *45·1*
α_{12}	2·77 *13·7*	10·9 *38·5*	25·6 *61·2*	49·5 *78·2*	85·8 *90·7*	138 *101*	210 *111*	303 *123*	419 *140*	555 *168*
α_{13}	10·3 *28·8*	38·9 *83·2*	82·6 *130*	138 *157*	203 *167*	272 *165*	344 *158*	415 *152*	481 *149*	540 *153*
α_{14}	0·00157 *0·0134*	0·00551 *0·0335*	0·0136 *0·0544*	0·0318 *0·0802*	0·0752 *0·117*	0·181 *0·175*	0·439 *0·275*	1·05 *0·461*	2·42 *0·826*	5·31 *1·58*
α_{15}	0·0986 *0·869*	0·366 *2·28*	0·903 *3·66*	2·03 *5·11*	4·48 *6·88*	9·70 *9·33*	20·5 *13·1*	41·6 *19·1*	80·8 *29·2*	149 *47·2*
α_{16}	2·42 *17·9*	9·44 *49·2*	22·9 *78·4*	47·6 *104*	92·4 *128*	171 *155*	301 *189*	508 *236*	819 *305*	1260 *416*
α_{17}	16·7 *80·7*	65·4 *228*	151 *362*	286 *459*	485 *525*	767 *576*	1150 *623*	1630 *681*	2230 *766*	2930 *903*
α_{18}	38·5 *108*	146 *312*	310 *488*	518 *590*	759 *626*	1020 *619*	1290 *594*	1560 *569*	1800 *558*	2030 *574*

Table 8.5   Coefficient Values for $n = 3$, Resistance Characteristic

P/p_m	0·1	0·2	0·3	0·4	0·5	0·6	0·7	0·8	0·9	1·0
β_1	0·00179 *0·00278*	0·0284 *0·0422*	0·141 *0·196*	0·436 *0·554*	1·03 *1·17*	2·05 *2·05*	3·62 *3·10*	5·80 *4·18*	8·62 *5·06*	12·0 *5·45*
β_2	0·00380 *0·00863*	0·0628 *0·138*	0·335 *0·690*	1·13 *2·13*	2·96 *5·02*	6·58 *9·78*	13·0 *16·5*	23·4 *24·7*	38·8 *32·6*	60·0 *37·2*
β_3	0·0538 *0·0834*	0·852 *1·27*	4·24 *5·89*	13·1 *16·6*	30·9 *35·1*	61·6 *61·4*	108 *93·0*	174 *125*	259 *152*	360 *164*
β_4	0·00268 *0·00740*	0·0456 *0·124*	0·255 *0·665*	0·912 *2·25*	2·57 *5·82*	6·21 *12·6*	13·4 *23·6*	26·4 *38·8*	47·8 *55·9*	80·0 *66·9*
β_5	0·0569 *0·129*	0·942 *2·06*	5·03 *10·3*	16·9 *32·0*	44·4 *75·2*	98·7 *147*	195 *248*	351 *370*	582 *490*	900 *557*
β_6	0·404 *0·626*	6·39 *9·50*	31·8 *44·2*	98·2 *125*	232 *264*	462 *461*	814 *698*	1300 *940*	1940 *1140*	2700 *1230*
β_7	0·00403 *0·0111*	0·0695 *0·189*	0·395 *1·04*	1·44 *3·58*	4·11 *9·45*	10·0 *20·7*	21·7 *39·0*	42·6 *64·5*	76·6 *92·9*	127 *111*
β_8	0·190 *0·442*	3·09 *6·90*	16·0 *33·5*	52·0 *99·8*	131 *225*	280 *422*	533 *686*	925 *992*	1490 *1280*	2240 *1430*
β_9	0·753 *1·17*	11·9 *17·7*	59·4 *82·5*	183 *232*	433 *492*	862 *860*	1520 *1300*	2440 *1750*	3620 *2130*	5040 *2290*
β_{10}	0·00646 *0·0202*	0·115 *0·360*	0·689 *2·12*	2·68 *7·98*	8·23 *23·2*	21·7 *56·1*	50·8 *117*	108 *213*	209 *334*	367 *418*

β_{11}	0·299 *0·893*	5·06 *14·7*	28·0 *77·7*	99·0 *257*	275 *649*	652 *1370*	1380 *2500*	2660 *4030*	4730 *5700*	7780 *6750*
β_{12}	3·65 *8·45*	59·5 *132*	310 *647*	1020 *1940*	2590 *4430*	5580 *8380*	10700 *13800*	18800 *20100*	30500 *26100*	46200 *29300*
β_{13}	11·3 *17·5*	179 *266*	891 *1240*	2750 *3490*	6500 *7380*	12900 *12900*	22800 *19500*	36500 *26300*	54300 *31900*	75600 *34300*
β_{14}	0·004 20 *0·0144*	0·0789 *0·272*	0·509 *1·76*	2·16 *7·37*	7·29 *24·0*	21·1 *64·9*	53·8 *151*	123 *304*	253 *519*	460 *680*
β_{15}	0·275 *0·968*	4·85 *16·9*	28·5 *96·9*	109 *353*	326 *990*	841 *2320*	1930 *4690*	4010 *8290*	7630 *12700*	13200 *15700*
β_{16}	6·40 *20·5*	107 *331*	579 *1690*	1990 *5400*	5380 *13200*	12400 *26800*	25500 *47400*	48000 *74400*	83600 *103000*	135000 *120000*
β_{17}	39·9 *92·9*	648 *1450*	3360 *7040*	10900 *20900*	27500 *47300*	58800 *88600*	112000 *144000*	194000 *208000*	313000 *269000*	470000 *301000*
β_{18}	79·1 *123*	1250 *1860*	6240 *8660*	19200 *24400*	45500 *51700*	90500 *90300*	159000 *137000*	256000 *184000*	380000 *223000*	529000 *240000*

Table 8.6   Coefficient Values for $n = 3$, Reactance Characteristic

P/p_m	0·1	0·2	0·3	0·4	0·5	0·6	0·7	0·8	0·9	1·0
α_1	0·0449 0·0695	0·178 0·264	0·393 0·546	0·682 0·865	1·03 1·17	1·43 1·42	1·84 1·58	2·27 1·63	2·66 1·56	3·00 1·36
α_2	0·0647 0·146	0·285 0·608	0·738 1·44	1·54 2·68	2·83 4·32	4·76 6·23	7·44 8·20	10·9 9·90	15·2 10·9	20·0 10·7
α_3	0·897 1·39	3·55 5·28	7·86 10·9	13·6 17·3	20·6 23·4	28·5 28·4	36·9 31·6	45·3 32·6	53·2 31·3	60·0 27·3
α_4	0·0309 0·0847	0·145 0·383	0·416 1·02	0·996 2·21	2·14 4·19	4·26 7·11	7·88 11·0	13·6 15·4	22·2 19·6	33·9 21·5
α_5	0·647 1·46	2·85 6·08	7·38 14·4	15·4 26·8	28·3 43·2	47·6 62·3	74·4 82·0	109 99·0	152 109	200 107
α_6	4·49 6·95	17·8 26·4	39·3 54·6	68·2 86·5	103 117	143 142	184 158	227 163	266 156	300 136
α_7	0·0525 0·144	0·253 0·670	0·736 1·83	1·74 3·99	3·63 7·48	6·89 12·5	12·1 18·7	19·8 25·4	30·4 31·0	43·9 32·3
α_8	2·41 5·58	10·1 22·3	24·7 50·0	48·2 87·6	83·5 133	133 182	199 229	282 267	381 286	490 275
α_9	9·42 14·6	37·3 55·4	82·5 115	143 182	217 246	299 298	387 332	476 343	559 328	630 286
α_{10}	0·0568 0·177	0·292 0·889	0·941 2·74	2·53 6·90	6·11 15·1	13·5 29·6	27·7 51·9	52·8 82·0	93·6 115	154 133

α_{11}	2·58 / 7·64	12·0 / 33·8	33·5 / 87·4	77·2 / 181	159 / 329	303 / 536	539 / 796	899 / 1080	1410 / 1330	2100 / 1420
α_{12}	30·9 / 71·1	131 / 287	324 / 651	644 / 1160	1130 / 1780	1830 / 2480	2770 / 3150	3970 / 3710	5400 / 4010	7000 / 3870
α_{13}	94·2 / 146	373 / 554	825 / 1150	1430 / 1820	2170 / 2460	2990 / 2980	3870 / 3320	4760 / 3430	5590 / 3280	6300 / 2860
α_{14}	0·0282 / 0·0957	0·159 / 0·536	0·578 / 1·91	1·77 / 5·58	4·83 / 14·2	11·9 / 31·9	27·1 / 63·7	56·5 / 113	108 / 174	189 / 216
α_{15}	1·81 / 6·31	9·09 / 30·8	28·3 / 90·8	73·5 / 217	171 / 453	364 / 846	723 / 1430	1340 / 2180	2320 / 2960	3750 / 3390
α_{16}	41·1 / 131	185 / 556	495 / 1370	1090 / 2700	2160 / 4650	3960 / 7270	6820 / 10400	11100 / 13800	17100 / 16500	24900 / 17400
α_{17}	253 / 586	1060 / 2340	2590 / 5250	5070 / 9200	8770 / 14000	14000 / 19100	20900 / 24100	29600 / 28000	40000 / 30000	51500 / 28800
α_{18}	494 / 766	1960 / 2910	4330 / 6010	7510 / 9540	11400 / 12900	15700 / 15700	20300 / 17400	25000 / 18000	29300 / 17200	33100 / 15000

Table 8.7   Coefficient Values for $n = 4$, Resistance Characteristic

P/p_m	0·1	0·2	0·3	0·4	0·5	0·6	0·7	0·8	0·9	1·0
β_1	0·00996 *0·0220*	0·158 *0·307*	0·785 *1·27*	2·42 *3·13*	5·74 *5·76*	11·5 *8·85*	20·4 *12·1*	33·1 *15·4*	50·2 *19·0*	71·9 *23·4*
β_2	0·0422 *0·165*	0·684 *2·28*	3·55 *9·36*	11·6 *23·1*	29·3 *43·3*	63·4 *68·7*	123 *98·5*	219 *133*	364 *176*	575 *235*
β_3	0·418 *0·924*	6·62 *12·9*	33·0 *53·4*	102 *131*	241 *242*	482 *372*	856 *509*	1 390 *649*	2 110 *799*	3 020 *982*
β_4	0·0564 *0·343*	0·925 *4·66*	4·89 *18·9*	16·5 *46·4*	43·6 *87·3*	99·5 *141*	206 *210*	394 *300*	711 *423*	1 220 *607*
β_5	0·886 *3·46*	14·4 *47·8*	74·5 *197*	243 *486*	616 *909*	1 330 *1 440*	2 580 *2 070*	4 590 *2 800*	7 650 *3 700*	12 100 *4 930*
β_6	4·39 *9·71*	69·6 *136*	346 *561*	1 070 *1 380*	2 530 *2 540*	5 060 *3 900*	8 980 *5 340*	14 600 *6 810*	22 100 *8 380*	31 700 *10 300*

Table 8.8   Coefficient Values for $n = 4$, Reactance Characteristic

P/p_m	0·1	0·2	0·3	0·4	0·5	0·6	0·7	0·8	0·9	1·0
α_1	0·159 *0·352*	0·631 *1·23*	1·40 *2·26*	2·42 *3·13*	3·67 *3·69*	5·10 *3·94*	6·65 *3·96*	8·27 *3·86*	9·91 *3·76*	11·5 *3·74*
α_2	0·490 *1·90*	2·08 *6·75*	5·13 *12·9*	10·2 *19·0*	18·0 *24·4*	29·3 *28·9*	44·9 *32·7*	65·5 *36·2*	91·5 *40·1*	123 *45·5*

Table 8.9 Coefficient Values for $n = 5$, Resistance Characteristic

P/p_m	0·1	0·2	0·3	0·4	0·5	0·6	0·7	0·8	0·9	1·0
α_3	4·78 / 10·6	18·9 / 36·9	41·9 / 67·8	72·7 / 93·9	110 / 111	153 / 118	200 / 119	248 / 116	297 / 113	345 / 112
α_4	0·473 / 2·85	2·09 / 10·2	5·52 / 19·9	12·1 / 30·8	24·0 / 42·3	44·8 / 54·9	79·3 / 69·1	134 / 86·2	216 / 108	336 / 140
α_5	7·35 / 28·5	31·2 / 101	77·0 / 194	153 / 285	270 / 366	440 / 433	674 / 490	983 / 543	1370 / 601	1850 / 683
α_6	35·9 / 79·2	142 / 277	314 / 509	545 / 704	826 / 830	1150 / 885	1500 / 890	1860 / 869	2230 / 845	2590 / 841
β_1	0·0645 / 0·117	1·02 / 1·73	5·12 / 7·76	15·9 / 20·8	37·9 / 41·7	76·2 / 68·7	136 / 98·6	224 / 128	342 / 156	495 / 184
β_2	0·462 / 1·31	7·50 / 19·8	38·8 / 91·4	126 / 256	317 / 538	682 / 936	1310 / 1420	2310 / 1950	3830 / 2510	6020 / 3100
β_3	3·61 / 6·54	57·4 / 97·0	287 / 435	889 / 1170	2120 / 2330	4270 / 3840	7640 / 5520	12500 / 7180	19200 / 8740	27700 / 10300
β_4	0·987 / 3·89	16·2 / 60·2	86·0 / 287	289 / 839	759 / 1850	1710 / 3390	3480 / 5430	6530 / 7860	11600 / 10600	19500 / 13700
β_5	12·9 / 36·6	210 / 553	1090 / 2560	3530 / 7170	8890 / 15100	19100 / 26200	36700 / 39800	64800 / 54700	107000 / 70100	169000 / 86800
β_6	50·6 / 91·6	803 / 9360	4010 / 6080	12400 / 16300	29700 / 32700	59800 / 53800	107000 / 77300	175000 / 101000	268000 / 122000	388000 / 144000

Table 8.10   Coefficient Values for $n = 5$, Reactance Characteristic

P/p_m	0·1	0·2	0·3	0·4	0·5	0·6	0·7	0·8	0·9	1·0
α_1	0·717 *1·30*	2·85 *4·81*	6·32 *9·58*	11·0 *14·5*	16·8 *18·5*	23·5 *21·2*	30·9 *22·4*	38·8 *22·3*	46·9 *21·4*	55·0 *20·4*
α_2	3·90 *11·0*	16·4 *42·5*	39·9 *90·7*	77·9 *150*	135 *212*	217 *270*	329 *318*	475 *354*	660 *379*	887 *401*
α_3	30·1 *54·5*	119 *202*	265 *402*	463 *607*	707 *778*	988 *890*	1 300 *939*	1 630 *935*	1 970 *899*	2 310 *858*
α_4	6·30 *24·7*	27·6 *99·8*	71·6 *227*	153 *407*	295 *634*	533 *895*	916 *1170*	1 510 *1450*	2 390 *1720*	3 650 *2010*
α_5	82·0 *230*	345 *893*	837 *1900*	1 640 *3140*	2 840 *4450*	4 560 *5670*	6 910 *6680*	9 980 *7430*	13 900 *7960*	18 600 *8430*
α_6	316 *572*	1 250 *2120*	2 790 *4220*	4 860 *6380*	7 420 *8170*	10 400 *9340*	13 600 *9860*	17 100 *9820*	20 700 *9440*	24 300 *9010*

Table 8.11   Coefficient Values for $n = 6$, Resistance Characteristic

P/p_m	0·1	0·2	0·3	0·4	0·5	0·6	0·7	0·8	0·9	1·0
β_1	0·484 *0·976*	7·69 *14·1*	38·5 *61·1*	120 *157*	286 *301*	579 *478*	1 040 *669*	1 720 *863*	2 650 *1060*	3 860 *1300*

Table 8.12   Coefficient Values for $n = 6$, Reactance Characteristic

P/p_m	0·1	0·2	0·3	0·4	0·5	0·6	0·7	0·8	0·9	1·0
α_1	3·95 *7·97*	15·7 *28·8*	34·9 *55·4*	61·1 *80·2*	93·5 *98·3*	131 *108*	174 *111*	219 *110*	267 *107*	315 *106*

Table 8.13   Coefficient Values for $n = 7$, Resistance Characteristic

P/p_m	0·1	0·2	0·3	0·4	0·5	0·6	0·7	0·8	0·9	1·0
β_1	4·11 *7·82*	65·4 *115*	328 *509*	1 020 *1 340*	2 450 *2 640*	4 980 *4 290*	8 980 *6 100*	14 900 *7 920*	23 000 *9 750*	33 800 *11 800*

Table 8.14   Coefficient Values for $n = 7$, Reactance Characteristic

P/p_m	0·1	0·2	0·3	0·4	0·5	0·6	0·7	0·8	0·9	1·0
α_1	25·7 *48·9*	102 *180*	228 *353*	399 *525*	613 *661*	864 *745*	1 150 *778*	1 450 *774*	1 780 *752*	2 110 *735*

8.5 References

1 MAGNUSSON, R.I.: 'Intermodulation noise in linear f.m. systems', *Proc. IEE*, 1962, 109 C, pp. 32–44 and (IEE Monograph 459E)

2 MEDHURST, R.G.: 'Explicit form of f.m. distortion products with white-noise modulation', *Proc. IEE*, 1960, pp. 120–126 107 C, (IEE Monograph 352E)

3 MEDHURST, R.G., and ROBERTS, J.H.: 'Explicit form of f.m. distortion products with white-noise modulation: extension and correction', *Proc. IEE*, 1960, 107 C, pp. 367–369 (addendum to IEE Monograph 352E)

4 SHIMBO, O., and LOO, C.: 'Digital computation of FM distortion due to linear networks', IEEE International Conference on Communications Philadelphia, 1968, pp. 482–486

5 MEDHURST, R.G., ROBERTS, J.H., and WALSH, W.R.: 'Distortion of SSB Transmission due to AM/PM conversion', *IEEE Trans.*, 1964, **CS-12**, (2), pp. 166–176

6 PAWULA, R.F.: 'The effects of quadratic AM-PM conversion in frequency-division multiplexed multiple access communication satellite systems', *IEEE Trans.*, 1971, **COM-19**, (3), pp. 345–349

7 SHIMBO, O.: 'Effects of intermodulation, AM-PM conversion and additive noise in multi-carrier TWT systems', *Proc. IEEE*, 1971, **59**, (2), pp. 230–238

8 MEDHURST, R.G., and ROBERTS, J.H.: 'Evaluation of distortion in f.m. trunk radio systems by a Monte Carlo method', *Proc. IEE*, 1966, **113**, (4), pp. 570–580

9 MEDHURST, R.G., and CLAYTON, F.M.: 'Validity of first-order f.m. distortion theory as applied to trunk radio systems', *Proc. IEE*, 1967, **114**, (7), pp. 903–906

10 HAMER, R.: 'The design of multi-channel telephony radio relay systems: intermodulation noise power due to transmission networks'. Post Office Engineering Department Radio Report 2630, 1958

Chapter 9

Devices for threshold extension and *S/D* improvement

9.1 Introductory material

Over recent years several special types of f.m. demodulator have been built and analysed which have the aim of improving on the range of useful operation of the conventional f.m. receiver. Such demodulators are usually known as threshold extending devices and three such will be discussed here. These are:

(*a*) frequency feedback demodulator (f.m.f.b.)
(*b*) dynamic tracking filter (d.t.f.)
(*c*) phase lock loop (p.l.l.)

Circuits have also been proposed for improving the signal-to-distortion ratio in situations where this would be very poor if conventional receiver designs were used.

A large body of material has been published on these topics (a useful bibliography on (a), (b) and (c), covering the period up to 1970 is included in Reference 1, while Reference 2 is a guide to much information regarding the p.l.l.) and again attention will be directed at cases in which the frequency modulation on the input carrier is modelled by a band of Gaussian noise. There is a direct application to f.m. f.d.m. systems, therefore, but the theory applies to any analogue system to which such a model for the modulation is appropriate.

Performance will be described by means of a curve showing how the interference appearing in any baseband channel varies with the input carrier-to-noise ratio. As with a conventional receiver, such a curve usually exhibits a threshold knee near which a small decrease in ρ, the input carrier-to-noise ratio, is accompanied by a much larger than proportional increase in the interference level measured in a baseband channel. The three devices listed above operate in various ways in order to extend the linear (above-threshold) region of operation beyond that of the conventional f.m. receiver, so that the knees in their performance curves appear at lowered values of the carrier-to-noise ratio.

The f.m. clicks which were described in Section 5.1 herald the arrival of the threshold and, as for the conventional receiver, the effect is first apparent in the lowest baseband channels. Owing to the slope of 6 dB per octave in the spectrum of the thermal noise (see eqn. 5.22) the interference level associated with the clicks is much lower than the level measured concurrently in the highest baseband channels, and, to a large extent, the exact threshold points are a matter of subjective judgement. To overcome this difficulty, and to provide a working basis, it is usually stated that threshold is to coincide with a departure of 1 dB from the above-threshold linear law

$$\frac{D}{S} = \left(\frac{p_m - p_0}{2\omega_B}\right)\left(\frac{p}{p_m}\right)^2\left(\frac{p_m}{\omega_\Delta}\right)^2 \frac{1}{\rho} \qquad (9.1)$$

which, when D/S and ρ are expressed in decibels, plots as a straight line.

Taking $2\omega_B$ as the alloted bandwidth (with the noise spread uniformly across it) eqn. 9.1 shows that by increasing the f.m. index ω_Δ/p_m the distortion-to-signal ratio can be reduced. It must be remembered that no contribution from distortion due to spectrum truncation or demodulator imperfections is included, but the general principle of trading bandwidth for an improvement in S/D is widely exploited in f.m. system designs.

Perhaps the best known example of this, and of the use of threshold extension in general, arises in satellite communications. Here the vast distances involved mean that at the ground station the signal levels can be extremely small, and every expedient must be used to combat the effects of noise.

The satellite may handle several r.f. carriers, each frequency modulated by a large number of telephone channels arranged in frequency-division multiplex. Large modulation indices ($\omega_\Delta/p_m > 1$) are used to realise the advantage referred to above.

Eqn. 9.1 is common to all demodulator types working above their thresholds and is obtained by taking the output (in terms of phase) to be $\mu(t) + (I_S/A)$, that is, the desired phase modulation is disturbed only by the quadrature noise component normalised by the carrier amplitude. Thus, the formula holds only when sufficient bandwidth is available to ensure that I_S/A dominates distortion generated by bandwidth restriction. Note also that subsequent filtering at the output will not change the value of D/S when eqn. 9.1 applies.

Clearly it is desirable to make $2\omega_B$ as small as possible concordant with the bandwidth demanded by the large deviation carrier which, it will now be assumed, is present at the receiver input. Before investigating the performance of specially designed receivers, therefore, it is pertinent to examine how much benefit can be derived from preceding a conventional demodulator with a narrowed i.f. filter. Also, since the appearance of individual clicks signals the threshold, it is of interest to examine the effect of completely removing clicks by using impulse detection techniques. Such methods can usually be described as amplitude sensitive (because dips in the envelope and clicks tend to be correlated), and their success had been investigated both experimentally and by computer simulation.[3-8]

9.2 I.F. filter bandwidth

To be specific, it will be assumed that the f.m. index is given by $\omega_\Delta/p_m = 2$, and that the filter receiving noise plus this large deviation carrier (the power spectrum has the Gaussian form of eqn. 7.26) is a truncating network of bandwidth $2\alpha p_m$. Initially α will be taken as 8 so that only 0·01% of the carrier power is excluded by the filter, then the effect of reducing α will be examined.

The carrier-to-noise ratio ρ_T at which threshold appears can be read from Fig. 5.2 (for convenience we confine attention to the top baseband channel) and the ordinate of the graph is then given by $1/(2\alpha)$, as $2\omega_B = 2\alpha p_m$. Typical values for α could be 3, 4, 5 or 6 and, for these, Fig. 5.2 shows that ρ_T lies in the range 7 dB to 8·5 dB, but it must be remembered that for each ρ_T, the noise is measured in an input bandwidth that is fixed by α.

The receiver performance curve will exhibit a linear portion provided any truncation distortion that is generated when α becomes small is significantly lower in level than the distortion predicted by eqn. 9.1 (with any distortion arising, for example, from discriminator nonlinearity being equally small). This requirement can be expressed (using eqn. 9.1 with $\omega_\Delta/p_m = 2$ and $p_0 = 0$) by the following inequality

$$\frac{1}{8\alpha}\left(\frac{S}{D}\right) > \rho > \rho_T \qquad (9.2)$$

It can be argued that an exercise of this kind should be carried through with an i.f. filter that has been chosen to be optimum in some sense, rather than a truncating network; the desired filter would

be the one that excludes the maximum amount of noise while
introducing the least distortion after carrier demodulation. This nonlinear optimisation problem is best handled by drawing on experience
gained from the results of analysis, computer simulations, and
measurements on a variety of filters.

However, the distortion levels shown on Figs. 7.6—7.10 for the
perfect truncating filter (zero phase characteristic but infinitely sharp
cut-off in amplitude) are reasonably representative in the present
context, so Fig. 7.9 gives S/D in equality 9.2.

Ideally, before a minimum value for α can be deduced from the
inequality 9.2, the largest value of ρ for which the linear law
eqn. 9.1 is to hold must be specified, but for $\alpha = 3, 4, 5$ and 6, the
left-hand side has the values $-3 \cdot 8 \, dB$, $0 \cdot 5 \, dB$, $7 \cdot 0 \, dB$ and $15 \cdot 0 \, dB$,
so if α is taken below 5, the right-hand side of the inequality will not
be met.

Taking $\alpha = 6$ (an i.f. bandwidth of twelve times the maximum
modulating frequency) Fig. 5.2 shows that the threshold occurs when
$\rho_T = 7 \cdot 8 \, dB$, while with the original bandwidth corresponding to
$\alpha = 8$, we find $\rho_T = 8 \cdot 4 \, dB$. In the former case, the noise is measured
in a bandwidth of twelve times the maximum modulating frequency,
i.e. 12/16 of the bandwidth used when $\alpha = 8$. Thus, the signal power
at which the threshold is reached is reduced by a factor of $\{8 \cdot 4 -
7 \cdot 8 + 10 \log_{10} (16/12)\} dB$ or $1 \cdot 85 \, dB$, and this is the threshold
extension realized in top channel.

This extension is obtained by reducing the i.f. bandwidth to such
an extent that the linear portion of the receiver performance curve
may be almost eliminated. In practice, therefore, α is likely to exceed
6 is such an example, and less threshold extension is then available.

A somewhat similar investigation was done by Muehldorf[9] who
used an i.f. filter so optimised that it provides the minimum mean
square error estimate of the carrier wave.[10] With a bandwidth
corresponding to $\alpha = 6 \cdot 6$, an extension of between $1 \cdot 5 \, dB$ and $2 \cdot 0 \, dB$
is predicted, but, as no account of distortion was taken, Muehldorf's
results are likely to be optimistic.

There is more scope for improvement when the f.m. index is small
as preservation of the first-order sidebands is the main requirement,
but such cases barely exhibit a threshold knee in their performance
curves. It is then more fitting to seek improvements in the signal-to-
distortion ratio (as opposed to threshold extension), by balancing
the benefit gained from filtering out noise against the intermodulation
distortion that is generated. Such optimisation of the i.f. bandwidth
can be beneficial well below the threshold in large f.m. index cases

(some examples are discussed later in Section 9.22), but no dramatic improvement in terms of threshold extension can be realised by narrowing a wide input bandwidth although an extension of as little as 1 dB can represent the difference between an acceptable or an unacceptable receiver design in some applications.

9.3 Click elimination schemes

Clicks herald the arrival of the f.m. threshold, and when they are distinct (before they become so numerous that they merge into a continuously distributed interference) some form of impulse cancellation may improve demodulator performance. Such methods usually involve the setting of thresholds to indicate the presence of a click, and a holding circuit then performs a linear interpolation to span the short interval of time (typically the reciprocal of the semi-bandwidth of the i.f. filter) occupied by each detected click.

The performance of a demodulator incorporating such a click elimination scheme was modelled on a digital computer by Malone[4] for the case of single tone modulation, and the conclusion reached was that a threshold extension of 1·5 dB to 2·0 dB is obtainable.

Having attributed the threshold to clicks it might seem surprising that their elimination results in such small extensions, but we must remind ourselves that picturing the instantaneous frequency as the sum of two independent components, one of which is a sequence of randomly occurring impulses of area $\pm 2\pi$, is a convenience that holds in the immediate vicinity of the threshold but, evidently, loses acceptance as little as 2 dB below the threshold. Again this seems to be at variance with earlier results in which the Rician model, as described above, offers high accuracy at carrier-to-noise ratios as low as 3 dB, but then it was the power spectrum of the instantaneous frequency that was of interest. Thus, the model seems to be well suited to spectral calculations but not necessarily to other uses such as when the distribution of peaks in the instantaneous frequency is important.

As discussed in Section 5.1, a click can be associated with the double event of the quadrature noise component I_s passing through zero when the sum of the in-phase noise component I_c, and A, the carrier amplitude, is a small negative quantity. At such times, therefore, the envelope

$$\sqrt{(A + I_c)^2 + I_s^2}$$

has a smaller value than at non-click instants and, indeed, it has been observed experimentally, and can be demonstrated theoretically,[6, 7] that high correlation exists between the appearance of f.m. clicks and dips in the composite envelope of the carrier plus noise sum; demodulators have been proposed that exploit this fact[3-8] and so may be termed amplitude sensitive.

These devices, operating from a common observation, have also come to the common conclusion that about 1·5dB to 2·0dB of extension is available. Glazer, using his derived probability distribution for click amplitudes,[11] has argued that these figures are fundamental to such an method of click elimination,[5] and has shown that, even if 96% of all clicks could be detected and removed, this would still provide only about 3dB of extension. A very efficient click detection and elimination scheme might realise such an improvement therefore, and an extension of 3·5dB has been reported.[7]

Another way of eliminating a click would be to cause the instantaneous frequency to be multiplied by some quantity which is small when the click occurs and which is constant (ideally unity) during the period between clicks. From the foregoing observations the envelope or some suitable function of the envelope suggests itself for this purpose, but it transpires that such techniques are most effective in improving *S/D* ratios many decibels below threshold rather than providing threshold extension.

An analysis of envelope multiplication methods is deferred until Section 9.21, and three conventional threshold extending demodulations are considered next.

9.4 Threshold extending demodulators: the f.m.f.b.

Block diagrams of the three threshold extending devices to be considered are shown. Fig. 9.1 refers to the frequency feedback demodulator (f.m.f.b.), Fig. 9.2 to the dynamic tracking filter (d.t.f.), and Figs. 9.3 and 9.4 to the phase lock loop (p.l.l.).

Attention will be confined to their steady-state operation in noise and the click analysis described in Chapter 5 will be a tool that is frequently used. The f.m.f.b. and d.t.f. have a closer affinity with each other than with the p.l.l., and the f.m.f.b. is used to describe the general style of the analysis.

Any stated figure for threshold extension should be qualified by a statement giving the operating conditions that prevail. The extension depends on the type and depth of modulation that is present on the input carrier, and in the f.m. f.d.m. situation to be examined here, it also depends on which baseband channel is of interest and whether or not the baseband is pre-emphasised.

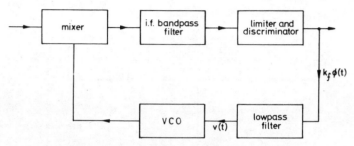

Fig. 9.1 Block diagram of the f.m. feedback demodulator

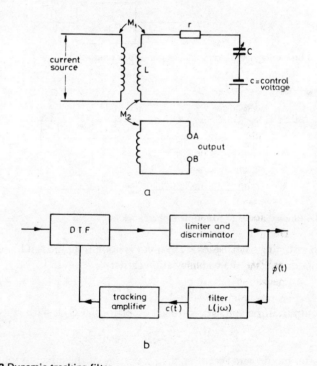

Fig. 9.2 Dynamic tracking filter
  a Series-damped form *b* Block diagram

Figs. 9.1 to 9.4 make it clear that many circuit parameters are involved as well, and so, in the interests of clarity, the discussion will nearly always refer to the highest baseband channel of a non-pre-emphasised system that uses the most commonly adopted circuit components. Also, when ρ or ρ_T is written for the carrier-to-noise ratio it is to be understood that the noise is measured in the Carson bandwidth of $2\omega_B$ as given by eqn. 4.13.

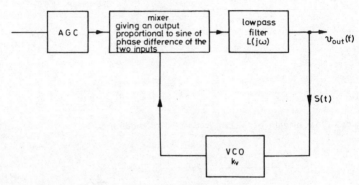

Fig. 9.3 Block diagram of the analogue phase lock loop

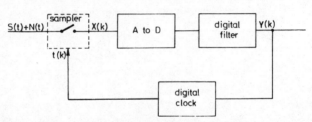

Fig. 9.4 Block diagram of the discrete phase lock loop

On assuming, initially, that the input is noise free, the f.m.f.b. de-modulator receives the wide deviation carrier

$$A \cos \left[\omega_0 t + \mu(t)\right] \tag{9.3}$$

The output of the voltage controlled oscillator (VCO) is written

$$V \cos \left[(\omega_0 - \omega_I)t + k_v v(t)\right] \tag{9.4}$$

and after mixing and accepting the i.f. portion of the mixer output, the narrow-band wave presented to the bandpass filter in the loop is

$$\frac{AV}{2} \cos \left[\omega_I t + \{\mu(t) - k_v v(t)\}\right] \tag{9.5}$$

Comparing eqns. 9.3 and 9.5 it is seen that the phase modulation $\mu(t)$ which gives rise to the wide deviation carrier has been modified to $\{\mu(t) - k_v v(t)\}$. Now $v(t)$ is fed back to the VCO from the output, and by appropriate design $\{\mu(t) - k_v v(t)\}$ is arranged to be an almost distortion-free replica of $\mu(t)$ with the property that the deviation produced by the frequency modulation $\{\dot{\mu}(t) - k_v \dot{v}(t)\}$ is small. As a consequence, the i.f. wave shown in eqn. 9.5 can be accommodated in a much smaller bandwidth than the bandwidth demanded by eqn. 9.3 and satisfactory demodulation of the f.d.m. assembly of channels can still be achieved. Restricting the i.f. filter passband has the outcome, when noise is reinstated in the analysis, that the carrier-to-noise ratio at which the threshold sets in is lowered, and threshold extension is obtained.

To reduce the number of variables, the transfer characteristic of the lowpass filter will be taken as

$$L(j\omega) = \frac{1}{1 + j\left(\dfrac{\omega}{p_m}\right)} \tag{9.6}$$

and that of the bandpass filter (in lowpass equivalent form) as

$$H(j\omega) = \frac{1}{1 + j\left(\dfrac{\omega}{\alpha p_m}\right)} \tag{9.7}$$

These single-pole forms have bandwidths expressed in terms of p_m the maximum modulating frequency; $2\alpha p_m$ is then the 3 dB-bandwidth of the i.f. filter, where α is a numerical factor. Further to the analytical simplicity of adopting the single-pole form, is the fact that this type of i.f. filter is the one commonly chosen for the loop because of the stability that is realised through its use. Finding the optimum value of α is one of the major tasks. Owing to the important part that filtering plays, it is convenient to introduce a special notation to represent the filtered form of a signal. Thus, for example, we shall write

$$v(t) = L(j\omega) | k_f \phi(t) \tag{9.8}$$

With reference to Fig. 9.1, $v(t)$ is the output from the lowpass filter that receives a portion (fixed by the size of k_f) of the signal detected by the limiter-discriminator combination $[\phi(t)$ is the phase modulation that corresponds to the detected f.m.]. The merit of the notation lies in allowing the filter to be specified in the frequency domain and the filtered signal in the time domain, the forms in which they appear most naturally in the analysis. Thus the Fourier transform of $\phi(t)$ and the impulse response corresponding to $L(j\omega)$ do not have to be introduced.

When noise is present at the f.m.f.b. input, it is convenient to represent it as a sum of randomly-phased tones covering the frequency band $\omega_0 - \omega_B$ to $\omega_0 + \omega_B$, and then eqn. 9.3 is replaced by

$$A \cos [\omega_0 t + \mu(t)] + \sum_{q=-\omega_B}^{+\omega_B} b \cos [\overline{\omega_0 + q}t + \alpha_q] \qquad (9.9)$$

and the i.f. portion of the mixer output becomes

$$S(t) = \frac{AV}{2} \cos [\omega_I t + \{\mu(t) - k_v v(t)\}]$$

$$+ \frac{V}{2} \sum_{q=-\omega_B}^{+\omega_B} b \cos [\overline{\omega_I + q}t + \alpha_q - k_v v(t)] \qquad (9.10)$$

This wave is passed into the i.f. bandpass filter and (using the current notation) the output can be written

$$H(j\omega)|S(t) \qquad (9.11)$$

As the filter is a linear device, this output will be given by summing the separate responses to the two terms making up eqn. 9.10, but these responses are not amenable to rigorous analysis because $v(t)$, being a signal that is fed back from the output, is made up not only of modulation, distortion, and noise components but also of interactions (distortion × noise, distortion × distortion etc.) between these three.

However, the type of performance curve to be derived for the f.m.f.b. is like that discussed earlier (Fig. 5.1) for the conventional receiver in that it is determined basically by the mean square values of noise and modulation parameters. Consequently, the analysis concentrates on evaluating r.m.s. values. With the noise term in eqn. 9.10, for example, it is seen that each independently-phased tone in the noise representation is phase modulated by $k_v v(t)$ and thus the mean square value (or noise power) is unaltered and, moreover, the ratio of carrier power to noise power at the stages of the analysis represented by eqns. 9.9 and 9.10 (at input and after the mixer) are the same.

When the i.f. filter is of the single-pole variety, it has a noise bandwidth of $\pi \alpha p_m$, and as $2\omega_B$ is the bandwidth of the noise at the receiver input, the reduction in noise power due to passage through the filter will be assumed to be given by $\pi \alpha p_m / 2\omega_B$.

Thus, the output of the i.f. bandpass filter is written

$$H(j\omega)\left|\frac{AV}{2} \cos (\omega_I t + \{\mu(t) - k_v v(t)\}) + N_F(t) \qquad (9.12)\right.$$

where $N_F(t)$ indicates a noise that is, effectively, the result of passing the input noise through the i.f. filter.

In the spirit of the remarks made above concerning the preoccupation with r.m.s. values, a frequency deviation index will be defined as follows

$$\beta_F = \frac{1}{p_m} \sqrt{\langle \{\dot{\mu}(t) - k_v \dot{v}(t)\}^2 \rangle} \tag{9.13}$$

and the corresponding mean square phase deviation ψ_{mix} by

$$\psi_{mix} = \langle \{\mu(t) - k_v v(t)\}^2 \rangle \tag{9.14}$$

Later, β_F and ψ_{mix} will be compared with their input counterparts ω_Δ / p_m and $\psi_\mu(0)$, the design aim being to make them as small as possible (especially β_F) so that the i.f. bandwidth factor α can be reduced to a value that strikes a compromise between excluding as much noise as possible and allowing an acceptable amount of the wanted signal to appear in the demodulator output.

Regarding the limiter-discriminator combination as a perfect frequency detector, the next item for consideration is the instantaneous frequency of wave shown in eqn. 9.12. This problem has much in common with the subject matter of Chapter 7, the difficulty of treatment being compounded by the complicated nature of $v(t)$ and the presence of the noise $N_F(t)$.

If eqn. 9.12 is rewritten in the form of a wave with simultaneous amplitude and phase modulation, that is, as

$$U(t) \cos [\omega_I t + \phi(t)] \tag{9.15}$$

then $\phi(t)$ and $v(t)$ are connected by eqn. 9.8 and an assessment of performance relies on finding an approximate but reasonably accurate expression for $v(t)$.

9.5 $v(t)$ and the demodulator output

Comparing eqns. 9.12 and 9.15, the explicit expression for $\phi(t)$ is

$$\phi(t) = \tan^{-1} \left\{ \frac{A e^{\alpha(t)} \sin [\mu(t) - k_v v(t) + \beta(t)] + I_{SF}}{A e^{\alpha(t)} \cos [\mu(t) - k_v v(t) + \beta(t)] + I_{CF}} \right\} \tag{9.16}$$

or, letting $\theta_1(t)$ stand for $\{\mu(t) - k_v v(t) + \beta(t)\}$

$$\phi(t) = \theta_1(t) + \tan^{-1} \left\{ \frac{I_{SF} \cos \theta_1(t) - I_{CF} \sin \theta_1(t)}{A e^{\alpha(t)} + I_{SF} \sin \theta_1(t) + I_{CF} \cos \theta_1(t)} \right\} \tag{9.17}$$

here I_{SF} and I_{CF} are the in-phase and quadrature components of the noise $N_F(t)$, while $e^{\alpha(t)}$ and $\beta(t)$ are, respectively, the amplitude modulation and the phase error introduced onto the signal component of eqn. 9.10 by the i.f. filter. Hopefully, $\alpha(t)$ here will not be confused with the bandwidth parameter α used in eqn. 9.2 and, for example, in Section 7.10.

The form of eqn. 9.17 has been met before in Section 5.3 where it was shown that above the threshold a modulation term like $\theta_1(t)$ can be placed equal to zero in the inverse tangent without introducing a significant change in the power level of the interference, indeed an approximation as simple as eqn. 5.22 is fully acceptable. However, the presence of $\theta_1(t)$ will affect the threshold point by modifying the expected number of clicks occurring per second in $\phi(t)$ (such a click is likely to be present if $I_{SF} \cos \theta_1(t) - I_{CF} \sin \theta_1(t)$ passes through zero when $Ae^{\alpha(t)} + I_{SF} \sin \theta_1(t) + I_{CF} \cos \theta_1(t)$ is negative, and since these conditions can arise when a click would not be experienced at the output of a conventional f.m. detector the f.m.f.b. can be responsible for some extra clicks). It has also been shown that, at least for Gaussian modulation, the click rate depends on three parameters:

the carrier-to-noise ratio
the noise parameter $-r_N''(0)$, defined in eqn. 5.17
the r.m.s. frequency deviation.

These three have their counterparts in eqn. 9.17 (the deviation index will be taken as β_F, for example) so an expression for the click rate can be readily obtained.

The amplitude modulation $e^{\alpha(t)}$ is seen to be a factor multiplying the carrier amplitude A, and, as the carrier power is proportional to A^2, this factor, which, in general, is slowly varying, can be viewed as causing the power of the useful signal to fluctuate. The quantity $A^2 \langle e^{2\alpha(t)} \rangle$ is the mean square value of the envelope of the filtered carrier and is given by an integral such as eqn. 4.31. Allowable filter bandwidths cause this fluctuation to be small, corresponding, typically, to a change in the input signal level of a fraction of a decibel.

These observations, together with the fact (see eqn. 5.18 and Table 5.1) that an accurate analysis of the conventional f.m. receiver can be realised by assuming the click noise to be an incoherent addition to the above-threshold interference, leads to the following simplified expression for $\phi(t)$

$$\phi(t) = \theta_1(t) + I_{SF} + N_c(t) \tag{9.18}$$

where $N_c(t)$ is a click noise component. Recalling that

$$\theta_1(t) = \{\mu(t) - k_v v(t) + \beta(t)\}$$

one more step is required and this is the recognition that $\beta(t)$, the phase error, will contain a contribution that is coherent with $\mu(t) - k_v v(t)$. It is therefore preferable to write $\theta_1(t)$ as follows

$$\theta_1(t) = B(j\omega)|\{\mu(t) - k_v v(t)\} + \gamma(t)$$

where $B(j\omega)$ is a coherence factor [the simplest viewpoint takes $B(j\omega)$ to be $H(j\omega)$, as shown in Section 4.5] and $\gamma(t)$ refers entirely to distortion of the baseband signal $\mu(t) - k_v v(t)$. Then, using eqn. 9.8

$$\frac{1}{k_f} v(t) = L(j\omega) . B(j\omega) \bigg| \{\mu(t) - k_v v(t)\} \qquad (9.19)$$

$$+ L(j\omega) \bigg| \bigg| \left\{ \frac{I_{SF}}{A} + N_c(t) + \gamma(t) \right\}$$

from which the following expression for $v(t)$ is obtained

$$v(t) = \frac{k_f L(j\omega) B(j\omega)}{[1 + (F-1)L(j\omega)B(j\omega)]} \bigg| \mu(t)$$

$$+ \frac{k_f L(j\omega)}{[1 + (F-1)L(j\omega)B(j\omega)]} \bigg| \bigg| \left\{ \frac{I_{SF}}{A} + N_c(t) + \gamma(t)] \right\}$$

$$(9.20)$$

where $F = 1 + k_f k_v$ is the feedback factor. Also

$$\{\mu(t) - k_v v(t)\} = \frac{1}{[1 + (F-1)L(j\omega)B(j\omega)]} \bigg| \mu(t)$$

$$- \frac{(F-1)L(j\omega)}{[1 + (F-1)L(j\omega)B(j\omega)]} \bigg| \bigg| \left\{ \frac{I_{SF}}{A} + N_c(t) + \gamma(t) \right\} (9.21)$$

The f.m. signal detected by the limiter-discriminator combination is $d\phi(t)/dt = \dot\phi(t)$ and on taking the demodulator output, $v_0(t)$, from the lowpass filter

$$v_0(t) = \frac{1}{k_v} \frac{(F-1)L(j\omega)B(j\omega)}{[1 + (F-1)L(j\omega)B(j\omega)]} \bigg| M(t)$$

$$+ \frac{1}{k_v} \frac{(F-1)L(j\omega)}{[1 + (F-1)L(j\omega)B(j\omega)]} \bigg| \bigg| \left\{ \frac{\dot I_{SF}}{A} + \dot N_c(t) + \dot\gamma(t) \right\}$$

$$(9.22)$$

or

$$v_0(t) = \frac{1}{k_v} Z(j\omega) \bigg| \bigg| \left\{ [B(j\omega)|M(t)] + \frac{\dot I_{SF}}{A} + \dot N_c(t) + \dot\gamma(t) \right\}$$

$$(9.23)$$

each of the demodulators to be considered has an output that can be expressed in this way, and $Z(j\omega)$ which is often called the loop transfer characteristic, is given by

$$\frac{(F-1)L(j\omega)}{1+(F-1)L(j\omega)B(j\omega)}$$

Clearly, $Z(j\omega)$ plays no part in determining the output S/D ratio because it affects equally the frequency components of the useful signal (the first term in the curly bracket of eqn. 9.23) and the interference (the remaining terms in the curly bracket). $Z(j\omega)$ can be identified from a linearised analysis of the noise-free loop except that $B(j\omega)$ will then be replaced by $H(j\omega)$ (see eqn. 4.29 which gives $|B(j\omega)|^2$).

However, $Z(j\omega)$ plays a prominent role in determining β_F and ψ_{mix} which, it will be recalled, refer to the f.m. index and mean square phase deviation of the carrier presented to the i.f. bandpass filter.

9.6 Values of β_F and ψ_{mix}

Using eqns. 9.13 and 9.21

$$\beta_F^2 = \frac{1}{p_m^2} \int \left| \frac{Z(j\omega)}{(F-1)L(j\omega)} \right|^2 \frac{\omega_\Delta^2}{(p_m - p_0)} \, d\omega + \frac{1}{p_m^2} \int |Z(j\omega)|^2 \, W_I(\omega) d\omega$$

$$(9.24)$$

Here $W_I(\omega)$ is the spectral density of the interference term $\dot{i}_{SF}/A + \dot{N}_c(t) + \dot{\gamma}(t)$ and the integration ranges extend from the lowest to the highest frequencies of significance in the integrands.*

Taking the three terms in order, the spectral density of $\dot{i}_{SF}/A$ is given (compare with eqn. 5.22) by $(\omega^2/2\omega_B\rho)\,|H(j\omega)|^2$ and extends over $0 \leqslant \omega \leqslant \omega_B$. $\dot{N}_c(t)$ has a flat spectral distribution given by $4\pi\nu$ where ν is calculated by adapting eqn. 5.13. The contribution made by $\dot{\gamma}(t)$ can be judged from Figs. 7.12, 7.13, and is discussed more fully below.

Strictly, $\dot{N}_c(t)$ and $\dot{\gamma}(t)$ both depend on β_F and so some iterative procedure might be supposed necessary to cope with β_F appearing on both sides of eqn. 9.24. However, if the feedback factor F is momentarily assumed so large that $Z(j\omega) \approx 1/B(j\omega)$, it is seen that

$$\beta_F \approx \frac{1}{F}\left(\frac{\omega_\Delta}{p_m}\right) \tag{9.25}$$

This approximation ignores a noise contribution to β_F but it shows that the feedback round the loop acts to reduce the f.m. index of the input,

*Negative frequencies are not used here

and this same property causes any intermodulation distortion to be affected similarly. So $\dot{\gamma}(t)$ may be assessed, approximately, by regarding it as being the frequency distortion introduced by a single-pole bandpass filter on a carrier frequency modulated with flat noise producing an f.m. index of β_F. While this argument is somewhat crude (as eqn. 9.21 shows, the spectral density of $\dot{\mu}(t) - k_v \dot{v}(t)$ is not constant) an examination of specific cases (assisted by Figs. 7.12 and 7.13) produces the conclusion that the intermodulation distortion $\dot{\gamma}(t)$ plays a very minor part in optimising performance, owing to the distortion reducing property of the loop. Consequently, $\dot{\gamma}(t)$ will be dropped, and as a further simplification, the f.m. index will be taken to be $(1/F)(\omega_\Delta/p_m)$ in calculating ν. (Fortunately the f.m. index does not appear in the exponential which is the important term of eqn. 5.13.) Then

$$\beta_F = \left\{ \int \left| \frac{Z(j\omega)}{(F-1)L(j\omega)} \right|^2 \left(\frac{\omega_\Delta}{p_m} \right)^2 \frac{d\omega}{(p_m - p_0)} \right.$$
$$\left. + \int |Z(j\omega)|^2 \left\{ \frac{|H(j\omega)|^2}{2\omega_B \rho} \left(\frac{\omega}{p_m} \right)^2 + 4\pi\nu \right\} d\omega \right\}^{1/2} \quad (9.26)$$

where
$$\nu = \frac{(p_m/2\pi)}{\sqrt{\pi}} \left\{ \frac{2}{F^2} \left(\frac{\omega_\Delta}{p_m} \right)^2 + \frac{1}{\omega_B p_m^2} \frac{1}{\rho} \int \omega^2 |H(j\omega)|^2 d\omega \right\}^{1/2}$$

$$\exp - \left[\frac{\rho}{\frac{1}{\omega_B} \int |H(j\omega)|^2 d\omega} \right]$$

A similar exercise produces an expression for ψ_{mix} (eqn. 14 of Reference 12) and Figs. 9.5 and 9.6 show the resulting values plotted against the feedback factor expressed in decibels. The case shown refers to $\rho = 5 \, \mathrm{dB}$, and a 240 channel f.m. f.d.m. signal with an r.m.s. test-tone deviation of 1 Mhz ($\omega_\Delta/p_m = 2 \cdot 62$). No pre-emphasis is applied in Fig. 9.5, but the CCIR pre-emphasis law is present in Fig. 9.6.

Curves such as these may be drawn for a range of values of ρ to investigate how the minima that occur in both β_F and ψ_{mix} vary with F (the shallow minima in ψ_{mix} occur beyond the abscissae scales).

The value of α does not critically affect these curves, and taking $\rho = 5 \, \mathrm{dB}$ as representative of the below-threshold region, it is seen that with 13 dB of feedback the f.m. index of $2 \cdot 62$ is reduced to about unity. Thus, F is large, so lending support to eqn. 9.25.

Pre-emphasis has little effect on the β_F curves suggesting that there is little difference between the optimum i.f. bandwidths for pre-emphasised and non-pre-emphasised cases: ψ_{mix} is significantly reduced by pre-emphasis, however, thus paralleling the situation with the conventional receiver when the CCIR pre-emphasis law is enforced in that the r.m.s. frequency deviation ω_Δ is left unchanged but $\psi_\mu(0)$ is made much smaller.

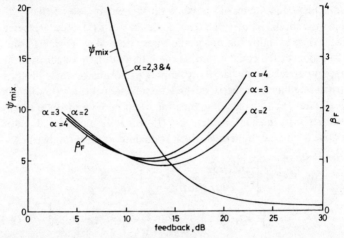

Fig. 9.5 Variation of ψ_{mix} and β_F with feedback
240 Channel System, 1 MHz r.m.s. test-tone deviation. Baseband range 60 kHz–1052 kHz
$\rho = 5$ dB
3 dB bandwidth of i.f. filter = 2.1α MHz
No pre-emphasis, single-pole i.f. and baseband filters

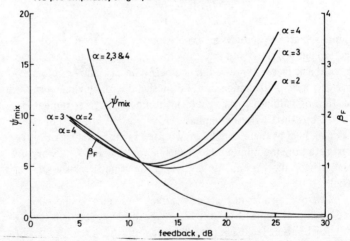

Fig. 9.6 Variation of ψ_{mix} and β_F with feedback, pre-emphasis applied to the baseband

240 Channel system, 1 MHz r.m.s. test-tone deviation

Baseband range 60 KHz–1052 KHz. $\rho = 5$ dB, 3 dB bandwidth of i.f. filter = 2.1α MHz

9.7 Baseband threshold curves for the f.m.f.b.

Eqn. 9.23 will yield an expression for the output D/S ratio (already the spectral densities of I_{SF}/A and $\dot{N}_c(t)$ are available from their use in eqn. 9.26), and attention is now directed at $B(j\omega) |M(t)$ which represents the undistorted output.

Unless account of $B(j\omega)$ is taken, there is no limit to the amount of threshold extension available through narrowing the loop filter except that, eventually, the noise will contribute $[1 - e^{-\rho_F}]^2$ as a coherence factor (the suffix F is added to ρ to indicate that the noise is measured in a bandwidth reduced by the loop filtering), and the distortion term $\dot{\gamma}(t)$ will become large.

The spectral density of $B(j\omega) |M(t)$. is given, effectively, by $\omega_\Delta^2/(p_m - p_0)$ times eqn. 4.29, and so we wish to estimate when the curly bracket of eqn. 4.29, begins to depart from unity, for it can be supposed that $|H(j\omega)|^2$ will be close to unity for all baseband frequencies. If we agree to ignore variations with baseband frequency, then eqn. 4.27 offers the best means of achieving our goal since it involves the power spectrum of the filtered wave and can be thrown into a fairly simple form for $\omega = 0$. We shall write, using eqn. 4.27

$$|B(0)|^2 = \lambda^2 = \left| \int_{-\infty}^{+\infty} \left\{ \frac{G(q)}{\frac{1}{2}A^2} \right\} \frac{1}{1 + \left(\dfrac{q}{\alpha p_m}\right)^2} \, dq \right|^2 \quad (9.27)$$

and in the present context $G(q)$ can be given the Gaussian form of eqn. 7.26 with ω_Δ/p_m replaced by β_F, since the integral is not too dependent on the shape of $G(q)$. Then λ, the coherence factor, is given by

$$\lambda = \frac{\alpha}{\beta_F} \sqrt{\frac{\pi}{2}} \left\{ 1 - \mathrm{erf}\left(\frac{\alpha}{\beta_F \sqrt{2}}\right) \right\} e^{\frac{1}{2} (\alpha/\beta_F)^2} \quad (9.28)$$

It is seen that λ approaches unity for large α/β_F, i.e. when little bandwidth restriction is applied to the reduced-deviation wave. For α/β_F small, $\lambda \to 0$. (A very similar result for λ was used in Reference 12).

This is the behaviour anticipated, although several approximate steps have been made along the way because of the severe difficulties that a fully rigorous solution encounters. Nevertheless, eqn. 9.28 offers a useful guide, and some typical values are shown in Table 9.1.

Bearing in mind that the threshold is said to occur at a departure of 1 dB from the linear law of eqn. 9.1, it is clear from Table 9.1 that, even if the receiver always responded to noise in a linear fashion, α/β_F could not be made as small as two.

Table 9.1 Coherence factor for f.m.f.b.

α/β_F	λ	λ dB
0·5	0·44	−7·1
1·0	0·65	−3·7
2·0	0·85	−1·4
3·0	0·92	−0·75
4·0	0·94	−0·56

An examination of the situation when this fanciful view of the receiver operation is not taken can be made by forming an expression for the output D/S ratio using eqn. 9.23 and balancing the effect of λ against the click noise contribution. This exercise reveals that $\alpha/\beta_F = 3$ represents a near-optimum condition.

The D/S ratio at any baseband frequency p is then well approximated by

$$\frac{D}{S} = \frac{2}{\sqrt{\pi}} \left(\frac{p_m - p_0}{p_m} \right) \left(\frac{p_m}{\omega_\Delta} \right)^2 \frac{1}{|H(jp)|^2}$$
$$\left\{ \frac{2}{F^2} \left(\frac{\omega_\Delta}{p_m} \right)^2 + \frac{1}{\omega_B p_m^2} \cdot \frac{1}{\rho} \int \omega^2 \, |H(j\omega)|^2 \, d\omega \right\}^{1/2}$$
$$\exp - \left[\frac{\rho}{\frac{1}{\omega_B} \int |H(j\omega)|^2 \, d\omega} \right] + \frac{(p_m - p_0)}{2\omega_B} \left(\frac{p}{p_m} \right)^2 \left(\frac{p_m}{\omega_\Delta} \right)^2 \cdot \frac{1}{\rho}$$

$$(9.29)$$

For completeness an intermodulation distortion term deriving from $\dot{\gamma}(t)$ can be added to eqn. 9.29. This has effect in the distortion-limited region[1] well above the threshold of the conventional receiver where (as eqn. 9.23 shows if $\rho \to \infty$) only $\dot{\gamma}(t)$ causes distortion in the output. This additional term* can be written[12] as

$$\frac{F^2}{2} \left(\frac{\beta_F}{\omega_\Delta/p_m} \right)^4 \left(\frac{D}{S} \right)_{p_m} \qquad \text{in top channel}$$

and

$$\frac{2}{F^2} \left(\frac{D}{S} \right)_{p_0} \qquad \text{in bottom channel}$$

When the loop filter is of the single pole variety, $(D/S)_{p_m}$, for example, can be read from Figures 7.12–7.14 with ω_Δ/p_m replaced by β_F. If $\beta_F \approx 1/F \, [\omega_\Delta/p_m]$ is accepted, then, when third-order distortion predominates, $(D/S)_{p_m}$ is proportional to F^{-4}, and so, in top channel, the added distortion term varies, power-wise, as F^{-6}. This was

*The lower suffix on D/S indicates the channel frequency

pointed out in Reference 13, which is one of the papers to appear[13, 14] dealing with the intermodulation performance of the f.m.f.b., i.e. the input is noise-free. The work of Chapter 7 suggests, however, that β_F will have to be 0·5 or less in order for the F^{-6} law to apply.

The theory leading to eqn. 9.29 has been used to obtain Fig. 9.7 where a comparison is made with a curve drawn through measured points. A single-pole filter has been assumed, and with Fig. 5.2 providing the datum for the conventional receiver, a threshold extension of 4·6 dB is revealed. In bottom channel, the theory predicts an extension of 4·9 dB.

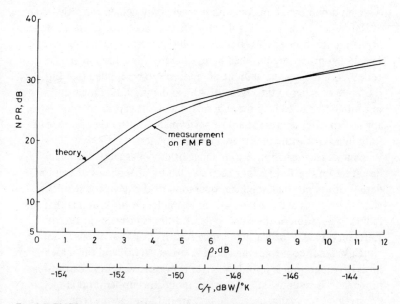

Fig. 9.7 FMFB comparison of theory with measurements

       Top channel of a 240 channel system. No pre-emphasis.
       I.F. filter bandwidth = 6·3 MHz
       13 dB feedback
       Threshold of a conventional demodulator occurs at $\rho = 8·7$ dB

$$C/T, \text{dbW}/^{\circ}K = \rho\ (\text{dB}) + \log_{10}\left(k\frac{2\omega_B}{2\pi}\right)$$

       where k is Boltzmann's constant ($1·38 \times 10^{-23}\ J^0\,K^{-1}$)
       and in this case $2\omega_B/2\pi =$ input noise bandwidth = 24 MHz

9.8 Discussion

There is a large amount of literature on the f.m.f.b., and it contains contributions that deal with design aspects not treated here (VCO linearity and discriminator distortion, for example) and eqn. 9.29 has been written in terms of a general loop filter characteristic $H(j\omega)$ so that forms other than the single-pole network, or a loop delay τ [multiply $H(j\omega)$ by $e^{-j\omega\tau}$], can be investigated. It is common practice to retain a single-pole form for the loop filter because of stability considerations, but the lowpass filter $L(j\omega)$ need not be as simple as has been assumed here. A unique design specification for this filter does not exist (p. 219 of Reference 1) and the position of the pole(s) can be varied or it can be arranged for the pole of the i.f. filter to be cancelled when $L(j\omega)$ and $H(j\omega)$ are multiplied together.

The effect of such design modifications on the coherence factor λ is largely unknown, however, and it is generally agreed (pp. 204–205 of Reference 1) that it is highly important to account for the presence of the modulation when searching for the preferred parameter values. The design procedure outlined here, whereby the minimum β_F of eqn. 9.26 indicates the amount of feedback to be applied (see Fig. 9.5), the value of α lies in the region of $3\beta_F$, and eqn. 9.29 allows the output D/S ratio to be plotted against the input carrier-to-noise ratio, appears to offer an assessment of performance in the f.m. f.d.m. case fully in accord with current engineering opinion.

As well as considering a wide range of design aspects, the large literature on the f.m.f.b. has been swelled by differences of opinion over details of the internal nonlinear operation of the device. Use of the click theory has been challenged for example, on the grounds that the radius of gyration of the single pole i.f. filter is infinite (p. 196 of Reference 1). The offending term is $\int \omega^2 |H(j\omega)|^2 d\omega$ of eqn. 9.29 which will not converge when eqn. 9.7 gives $H(j\omega)$ and the upper limit of integration is infinitely large. However, as a finite carrier-to-noise ratio is assumed at the f.m.f.b. input, this upper limit is constrained to a value usually judged from Carson's rule (eqn. 4.13) [$N(\omega)$ of eqn. 5.17 is taken to be zero for $|\omega| > \omega_B$] and so the integral will converge. Within the accuracy of Carson's rule, therefore, the theory can proceed, and it is the exponential term of eqn. 9.29 (containing an integral that does not have the troublesome behaviour) that is of greatest importance.

Most of the exchanges of opinion on points of the theory appeared in the mid-1960s, and, in a few cases, authors have included some discussion of the work of others.[12,15]

The case of $\omega_\Delta/p_m = 2{\cdot}62$ treated here is typical. With larger values of the f.m. index, the minimum in β_F occurs at larger values of the feedback factor F but an i.f. bandwidth factor α near to three times β_F (minimum) is still required, and a threshold extension of about 4 dB in top channel, and 5 dB in bottom channel, is a realistic summary. Working in terms of the ratio ω_Δ/p_m disguises the absolute values of ω_Δ and p_m and loop stability problems can be severe in practice if the loop phase shift has to be carefully controlled up to several tens of Megahertz, as may be the case in order to realize the threshold extensions predicted for very large capacity f.m. f.d.m. systems.

It is seen that the combined effect of compressing the deviation and applying judicious filtering can provide a worthwhile improvement over simply narrowing the input bandwidth (Section 9.2). The non-linearities of the problem are difficult to cope with and while no fundamental limit to the attainable extension has been sought from an information theoretic viewpoint, a limit has been shown to exist in terms of the coherence factor. This effect emerges in some form for all the demodulator types to be considered.

9.9 Dynamic tracking filter

The d.t.f. operates from the observation that, although the instantaneous frequency of a carrier that is frequency modulated by an information-bearing signal may swing across a wide frequency band, nevertheless, if the variations in frequency can be followed by a tuned circuit, satisfactory demodulation may be achieved, with a consequent saving in bandwidth.

When the carrier to be demodulated is accompanied by noise, the variable tuning properties of the device mean that only a narrow band of noise is received at any instant and the threshold of an f.m. receiver can consequently be extended.

Early designs such as the one developed by C.H. Gibbs and R. Hamer of the British Post Office for the first Telstar receiver at Goonhilly, used a normal varactor diode linearised by a diode network, but the practical difficulties of realising a suitable circuit for the dynamic filtering operation have become eased by the development in Japan of the hyper-abrupt-junction variable capacitor diode.[16] Both series damped and parallel forms of the circuit are now readily available. The series form is slightly more attractive than the parallel form from an engineering viewpoint as it offers simpler control of bandwidth variation and so attention will be confined to the series damped form shown in Fig. 9.2.

An appreciation of the facility provided by the hyper-abrupt-junction variable capacitor diode in realising a convenient circuit for the d.t.f. may be formed with reference to a simple LC filter, the familiar formula for the resonant frequency of which is

$$\omega_I = \frac{1}{\sqrt{LC}} \tag{9.30}$$

Now if the capacitor C were to become time varying and were to vary inversely as the square of a voltage V, the resonant frequency would become directly proportional to V.

The variable capacitor diode has an equivalent circuit[16] that consists of a variable capacitor and a resistance in series, and, over a satisfactory portion of the diode characteristic, the following relationship holds between the instantaneous charge q on the capacitor, and v, the voltage across it

$$C = \frac{dq}{dv} = \frac{K}{(v + V_0)^2} \tag{9.31}$$

where K and V_0 are constants. The diode thus possesses the characteristic required for the resonant frequency of an LC filter circuit that incorporates the device to be made to follow the applied voltage v. For the demodulation of an f.m. signal, v is arranged to be proportional to the instantaneous frequency of the modulated wave, and in the circuits shown in Fig. 9.2 this is achieved by the control voltage $c(t)$, which is derived from the demodulated baseband signal.

The time-varying nature of the capacitance associated with the diode complicates the working when the circuit equations are set up, making it difficult to appreciate which of the various parameters involved are the important ones. So a simplified view of the way the circuit operates is useful.

9.10 Simplified view

The centre frequency of the dynamic filter at any instant will be written

$$\frac{d}{dt} [\omega_I t + c(t)]$$

The frequency-sensitive characteristic of the device [which will be designated $A(j\omega)$] is to be thought of as extending out to either side of this frequency and the filter responds as to a carrier of frequency $\omega_I + \dot{c}(t)$ which is phase modulated by $[\mu(t) - c(t)]$.

The phase modulation $[\mu(t) - c(t)]$ is referred to as the tracking phase error, and if (in an r.m.s. sense, say) this represents a small deviation, then the bandwidth of $A(j\omega)$ can be correspondingly small. With $[\mu(t) - c(t)]$ we associate an f.m. index α_F defined (compare eqn. 9.13 in the case of the f.m.f.b.) as follows:

$$\alpha_F = \frac{1}{p_m} \sqrt{\langle [\dot{\mu}(t) - \dot{c}(t)]^2 \rangle} \qquad (9.32)$$

and an r.m.s. phase modulation index ϕ_d where

$$\phi_d^2 = \langle [\mu(t) - c(t)]^2 \rangle \qquad (9.33)$$

Assuming that ϕ_d, the r.m.s. tracking error, is small (this is substantiated later) the instantaneous frequency at the d.t.f. output may be written (see eqn. 4.29), ignoring distortion terms, as

$$\frac{d}{dt} [\omega_I t + c(t) + \{A(j\omega) | [\mu(t) - c(t)]\}] = \frac{d}{dt} [\omega_I t + \phi(t)]$$

where

$$\phi(t) = c(t) + \{A(j\omega) | [\mu(t) - c(t)]\} \qquad (9.34)$$

From Fig. 9.2 is seen that

$$c(t) = L(j\omega) | \phi(t)$$

So

$$\phi(t) = \left[\frac{A(j\omega)}{1 - L(j\omega) + A(j\omega)L(j\omega)} \right] | \mu(t) \qquad (9.35)$$

and

$$\mu(t) - c(t) = \left[\frac{1 - L(j\omega)}{1 - L(j\omega) + A(j\omega)L(j\omega)} \right] | \mu(t) \qquad (9.36)$$

The d.t.f. output is $\dot{\phi}(t)$, and when the analysis is carried through in detail, not neglecting noise and the nonlinearities, it can be shown[17] that

$$v_0(t) = \dot{\phi}(t) = \left[\frac{1}{1 - L(j\omega) + A(j\omega)L(j\omega)} \right] \Big|$$
$$\left\{ [A(j\omega) | M(t)] + \frac{I_1}{A} + \dot{N}_c(t) + \dot{\gamma}(t) \right\} \qquad (9.37)$$

and

$$\mu(t) - c(t) = \left[\frac{1 - L(j\omega)}{1 - L(j\omega) + A(j\omega)L(j\omega)} \right] \Big| \mu(t)$$
$$+ \left[\frac{L(j\omega)}{1 - L(j\omega) + A(j\omega)L(j\omega)} \right] \Big| \left(\frac{I_1}{A} + N_c(t) + \gamma(t) \right) \qquad (9.38)$$

Thus, the loop transfer function for the d.t.f. is given by

$$Z(j\omega) = \frac{1}{1 - L(j\omega) + A(j\omega)L(j\omega)} \qquad (9.39)$$

The curly bracket of eqn. 9.37 has been written so as to resemble the corresponding bracket in eqn. 9.23 for the f.m.f.b., and eqn. 9.38 may be compared to eqn. 9.21. Evidently there are close parallels to be drawn with the procedure followed in Section 9.6 to assess the f.m.f.b. performance.

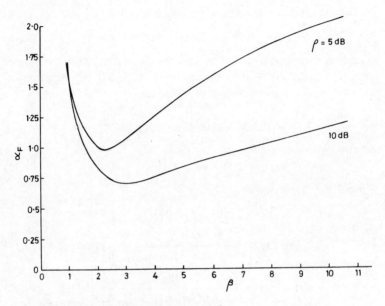

Fig. 9.8 Variation of DTF parameter α_F with β

240 channel system, r.m.s. test-tone deviation = 1·0 MHz
Baseband range 60 KHz–1052 KHz
3 dB bandwidth of lowpass filter = 1·052β MHz

9.11 Values of α_F and ϕ_d

The more detailed analysis of Reference 17, referred to earlier, shows that I_1/A of eqn. 9.38 has the same interpretation as I_{SF}/A of eqn. 9.21, namely it is a filtered version of I_s/A, the normalised quadrature component of the input noise, the filter in question being a single-pole network. $\dot{N}_c(t)$ is the corresponding click noise and $\dot{\gamma}(t)$ in eqn. 9.37 refers to distortion of the baseband signal $[\mu(t) - c(t)]$. To implement the equations, $L(j\omega)$ and $A(j\omega)$ have to be specified. For the former we take

$$L(j\omega) = \frac{T}{1 + j(\omega/\beta p_m)} \qquad (9.40)$$

where β is a bandwidth factor that plays a role in the theory closely similar to that of F in the f.m.f.b. analysis.

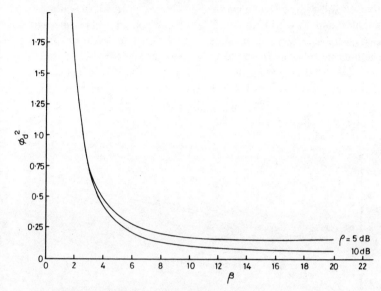

Fig. 9.9 Variation of DTF parameter ϕ_d^2 with β

        240 channel system, r.m.s. test-tone deviation = 1 MHz
        Baseband range 60 KHz–1052 KHz
        3 dB bandwidth of lowpass filter = 1.052β MHz

For $A(j\omega)$, a single-pole form (as suggested by Fig. 9.2) is adopted:

$$A(j\omega) = \frac{1}{1 + j\left(\dfrac{\omega}{\Delta_\omega}\right)} \qquad (9.41)$$

where $2\Delta\omega$ is called the 3 dB static bandwidth of the d.t.f. With $\omega_\Delta/p_m = 2.62$, Fig. 9.8 shows α_F plotted against β, and Fig. 9.9 shows ϕ_d^2 plotted against β, at two values of the input carrier-to-noise ratio. These curves have been drawn from expressions that correspond to eqn. 9.26, and it is seen that the minimum in α_F when $\rho = 5$ dB agrees very closely with the minimum of β_F shown on Fig. 9.5.

In contrast to the large values adopted by ψ_{mix} in f.m.f.b. working, it is seen that ϕ_d^2 will be close to 1 rad^2 when β lies near the minimum in α_F. A good approximation for ϕ_d^2 (Reference 17) is

$$\phi_d^2 = \left(\frac{\omega_\Delta}{p_m}\right)^2 \frac{1}{\beta}\tan^{-1}\left(\frac{1}{\beta}\right) + \left(\frac{p_m}{2\omega_B}\right)\frac{\beta}{\rho}\tan^{-1}\left(\frac{\omega_B}{p_m\beta}\right) \qquad (9.42)$$

The frequency deviation parameter α_F has the greatest influence on the d.t.f. design (just as β_F did in the case of the f.m.f.b.) and the fact that ϕ_d^2 and ψ_{mix} differ so markedly would have significance if a very detailed analysis of the intermodulation components $\dot{\gamma}(t)$ in the two cases were necessary. Fortunately, with the d.t.f., as with the f.m.f.b., the intermodulation does not play a significant part in deciding the available threshold extension. The coherence factor has equal significance, however, and because the minima in α_F and β_F are so comparable we conclude that $(\Delta_\omega/p_m)/\alpha_F \approx 3$ will again be a near optimum requirement.

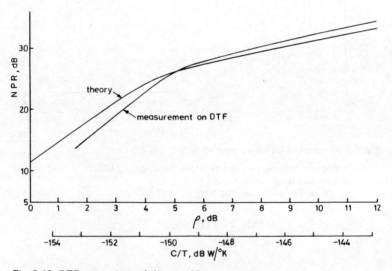

Fig. 9.10 DTF comparison of theory with measurements

Top channel of a 240 channel system
No pre-emphasis
3 dB static bandwidth = 6·3 MHz
3 dB bandwidth of lowpass filter = 3·15 MHz
Threshold of conventional demodulator occurs at $\rho = 8·7$ dB

$$C/T, \text{dBW}/^\circ\text{K} = \rho\,(\text{dB}) + 10\log_{10}\; k\,\frac{2\omega_B}{2\pi}$$

where k is Boltzmann's constant $(1·38 \times 10^{-23}\,\text{J}^\circ\text{K}^{-1})$ and in the present case $2\omega_B/2\pi$ = input noise bandwidth = 24 MHz

9.12 Comparison of theory and measurement

The d.t.f. is a difficult device to analyse in detail and the description given here strikes a compromise between the fierce complication represented by the nonlinearities and a quasi-static viewpoint. For a tractable analysis it seems necessary to regard the intermediate frequency ω_I as being much larger than any other frequencies involved, e.g. the modulation bandwidth and the instantaneous filter bandwidth, but the error incurred is difficult to assess. The ultimate justification for any simplifying steps that are taken lies in a comparison with measurement, and Fig. 9.10 shows such a comparison. In top channel, the theory predicted a threshold extension of 4·6 dB, and a measured value of 4·0 dB was achieved: both theory and measurements used $\beta = 3$ and $\Delta_\omega = 3p_m$. Further information on the d.t.f., which is seen to have a threshold extension capability comparable to that of the f.m.f.b., may be found in Reference 18.

9.13 Phase lock loop

The phase lock loop (p.l.l.) is a device which has many uses in communications engineering, ranging over synchronisation, acquisition, frequency synthesis, and the demodulation of angle modulated carriers. Both analogue and digital forms of the loop are currently used. In its analogue realisation (a.p.l.l.) a phase detector compares the phase of a received signal with that of a voltage-controlled oscillator (VCO) and the circuit corrects, or attempts to correct, for the difference. By feeding back to the VCO a portion of the phase detector output (suitably filtered), the instantaneous frequency of the VCO can be made to follow frequency changes in the input wave and it is this feature that leads to threshold extension, which is limited by the appearance of a click-like disturbance much as with the devices considered earlier. A typical circuit configuration is shown in Fig. 9.3.

In the digital form of the loop (the d.p.l.l., the d can also stand for discrete) the phase detector is replaced by a sampler and the VCO becomes a digital clock running at the nominal carrier frequency of the input. (See Fig. 9.4.) The phase of the input is tracked by taking samples at or near to the zero crossings of the received carrier wave, and in both the analogue and digital forms a locked condition is aimed at which means that a coherent or partially coherent detection facility is available. The term 'partially coherent' is used because, in practice, noise prevents a perfect phase match from being achieved at all times, and a phase error $\phi(t)$ is present.

In digital data systems which require coherent detection, a phase lock loop enables the reference signal to be derived either directly from the received carrier or by tracking an auxiliary carrier. For example, a low phase modulation index can be used to ensure that a large residual carrier component is present for this purpose.

A vast literature exists describing and analysing the performance of the loop and these divide into two main areas, transient analyses which refer to the initial behaviour when the loop is started up from rest, and steady-state analyses.

Typically, transient investigations concern themselves with the conditions under which locking can occur (the pull-in range and the locking range) and they also consider how long is likely to elapse before a lock is obtained (the expected time to lock or pull-in time). Usually noise is assumed not to be present and the differential equation that governs the loop operation is solved (often in an approximate way) to identify the conditions under which the desired mode of operation will ensue. For the digital device, a difference equation arises (rather than a differential equation) owing to the sampling taking place at discrete time instants.[20]

The transient behaviour will not be described further as our current interest is threshold extension. The steady-state performance of an a.p.l.l. when used to demodulate an f.m. f.d.m. carrier plus noise will be discussed first and this serves well to describe the loop operation.

9.14 P.L.L. as an f.m. demodulator

With reference to Figure 9.3, the input consisting of a frequency modulated carrier plus narrow-band Gaussian noise is written

$$A \cos [\omega_0 t + \mu(t)] + I_c \cos \omega_0 t - I_s \sin \omega_0 t \qquad (9.43)$$

If $S(t)$ is the output from the lowpass filter, the VCO output is

$$V \sin [\omega_0 t + k_v v(t)] \qquad (9.44)$$

where $dv(t)/dt = S(t)$, and k_v is a constant. Retaining only the low-frequency components out of the mixer, and employing the notation used in Section 9.4 to represent the operation of filtering, the output from the lowpass filter is given by

$$L(j\omega) \left| \left[\frac{VA}{2} \sin [k_v v(t) - \mu(t)] + \frac{V}{2} \{ I_c \sin [k_v v(t)] - I_s \cos [k_v v(t)] \} \right] \right.$$

but, on closing the loop, this expression must equal $S(t)$. Then, defining $\phi(t) = k_v v(t) - \mu(t)$ to be the phase error, the loop equation can be written

$$k_v v(t) = KL(j\omega) \left| \left\{ \sin \phi(t) + \frac{I_c}{A} \sin [\phi(t) + \mu(t)] \right. \right.$$

$$\left. \left. - \frac{I_s}{A} \cos [\phi(t) + \mu(t)] \right\} \right. \quad (9.45)$$

where $K = (VAk_v)/2$ has the dimensions of a radian frequency and is termed the loop gain factor. In engineering the loop it is convenient to keep K constant and so, since K depends on A, it is usual to pre-cede the loop with some form of automatic gain control (AGC). A limiter might be supposed to serve the same purpose but there is evidence that this degrades the threshold extension capability of the device.[22, 23] The combination of I_c and I_s in the curly bracket of eqn. 9.45 is seen, once again, to be in the form discussed in Section 5.3 (see eqn. 5.19), and for the reasons given there, it will be replaced by $-I_s/A$ thus simplifying eqn. 9.45 to

$$k_v v(t) = -KL(j\omega) \left| \left\{ \sin \phi(t) - \frac{I_s}{A} \right\} \right. \quad (9.46)$$

When the phase error is small, a linearised analysis in which $\sin \phi(t)$ is replaced by $\phi(t)$ can be carried through and then eqn. 9.46 provides

$$k_v v(t) = \left[\frac{jKL(j\omega)\omega}{KL(j\omega) + j\omega} \right] \left(\mu(t) + \frac{I_s}{A} \right) \quad (9.47)$$

$$= \left[\frac{KL(j\omega)}{KL(j\omega) + j\omega} \right] \left(M(t) + \frac{\dot{I}_s}{A} \right) \quad (9.48)$$

The square bracket contains the loop transfer characteristic that affects equally the spectra of the wanted signal $M(t)$ and the normalised quadrature noise component. Thus, when the p.l.l. output is taken from the lowpass filter (so causing it to be proportional to the left-hand side of eqns. 9.47 or 9.48) a distortion-to-signal ratio exactly agreeing with that provided above threshold by a conventional f.m. receiver is obtained. Note that this follows from approximating $\sin \phi(t)$ by $\phi(t)$, no limiter or discriminator is present in the simple circuitry of the p.l.l., and apart from supposing that eqn. 9.45 represents a stable operation, it has not even been necessary to specify $L(j\omega)$, the transfer character-istic of the lowpass filter.

Clearly, this is a low noise analysis and ϕ and $\sin \phi$ will never be precisely equal; thus some small distortion component will always be present at the output. It is appropriate to regard $\phi(t)$ as a random variable that is reduced modulo 2π and so its probability density function is defined on the interval $-\pi$ to π. It will be shown later that with low noise this distribution is closely Gaussian (the width of the density function being much less than 2π) and when this is so a first step in accounting for the sinusoidal nonlinearity is to write eqn. 9.46 as

$$k_v v(t) = KL(j\omega) \left| \left[e^{-\psi_\phi(0)/2} \{\phi(t) + [\sin\phi(t) - \phi(t)]\} - \frac{I_s}{A} \right] \right.$$

(9.49)

In this formulation, $\psi_\phi(0)$ is the mean square value of $\phi(t)$ and $[\sin\phi(t) - \phi(t)]$ is uncorrelated with $\phi(t)$. Exp $-\frac{1}{2}\psi_\phi(0)$ is the coherence factor (voltagewise) for a sinusoidal nonlinearity (Section 2.5), and it may also be recognised as Booton's equivalent gain, which Develet exploited in his early paper on the p.l.l.[24] Using eqn. 9.47 and the fact that $k_v v(t) = \phi(t) + \mu(t)$, the simplest solution for $\phi(t)$ is

$$\phi(t) = \left[\frac{-j\omega}{KL(j\omega) + j\omega} \right] \mu(t) + \left[\frac{KL(j\omega)}{KL(j\omega) + j\omega} \right] \frac{I_s}{A}$$

(9.50)

When $\mu(t)$ corresponds to a flat f.m. baseband and the noise also has a flat spectral distribution [the two members of eqn. 9.50 are then Gaussian processes and so $\phi(t)$ is one also], eqn. 9.50 gives the following for the mean square value of $\phi(t)$

$$\psi_\phi(0) = \left(\frac{\omega_\Delta}{p_m} \right)^2 \int_0^1 \frac{1}{\left| \dfrac{K}{p_m} L(jx) + jx \right|^2} \, dx + \left(\frac{p_m}{2\omega_B} \right) \frac{1}{\rho}$$

$$\int_0^{\omega_B/p_m} \left| \frac{\dfrac{K}{p_m} L(jx)}{\dfrac{K}{p_m} L(jx) + jx} \right|^2 dx$$

(9.51)

Assuming a form for $L(jx)$ is known (x is frequency normalised to the highest baseband frequency) an evaluation of this expression gives an indication of the minimum value of $\psi_\phi(0)$ and so shows whether exp $-\frac{1}{2}\psi_\phi(0)$ differs significantly from unity. (This is a minimum in the sense that, if $\sin\phi$ and ϕ differ appreciably, then eqn. 9.50, which is obtained on the assumption that $\sin\phi = \phi$, will not hold, and $\psi_\phi(0)$ will be larger than eqn. 9.51 predicts.) Departure of exp $-\frac{1}{2}\psi_\phi(0)$ from the value unity means that the device will have a linear portion on its performance curve (D/S versus ρ) that is poorer by about $4\cdot3\,\psi_\phi(0)$ decibels (in all baseband channels) than the ideal detector. This result ignores the distortion that will also be present in the output deriving from the difference between $\sin\phi(t)$ and $\phi(t)$ and which will give rise to further degradation.

The second of the two integrals in eqn. 9.51 gives an important parameter called the loop noise bandwidth ω_L. The upper integration limit is usually large (3 or greater) and ω_L is defined by

$$\frac{\omega_L}{p_m} = \int_0^\infty \left| \frac{\dfrac{K}{p_m} L(jx)}{\dfrac{K}{p_m} L(jx) + jx} \right|^2 dx \qquad (9.52)$$

Thus, in absence of modulation ($\omega_\Delta = 0$), $1/\psi_\phi(0)$ is equal to the carrier-to-noise ratio at the p.l.l. input with the noise measured in the bandwidth ω_L. When the p.l.l. is used as an f.m. demodulator, the term in ω_Δ (or its equivalent when the modulation differs from f.d.m.) is present and $L(j\omega)$ could be chosen so that $\psi_\phi(0)$ is minimised. The resulting filter characteristic would depend on the modulation parameters as well as the carrier-to-noise ratio but, being derived from a linearisation of the loop (and thereby ignoring the nonlinear behaviour) there is no guarantee that it would be the optimum from a threshold extension viewpoint.

As will become apparent, the threshold of performance is largely due to a phenomenon known as cycle slipping and, in general, three topics have to be considered when the optimum p.l.l. design is sought. These are:

(*a*) attenuation of the wanted output (the size of the coherence factor or Booton's equivalent gain factor)
(*b*) control of the intermodulation and distortion produced by bandwidth restriction
(*c*) minimisation of the rate at which cycle slips occur.

However, as an exact analysis of the loop performance with finite input bandwidth, and even the simplest form of loop filter, i.e. $L(j\omega) \equiv 1$, has yet to be achieved, balancing the content of (*a*), (*b*) and (*c*) in the optimum way is not a problem that can be rigorously solved. It is generally agreed that, as in the cases of the f.m.f.b. and d.t.f., item (*b*) is of minor importance in comparison[25] with (*a*) or (*c*).

9.15 Filter types

Phase lock loops have come to be classified according to the complexity of the filter used in the loop. As is seen from eqn. 9.48, if no filter is used at all $[L(j\omega) \equiv 1]$, the transfer characteristic has the form

$K/(K + j\omega)$ and in this case the term first order is used to describe the loop. A second-order loop, similarly, is one in which the filter used gives rise to a quadratic form in ω in the denominator of the transfer function, and so on.

One advantage of the filter is that it allows the designer flexibility to choose its shape and parameters so that, together with the loop gain factor K, some performance objective is attained. Such an objective is the minimisation of the r.m.s. phase error when steps in phase or frequency are applied at the input and white noise is present too, but the loop is operated above its threshold. This design-aim was studied in Reference 26, and, in the case of a frequency step input, the proportional-plus-integral filter was identified as a structure that provides stability over a wide range of loop gain variations. The characteristic of this filter will be written

$$L(j\omega) = 1 + \frac{a}{j\omega} \qquad (9.53)$$

where a is a parameter to be determined. The filter is not realisable by means of passive components but can be closely approximated by an amplifier circuit.[27;29] This filter is widely used and will be seen to produce a second-order loop. The most general form of the transfer function that gives a second-order loop is

$$L(j\omega) = \frac{1 + j\omega\tau_2}{\sigma + j\omega\tau_1} \qquad (9.54)$$

and eqn. 9.53 is seen to correspond to $\tau_1 = \tau_2 = 1/a$, with $\sigma \to 0$. Considerations of stability usually preclude the use of third- and higher-order loops and they are seldom used.

Gardner (pp. 73–76 of Reference 29) gives a useful review of the criteria governing the choice of loop filter, and here attention is confined to the first-order loop and the second-order loop that has eqn. 9.53 for its filter. The respective loop noise bandwidths ω_L are then given by

$$\omega_L = \frac{\pi}{2}K$$

and

$$\omega_L = \frac{\pi}{2}(K + a) \qquad (9.55)$$

On inserting the proportional-plus-integral form for $L(j\omega)$ in eqn. 9.51 it becomes

$$\psi_\phi(0) = \left(\frac{\omega_\Delta}{p_m}\right)^2 \int_0^1 \frac{x^2}{x^4 + x^2\left[\left(\frac{K}{p_m}\right)^2 - 2\frac{Ka}{p_m^2}\right] + \left(\frac{Ka}{p_m^2}\right)^2} \, dx$$

$$+ \frac{p_m}{2\omega_B} \frac{1}{\rho} \int_0^{\omega_B/p_m} \frac{\left(\frac{K}{p_m}\right)^2 \left[x^2 + \left(\frac{a}{p_m}\right)^2\right]}{x^4 + x^2 \left[\left(\frac{K}{p_m}\right)^2 - 2\frac{Ka}{p_m^2}\right] + \left(\frac{Ka}{p_m^2}\right)^2} \, dx$$

$$\approx \frac{1}{3}\left(\frac{\omega_\Delta}{p_m}\right)^2 \left(\frac{p_m^2}{Ka}\right)^2 + \left(\frac{p_m}{2\omega_B}\right) \frac{1}{\rho} \frac{\pi}{2}\left[\frac{K}{p_m} + \frac{a}{p_m}\right] \tag{9.56}$$

Eqn. 9.56 is obtained after making two approximating steps. In the first (modulation) integral the denominator of the integrand is assumed to be flat (with value $(Ka/p_m^2)^2$) while the upper limit of the second (noise) integral has been taken to be ∞, as in eqn. 9.52. The symmetry regarding the dependence of the two terms in eqn. 9.56 on K and a shows that a minimisation is achieved by taking $K = a$, then

$$\psi_\phi(0) = \frac{1}{3}\left(\frac{\omega_\Delta}{p_m}\right)^2 \cdot \left(\frac{p_m}{a}\right)^4 + \left(\frac{p_m}{2\omega_B}\right) \frac{\pi}{\rho}\left(\frac{a}{p_m}\right) \tag{9.57}$$

with

$$\frac{a}{p_m} = \left\{\frac{4}{3\pi}\left(\frac{\omega_\Delta}{p_m}\right)^2 \cdot \frac{2\omega_B}{p_m} \rho\right\}^{1/5} = \frac{\omega_L}{\pi p_m} \tag{9.58}$$

Appearance of the fifth root of ρ shows that the values of a/p_m given by eqn. 9.58 remain fairly constant as ρ is varied. $K/p_m = a/p_m \approx 3$ is typical when the parameters of satellite applications are inserted in eqn. 9.58, and this conclusion can be used to check back on the validity of the approximations that led to eqn. 9.56. In the absence of a loop filter $[L(j\omega) \equiv 1]$ the mean square phase error is given by

$$\psi_\phi(0) = \left(\frac{\omega_\Delta}{p_m}\right)^2 \left(\frac{p_m}{K}\right) \tan^{-1}\left(\frac{p_m}{K}\right) + \left(\frac{p_m}{2\omega_B}\right) \frac{1}{\rho}\left(\frac{K}{p_m}\right) \tan^{-1}\left(\frac{\omega_B}{K}\right) \tag{9.59}$$

from which, on comparison with eqn. 9.57, it is apparent that the proportional-plus-integral filter significantly reduces the contribution made by the modulation term to the error.

It may be noticed that eqns. 9.59 and 9.42 have identical forms, with K/p_m and β playing interchangeable roles. The common objective of attempting to track the instantaneous frequency leads to close parallels in the operating equations of different threshold extending devices.

9.16 Performance when sin ϕ and ϕ begin to differ

The approximation sin $\phi = \phi$ is intuitively acceptable at low input noise levels and leads to the solution shown in eqn. 9.50 for $\phi(t)$.

Then $\phi(t)$ is the sum of two independently distributed Gaussian variates and $\dot{\phi}(t)$ will also be Gaussian and uncorrelated with $\phi(t)$.

By examining the frequency with which $\phi(t)$ crosses the level $\pi/2$ (with $\dot{\phi}(t)$ positive, say) an idea can be formed of when the linearising approximation breaks down. On some of these occasions inertial effects in the loop will cause $\phi(t)$ to return to the stable region $(-\pi/2 < \phi < \pi/2)$ almost immediately, but on others $\phi(t)$ will proceed to increase through π whereupon a cycle slip is likely to occur and the loop, having momentarily lost lock, will usually re-lock about $\phi = 2\pi$, i.e. the next stable region of the phase detector characteristic. A phase step of $+2\pi$ (the positive sign being attached because $\dot{\phi}(t)$ was assumed to be positive) may therefore be expected to be added to I_s/A on the right-hand side of eqn. 9.47 each time a forward cycle slip occurs.

This behaviour is reminiscent of the click noise phenomenon described in Section 5.1 for the conventional f.m. receiver and, indeed, observations of the p.l.l. output reveal that individual pops or clicks are present and cause a thresholding effect similar to that occurring with the f.m.f.b., d.t.f., or the conventional receiver.

Letting $p(\phi, \dot{\phi})$ be the joint density function of ϕ and $\dot{\phi}$, ν_γ the expected number of times per second that ϕ passes through the value γ (forward and backward crossings both being included) is given by an integral of the following type

$$\nu_\gamma = \int_{-\infty}^{+\infty} |\dot{\phi}| \, p(\gamma, \dot{\phi}) d\dot{\phi} \qquad (9.60)$$

The simplest cases of integrals like this occur when ϕ and $\dot{\phi}$ are independent as is the case when a linearisation of the loop is performed. Then, when $\dot{\phi}$ is Gaussian

$$\nu_\gamma = p(\gamma) \cdot \sqrt{\frac{2\sigma_1^2}{\pi}} \qquad (9.61)$$

where $\sigma_1^2 = \langle(\dot{\phi})^2\rangle$ is the mean square value of $\dot{\phi}$. This result shows that ν_γ is proportional to the density function of ϕ (which is also Gaussian when eqn. 9.50 holds), the factor of proportionality being determined by whatever value the loop and input parameters (filter type, carrier-to-noise ratio, modulation index, loop gain factor etc.) cause $\langle(\dot{\phi})^2\rangle$ to have.

Eqn. 9.61 has been fairly extensively used to assess p.l.l. performance with γ given values such as $\pi/2$ or π (References 23 and 27) but, strictly, it is true only for vanishingly small phase errors, and placing $\gamma = \pi/2$, say, and comparing the result when $\gamma = \pi$ reveals a gigantic change in ν_γ since passages through π are then predicted as events of

much greater rarity than passages through $\pi/2$. The region of validity
of eqn. 9.61 is being exceeded, and in practice such a large difference
in the rates of crossing the $\pi/2$ and π levels is not observed when the
threshold appears, and these events are not so remotely correlated as
is suggested by eqn. 9.61 (see below eqn. 9.81).

As mentioned above, the threshold is associated with the appearance
of a new click-like disturbance in the output and it may be recalled
(see eqns. 5.5 and 5.16) that the click rate for the conventional
receiver is given by

$$\nu = \frac{1}{2\pi} \sqrt{\frac{-r_N''(0)}{\pi\rho}} \, e^{-\rho} \tag{9.62}$$

while it can be shown (using eqn. 5.1 of Reference 30 with $\theta = \pi/2$)
that the expected number of times per second that the phase angle of
unmodulated carrier plus noise passes through $\pi/2$ is given by

$$\frac{1}{\pi} \sqrt{-r_N''(0)} \, e^{-\rho} \tag{9.63}$$

These are merely illustrative examples and should not be viewed as
having too close an analogy in the p.l.l., but eqns. 9.62 and 9.63 are seen
to have the same exponential factor and differ by $2\sqrt{\pi\rho}$ which amounts
typically, to an order of magnitude. More importantly, neither eqn.
9.62 or 9.63 can be obtained from a linearised analysis and thus it
cannot be expected that the result which is the counterpart of eqn.
9.62 for the p.l.l. can be obtained without recognising the $\sin\phi$ nonlinearity.

The threshold extension provided by the f.m.f.b., for example, stems
from the click rate obeying a law like eqn. 9.62 but with ρ increased
by a factor which is approximately the ratio of the input bandwidth to
the noise bandwidth of the loop filter. The rate of cycle slipping which
is the corresponding quantity in the case of a p.l.l. will be shown to
involve the loop bandwidth ω_L in a similar role.

9.17 Joint density function

This section discusses the joint distribution of the phase error and its
derivative. Keeping the assumption of a Gaussian modulation on the
received signal, reference is made to eqn. 9.45. By introducing the
inverse filter characteristic $L^{-1}(j\omega)$ and noting that $k_v v(t) = \phi(t) + \mu(t)$, eqn. 9.45 can be written

$$\dot{\phi}_1 + \sin\phi = n(t) + \dot{\mu}_1 \tag{9.64}$$

The time dependence of $\dot{\phi}_1$, ϕ and $\dot{\mu}_1$ is tacitly assumed and

$$\dot{\phi}_1 = L^{-1}\left|\left[\frac{\dot{\phi}(t)}{K}\right]\right| \tag{9.65}$$

$$\dot{\mu}_1 = -L^{-1}\left|\left[\frac{\dot{\mu}(t)}{K}\right]\right| \tag{9.66}$$

For example, with the proportional-plus-integral type of loop filter

$$L(j\omega) = 1 + \frac{a}{j\omega} \quad \text{so } L^{-1}(j\omega) = \frac{j\omega}{a + j\omega}$$

$n(t)$ is a noise-like disturbance that is given by

$$n(t) = \frac{I_c}{A}\sin\left[\phi(t) + \mu(t)\right] - \frac{I_s}{A}\cos\left[\phi(t) + \mu(t)\right] \tag{9.67}$$

Note that the mean square value of $n(t)$ is $1/(2\rho)$. The probability density function of ϕ, $p(\phi)$, to be obtained from eqn. 9.64 will have a period of 2π and in terms of $\Phi(u)$ the characteristic function of ϕ, we have (corresponding to eqn. 2.23)

$$p(\phi) = \frac{1}{2\pi}\sum_{m=-\infty}^{+\infty}\Phi(m)\,e^{jm\phi} \quad -\pi \leqslant \phi \leqslant \pi \tag{9.68}$$

Ideally the working would proceed with ϕ and $\dot{\phi}$ but greater progress can be made with the pair ϕ and $\dot{\phi}_1$ and an extension of eqn. 9.68 allows their joint density function $p(\phi, \dot{\phi}_1)$ to be written

$$p(\phi, \dot{\phi}_1) = \frac{1}{(2\pi)^2}\int_{-\infty}^{\infty}\sum_{m=-\infty}^{+\infty}\Phi(m, u)\exp\{j(m\phi + u\dot{\phi}_1)\}du \tag{9.69}$$

Here $\Phi(m, u)$ is the joint characteristic function of ϕ and $\dot{\phi}_1$, i.e. $\Phi(m, u) = \langle\exp j(m\phi + u\dot{\phi}_1)\rangle$. The right-hand side of eqn. 9.64 has a mean square value of $1/(2\rho) + \langle(\dot{\mu})^2\rangle = \sigma_R^2$ and its characteristic function will be taken to be the Gaussian form

$$\exp-\left(\frac{\sigma_R^2 u^2}{2}\right)$$

Thus, from eqn. 9.64

$$\langle\exp j(u[\dot{\phi}_1 + \sin\phi])\rangle = \exp-\left(\frac{\sigma_R^2 u^2}{2}\right) \tag{9.70}$$

or using

$$\sum_{m=-\infty}^{+\infty}J_m(u)\exp jm\phi = \exp(ju\sin\phi)$$

$$\sum_{m=-\infty}^{\infty}J_m(u)\,\phi(m, u) = \exp-\left[\sigma_R^2\frac{u^2}{2}\right] \tag{9.71}$$

An inversion of this relationship would yield $\Phi(m, u)$ so giving an expression for $p(\phi, \dot{\phi}_1)$, and the form of the left-hand side of eqn. 9.71 suggest that the addition formula (or summation formula) for Bessel functions (p. 979 of Reference 31) is likely to offer a means of obtaining an inversion. The formula may be written as follows:

$$\sum_{m=-\infty}^{+\infty} J_m(u) Z_m(v) e^{jm\alpha} = Z_0 \{\sqrt{u^2 + v^2 - 2uv \cos \alpha}\} \quad (9.72)$$

where Z_m is a general member of the Bessel family $(J_m, N_m, I_m$ etc.) and the restriction $|u| < |v|$ is to be observed if Z_m is not J_m. Consequently, consider the following form for $\Phi(m, u)$

$$\Phi(m, u) = \int_{-\infty}^{+\infty} p_R(z) \frac{Z_m[f(z, u)] e^{jm\alpha(z, u)}}{Z_0 \{\sqrt{u^2 + f^2(z, u) - 2uf(z, u) \cos \alpha(z, u)}\}} e^{juz} dz$$
$$(9.73)$$

where $p_R(z)$ is the probability density function of the right-hand side of eqn. 9.64.

It is seen that eqn. 9.71 is satisfied for general functions $f(z, u)$ and $\alpha(z, u)$ subject only to the restriction that $|f(z, u)| > |u|$ if Z_m is chosen not to be J_m. The generality of eqn. 9.73 is remarkable [$p_R(z)$ need not be Gaussian and no assumption about the loop filter has been made] and it emphasises a common feature of analyses of the phase lock loop when attacked by the current method or in other ways, in that solutions can often be produced but their uniqueness is in question.

Eqn. 9.73 ensures that every first-order moment of the left-hand side of eqn. 9.64 equals the corresponding moment of the right-hand side, but apart from demanding such properties as realness and evenness it is not possible to identify $f(z, u)$, $\alpha(z, u)$ or Z explicitly.

This situation stems from the fact that determination of a probability density function implies a knowledge of all the corresponding moments, and, when $\dot{\phi}_1$ and ϕ are tied together by only the one equation 9.64, no amount of analytical manipulation short of actually solving the equation will allow $\langle (\dot{\phi}_1)^n \cdot \phi^m \rangle$ to be determined for all integers n and m. The best that can be achieved is a balance of moments such, as is provided by eqn. 9.73.

When ϕ is small, linearisation of the analysis shows $\dot{\phi}_1$ and ϕ to be Gaussian, but, when ϕ is not so small, a formidable task is presented by the requirement that the equation (with a particular noise record on the right-hand side) be solved for both ϕ and $\dot{\phi}$ (or $\dot{\phi}_1$) and the results used to estimate a joint density function.

An alternative approach which has been resorted to on numerous occasions is the Fokker–Planck technique in which a (partial) differential equation is set up that has the required density function as its solution.

Unfortunately, the coefficients of the equation involve certain conditional expectations that rely for their evaluation on the density function which is being sought, and so a kind of circular impasse is met.

However, if the input noise is assumed to be flat and of infinite bandwidth, then an equation is obtained that is free of the offending coefficients. Most of the currently available analytical results have been produced by this means but it is a means that is incompatible with relating the input carrier-to-noise ratio and output signal-to-noise ratio of the p.l.l., as the former is then zero.

The equation in question (see eqn. 70 of Reference 32) is difficult to solve with a single variable (ϕ, for example) even for the first-order loop and is prohibitively difficult for higher-order loops although certain features of its solution can be inferred.

It can be expected that results produced on the assumption of an infinitely wide noise bandwidth would be acceptable for a sufficiently large ratio of input bandwidth to loop bandwidth but how large this ratio has to be is unclear.

The threshold extending property of the p.l.l. is only one reason for its many uses in communications engineering, and the results produced by the Fokker Planck technique have certainly proved their value for design purposes in many instances, but they represent a limiting situation, and in view of the difficulties outlined above, the joint characteristic function given in eqn. 9.73 is worthy of further consideration.

9.18 Two marginal distributions

The characteristic function for $\dot{\phi}_1$ is obtained by placing $m = 0$ in eqn. 9.73, and

$$\Phi(0, u) = \int_{-\infty}^{+\infty} p_R(z) \frac{Z_0 [f(z, u)] \exp juz}{Z_0 [\sqrt{u^2 + f^2(z, u) - 2uf(z, u) \cos \alpha(z, u)}]} \, dz \tag{9.74}$$

Assuming that f and α do not depend on z (this parallels a separable solution of a differential equation) we have

$$\Phi(0, u) = \frac{Z_0 [f(u)]}{Z_0 [\sqrt{u^2 + f^2(u) - 2uf(u) \cos \alpha(u)}]} \exp - \left[\frac{\sigma_R^2}{2} u^2 \right] \tag{9.75}$$

Recalling eqn. 9.64, and placing $\sin \phi$ on the right-hand side, it is seen that if $\sin \phi$ is ascribed a characteristic function of $J_0(u)$ (corresponding to a large noise disturbance so ϕ is uniformly distributed and independent of $n(t)$ and $\dot{\mu}_1$) then for very large noise

$$\Phi(0, u) = J_0(u) \exp - \left[\frac{\sigma_R^2}{2} u^2 \right] \qquad (9.76)$$

Eqn. 9.76 is to be compared with eqn. 9.75 and when the noise is severe (σ_R^2 is large), it is the small u region that is of most importance where $J_0(u) = 1 - u^2/4 + \dots$

An examination of possible simple forms for $f(u)$ and $\alpha(u)$ reveals that, if Z_0 is chosen to be I_0 (a modified Bessel function of the first kind) with

$$f(u) = a_1 + b_1 u^2$$

(where a_1 and b_1 are to be determined, and to comply with eqn. 9.72, $a_1 + b_1 u^2 > |u|$ so $a_1 b_1 > \frac{1}{4}$) and

$$\alpha(u) = \frac{\pi}{2} \operatorname{sgn} u$$

$$\left. \begin{array}{c} \\ \\ \\ \\ \\ \end{array} \right\} \qquad (9.77)$$

then

$$\frac{I_0(a_1 + b_1 u^2)}{I_0(\sqrt{u^2 + (a_1 + b_1 u^2)^2})} = 1 - \frac{1}{2} \frac{I_1(a_1) u^2}{a_1 I_0(a_1)} + \dots \qquad (9.78)$$

and this, for small a_1, approaches $1 - u^2/4 + \dots$ These are the leading terms in $J_0(u)$ for small u, so eqns. 9.75 and 9.76 have been matched. With the choices shown in eqn. 9.77 and with $Z_m = I_m$, the marginal distributions for ϕ and $\dot{\phi}_1$ become [33]

$$p(\phi) = \frac{e^{a_1 \cos \phi}}{2\pi I_0(a_1)} \qquad -\pi \leqslant \phi \leqslant \pi \qquad (9.79)$$

and

$$p(\dot{\phi}_1) = \frac{1}{2\pi} \int_{-\infty}^{+\infty} e^{-\sigma_R^2 (u^2/2)} \frac{I_0(a_1 + b_1 u^2)}{I_0[\sqrt{u^2 + (a_1 + b_1 u^2)^2}]} \exp ju\dot{\phi}_1 \, du \qquad (9.80)$$

The first of these will be recognised as the phase error distribution usually attributed to Tikhonov[34,35] who derived it for the first-order loop using the Fokker-Planck technique. Published analyses of the 2nd-order loop using the same technique[32,36] have also concluded that the phase error has such a distribution and this has been corroborated by computer simulation.[37] Small ϕ and large a_1, give

$$p(\phi) \approx \frac{e^{-a_1 \phi^2/2}}{\sqrt{2\pi/a_1}} \qquad (9.81)$$

which is the expected Gaussian distribution for ϕ and shows that a_1 is then the reciprocal of the mean square value of ϕ as given by eqn. 9.57 or 9.59, but a_1 must vary monotonically with ρ (the input carrier-to-noise ratio) for when a_1 is small $p(\phi)$ approaches a uniform distribution, as has been supposed in producing eqn. 9.76. The large difference between $p(\pi/2)$ and $p(\pi)$, when eqn. 9.81 is used, is evident.

Because $\sin\phi$ is bounded, eqn. 9.64 suggests that $\dot{\phi}_1$ will have almost the same distribution as $n(t) + \dot{\mu}_1$ when the noise is severe and so the interesting conclusion emerges that $\dot{\phi}_1$ will have a distribution which is close to the Gaussian form whenever ρ is very large or very small. As $\dot{\phi}$ is related to $\dot{\phi}_1$ by a linear filtering operation, it seems a fair inference that $\dot{\phi}$ will exhibit a similar behaviour (Reference 38 adds some support to this conclusion).

In practical cases it is the region in between these extremes of ρ that is of interest and it must be remarked that eqn. 9.80 cannot run into the correct Gaussian distribution for $\dot{\phi}_1$ when ρ is large (because eqn. 9.74 has not entailed solving eqn. 9.64 for $\dot{\phi}_1$) although, as eqn. 9.78 shows, satisfactory behaviour in the important case of small ρ is achieved.

It is seen that agreement with the conclusion of the Fokker-Planck approach regarding the analytical form for the distribution of $\phi(t)$ has been reached, and a distribution for $\dot{\phi}_1(t)$ also has been derived. The generality of eqn. 9.73 is such that its use in eqn. 9.69 (Reference 33) gives insight into the general form for the joint distribution of ϕ, and $\dot{\phi}_1$, and this is especially useful in the case of the first-order loop for then $\dot{\phi}/K$ and $\dot{\phi}_1$ are identical. However, further effort lies in the precise identification of the parameters a_1 and b_1 (it seems particularly difficult, to specify b_1 (see eqn. 9.77) and tighten the requirement that $a_1 b_1 > 1/4$). The b_1 problem will not be pursued here but when eqn. 9.81 holds it is clear that $1/a_1 = \psi_\phi(0)$, so $1/a_1$ is given by eqn. 9.57 or 9.59. If the noise level prevents a linearisation of the loop these formulae must underestimate the mean square phase error and, in particular, eqn. 9.58 will not indicate the preferred loop bandwidth (or filter factor) for operation in the threshold region. Experience suggests, however, that the error is small (reflected perhaps by the weak dependence on ρ shown by eqn. 9.58) and an investigation of the p.l.l. threshold can be made by assuming that eqn. 9.57 and 9.59 hold in the threshold region as well as above it,[*]and give the reciprocal of a_1.

9.19 P.L.L. threshold extension

The click-like disturbances that signal the p.l.l. threshold can be treated in a manner that closely parallels the analysis of the threshold of the conventional or f.m.f.b. receivers. Dropping the loop transfer character-

---

[*]See p. 1952 of Reference 27 for supporting evidence

istic and using eqns. 9.48 and 9.49, the output near threshold, $v_0(t)$, can be modelled by

$$v_0(t) = e^{-\psi_\phi(0)/2} M(t) + \frac{\dot{I}_s}{A} + \sum_k 2\pi\delta(t - t_k) - \sum_l 2\pi\delta(t - t_l) \tag{9.82}$$

t_k and t_l are the instants at which impulses with area 2π or -2π appear, and the coherence factor has been taken as $\exp - [\psi_\phi(0)/2]$.

As has been mentioned in Section 5.1, it is the impulse rate that governs the spectral density of the train of impulses and so we again turn attention to eqn. 9.60.

The difficulties encountered in fully specifying $p(\phi, \dot{\phi})$ have been discussed in Section 9.17, but we have examples from which to judge the form of the expected result for the click-rate. In particular, eqn. 9.62 for the conventional receiver, and the expression for ν below eqn. 9.26 for the f.m.f.b., show a form very similar to eqn. 9.61 which is obtained when ϕ and $\dot{\phi}$ are assumed to be independent. Consequently, this assumption will be retained so that using eqn. 9.79 and the asymptotic formula $I_0(a_1) \approx e^{a_1}/\sqrt{2\pi a_1}$ the following is obtained:

$$\nu_\gamma = \sqrt{\frac{a_1 \sigma_1^2}{\pi}} e^{-a_1(1 - \cos\gamma)} \tag{9.83}$$

As with the examples quoted above, it is the exponential factor that is important in deciding the available threshold extension, and as the impulse train has a flat spectral density over the baseband frequency range a convenient way of judging performances is to compare the arguments of the respective exponentials.

A performance superior to that of the f.m.f.b. will be realised by the p.l.l. if

$$a_1(1 - \cos\gamma) > \rho_T \left[\frac{2\omega_B}{2\alpha p_m}\right] \frac{2}{\pi} \tag{9.84}$$

Here, the right-hand side is the argument of the exponential term of eqn. 9.29 when the f.m.f.b. loop filter is a single pole network, ρ_T is the value of the input carrier-to-noise ratio at which the f.m.f.b. threshold occurs, and it will be recalled that $\alpha \simeq 3$ represents a near optimum when the coherence factor effect is also taken into consideration. (This assumes the same modulation parameters as were used in Section 9.6, i.e. $\omega_\Delta/p_m = 2.62$).

The description of cycle slipping behaviour given earlier indicates that a loss of lock transient may be expected if $|\phi(t)|$ exceeds $\pi/2$, but the situation is not a simple one as occasions arise when inertial effects in the loop can cause a return to the stable region ($|\phi(t)| < \pi/2$) even though $\phi(t)$ has exceeded $\pi/2$ by a good margin. Strictly, therefore, no single value for γ in eqn. 9.84 is appropriate, but Smith[39] has given an experimentally determined value of $1 \cdot 81$ radians for the phase excursion beyond which loss of lock occurs with very high probability. Rewrite eqn. 9.84 as follows:

$$\alpha \frac{\pi}{2} \frac{(1 - \cos \gamma)}{\rho_T} \left(\frac{p_m}{\omega_B} \right) > \frac{1}{a_1} \qquad (9.85)$$

In the threshold region $1/a_1 > \psi_\phi(0)$, where eqn. 9.57 gives $\psi_\phi(0)$ when a proportional-plus-integral loop filter is adopted, so it is certainly required that

$$\alpha \frac{\pi}{2} \frac{(1 - \cos \gamma)}{\rho_T} \left(\frac{p_m}{\omega_B} \right) > \frac{1}{3} \left(\frac{\omega_\Delta}{p_m} \right)^2 \left[\frac{p_m}{a} \right]^4 + \left(\frac{p_m}{2\omega_B} \right) \frac{\pi}{\rho_T} \left[\frac{a}{p_m} \right]$$

(where a/p_m is given by eqn. 9.58), or

$$\alpha > \frac{5}{4} \left(\frac{a}{p_m} \right) \frac{1}{(1 - \cos \gamma)} \qquad (9.86)$$

The design procedures for the f.m.f.b. and p.l.l. reveal that α and a/p_m should be given comparable values (both are in the region of 3 for satellite applications) while, on accepting the value of $1 \cdot 81$ radians for γ, we see that $5/4(1 - \cos \gamma) = 1 \cdot 01$. Thus, eqn. 9.86 says that, if a superior performance is provided by the p.l.l., the margin over the f.m.f.b. is very small and is unlikely to be predicted with high accuracy until some major advance in the theory is made, such as correctly accounting for the way in which $\phi(t)$ and $\dot{\phi}(t)$ are correlated.

Practical experience with the p.l.l. confirms the conclusion that very comparable performance with the f.m.f.b. or d.t.f. is realised in many situations so that the choice between the various types of threshold extending devices is often made in favour of the p.l.l. purely because of its simple construction.

A situation in which the p.l.l. might not be preferred is that in which the input signal carries an extremely large f.m. index, for, as is seen from eqn. 9.57, a contribution to the mean square phase error arises from modulation. If an excessively large loop gain factor is required to eliminate the modulation term, this could enlarge the second (noise) term of eqn. 9.57 to an unacceptable value.

9.20 Digital p.l.l. and the discrete p.l.l.

With the advent of solid-state circuitry, digital forms of the p.l.l. have been proposed that are more compact, more reliable, and cheaper than their analogue counterparts, as well as having the advantage of freedom from drift.

Reference 19 provides a review of the many realisations that have been discussed in the literature. Some of these cause the input signal and noise to be processed in the same way as occurs in the a.p.l.l. (so the mathematical treatment is the same) but, more generally, a direct tracking of the zero crossings of the input is attempted by taking samples and using processed versions of the samples to correct the period of a digital clock until a locked condition is achieved.

In some designs this sampling is done with a uniform time spacing (Z-transform methods are then a useful tool in the analysis) but an interesting variation occurs with the discrete p.l.l. which is shown in block diagram form in Fig. 9.4. The sampler detects the error in phase, and the digital clock introduces a phase correction at one discrete instant per cycle of the incoming carrier, the sampling being nonuniform.

Writing $S(t) + N(t)$ for the input (as in eqn. 9.43, where again it will be supposed that the phase modulation $\mu(t)$ is a Gaussian process and the noise is also Gaussian), the kth sample of the input is called $X(k) = S(t_k) + N(t_k)$. The sequence $X(k)$ is passed through the A/D converter and digital filter to give $Y(k)$ which is used to control the period of the digital clock.

With $T = 2\pi/\omega_0$ as the nominal period, $Y(k)$ corrects T so that the next clock period $T(k + 1)$ is given by

$$t_{k+1} - t_k = T(k + 1) = T - Y(k) \tag{9.87}$$

the successive corrections having the aim of causing the positive-going zero crossing to be tracked. When the digital filter is the equivalent of the proportional-plus-integral filter of eqn. 9.53

$$Y(k) = \Delta_1 X(k) + \Delta_2 \sum_{l=0}^{k} X(l) \tag{9.88}$$

where $\check{\Delta}_1$ and Δ_2 are gain constants ($\Delta_2 = 0$ for a first-order loop). Ideally, $\dots t_1, t_2 \dots t_k$ are the times when positive-going zero crossings of the carrier wave occur so $\phi(k) = \omega_0 t_k + \mu(t_k)$ reduced modulo 2π is a measure of the phase error, and the first-order loop equation can be written

$$\left[\frac{\phi(k+1)-\phi(k)}{K_1}\right] + \sin\phi(k) = \frac{N(t_k)}{A} - \left[\frac{\mu(t_{k+1})-\mu(t_k)}{K_1}\right]$$

$$(9.89)$$

Here $K_1 = A\omega_0\Delta_1$ is called the loop gain, and this difference equation can be compared with eqn. 9.64 in the case of the analogue p.l.l. The right-hand side of eqn. 9.89 is a Gaussian variate and, for fixed k, its mean square value σ_R^2 is given by

$$\sigma_R^2 = \frac{1}{2\rho} + 2 \left\langle \frac{\psi_\mu(0) - \psi_\mu(T - \Delta_1 X(k))}{K_1^2} \right\rangle \qquad (9.90)$$

The angle brackets refer to the time interval between samples at t_{k+1} and t_k being itself a random variable, and this circumstance together with the sinusoidal characteristic on the left-hand side of eqn. 9.89 points up the nonstationary and nonlinear nature of the analysis.

To investigate the distribution of $\phi(k)$ for some particular k, eqn. 9.89 can be manipulated in the manner described with the a.p.l.l. equation, to give

$$\sum_{m=-\infty}^{+\infty} J_m(u)\,\Phi\left(m - \frac{u}{K_1}, \frac{u}{K_1}\right) = \exp-\left[\tfrac{1}{2}\sigma_R^2 u^2\right] \qquad (9.91)$$

where

$$\Phi(u_1, u_2) = \langle \exp j\,[u_1\phi(k) + u_2\phi(k+1)]\rangle$$

From the analysis of Section 9.17, an inversion of eqn. 9.91 has eqn. 9.73 as a possible solution for $\Phi(m - u/K_1, u/K_1)$. This is a general inversion holding for all values of u and so, arguing as in Section 9.17, by placing $u = 0$ we obtain $\Phi(m, 0) = \langle \exp jm\phi(k)\rangle = I_m(a_2)/I_0(a_2)$ where a_2 is a constant to be determined. The distribution of $\phi(k)$ is therefore concluded to have the Tikhonov form of eqn. 9.79.

As with the a.p.l.l., for a low-noise input, the approximation $\sin\phi(k) = \phi(k)$ is plausible, and then a Gaussian distribution for $\phi(k)$ may be anticipated with eqn. 9.89 becoming

$$\phi(k+1) - [1 - K_1]\,\phi(k) = K_1\frac{N(t_k)}{A} - [\mu(t_{k+1}) - \mu(t_k)]$$

$$(9.92)$$

It is evident, however, that the behaviour of an iteration of this equation [starting from some initial value ϕ_0 for $\phi(k)$] depends critically on the size of K_1. For a statistically stable state to be maintained, $|1 - K_1|$ must not exceed unity ($K_1 < 2$) and this is a feature of the discrete p.l.l. that is absent with analogue versions of the loop (see Reference 20 where it is stated that $K_1 \equiv 1$ leads to the most rapid convergence to the statistical steady state).

Using eqn. 9.92, σ_L^2, the common variance of $\phi(k)$ and $\phi(k+1)$ in the stable state, satisfies

$$\sigma_L^2 = [1 - K_1]^2 \sigma_L^2 + (K_1 \sigma_R)^2$$
$$+ 2K_1(1 - K_1) \left\langle \phi(k) \left[\frac{N(t_k)}{A} - \left\{ \frac{\mu(t_{k+1}) - \mu(t_k)}{K_1} \right\} \right] \right\rangle$$

$$(9.93)$$

When $K_1 \equiv 1$, therefore

$$\sigma_L^2 = \sigma_R^2 \approx \frac{1}{2\rho} + 2[\psi_\mu(0) - \psi_\mu(T)] \qquad (9.94)$$

and the distribution density of $\phi(k)$ is given by

$$p(\phi) = \frac{e^{a_2 \cos \phi}}{2\pi I_0(a_2)} \approx \sqrt{\frac{a_2}{2\pi}} e^{-a_2 \phi^2/2} \text{ with } a_2 = \frac{1}{\sigma_L^2} \qquad (9.95)$$

Clearly, the greater the jittering of the zero crossings of the carrier (caused by a significant phase modulation) the more difficult it is for the loop to lock and, as with the a.p.l.l., the second-order loop offers better performance in this respect that the first-order loop.[19]

By recalling Stumpers' definition of instantaneous frequency and its relationship to the zero crossings of the carrier (see eqns. 3.5 to 3.7) it is evident that the d.p.l.l. can be used to obtain a continuous estimate of the frequency of an input f.m. wave (Reference 21 describes a frequency demodulator based on these principles). However, the thresholding behaviour is especially difficult to analyse because of the nonlinear and nonstationary features referred to earlier, and this is an area which is largely unexplored.

9.21 Envelope multiplication techniques

Here, various ways of using the envelope of the signal-plus-noise sum to improve poor S/D ratios (below threshold) are examined. So, letting $V_F(t)$ be the output from a modified receiver, consider

$$V_F(t) = F[R(t)] \cdot \dot{\theta}(t) \qquad (9.96)$$

where $R(t)$ is the envelope, $F[R(t)]$ is the function of $R(t)$ used for multiplication, and $\dot{\theta}(t)$ is the instantaneous frequency, given by

$$\frac{P(t)\dot{Q}(t) - Q(t)\dot{P}(t)}{P^2(t) + Q^2(t)} = \frac{P(t)\dot{Q}(t) - Q(t)\dot{P}(t)}{R^2(t)}$$

With a modulated carrier-plus-noise $P(t) = A \cos \mu(t) + I_c$ and $Q(t) = A \sin \mu(t) + I_s$ (at this stage it is assumed that the i.f. bandwidth is so large that it introduces no truncation distortion) and then

$$V_F(t) = \frac{F[R(t)] A^2}{R^2(t)} \left\{ M(t) + \left[\frac{\dot{i}_s}{A} \cos \mu(t) - \frac{\dot{i}_c}{A} \sin \mu(t) \right. \right.$$
$$\left. \left. + M(t) \left(\frac{I_c}{A} \cos \mu(t) + \frac{I_s}{A} \sin \mu(t) \right) \right] + \frac{I_c \dot{i}_s - I_s \dot{i}_c}{A^2} \right\} \quad (9.97)$$

The curly bracket consists of three mutually uncorrelated members which, in order of writing, may be called signal, signal × noise and noise × noise contributions.

As the envelope will always contain a d.c. component, it is seen that multiplication by a function of $R(t)$ that is of degree higher than two (typified by $F[R(t)] = b_3 R^3(t) + b_4 R^4(t) + \ldots$) cannot be expected to lead to an improvement in the balance of signal and distortion or noise: consequently, for multiplication by a function of the envelope to be profitable, the degree of the function in $R(t)$ should not exceed two. Clearly, the simplest cases are multiplication by the envelope, multiplication by the square of the envelope, or some combination of the two such as multiplying according to the envelope level, and, then, only when the result is likely to be beneficial.

Now, in eqn. 9.97, $M(t)$ is multiplied by

$$\frac{F[R(t)] A^2}{R^2(t)} \left[1 + \left\{ \frac{I_c}{A} \cos \mu(t) + \frac{I_s}{A} \sin \mu(t) \right\} \right] \quad (9.98)$$

Consequently, if this expression, when averaged over the noise parameters, has a value of λ, say, the useful signal in the output will be given by $\lambda M(t)$, and λ is the coherence factor on a voltage basis. Recalling that $\mu(t)$, I_s and I_c are mutually uncorrelated Gaussian variables, the required averaging is provided by a triple integral but by simple changes of variable this can be much reduced and a compact form for λ is

$$\lambda = 2\rho \int_0^\infty F(x) e^{-\rho(1+x^2)} I_1(2\rho x) dx \quad (9.99)$$

where $I_1(x)$ is a modified Bessel function of the first kind of unity order.

This, then, is a general expression for the coherence factor (as a voltage ratio) for the technique of multiplying by a function of the envelope.

By taking $F(R) = R^m$, eqn. 9.99 yields

$$\lambda = \Gamma\left(\frac{m}{2} + 1\right)\left(\frac{1}{\rho}\right)^{m/2-1} {}_1F_1\left(1 - m/2 : 2 : -\rho\right) \qquad (9.100)$$

and the explicit results for $m = 0$, 1 and 2 are shown in Table 9.2.

Table 9.2   Coherence factor

m	FMFB (voltagewise)
0	$1 - e^{-\rho}$
1	$\sqrt{\rho}\,\tfrac{1}{2}\sqrt{\pi}\left[I_0(\rho/2) + I_1(\rho/2)\right]e^{-\rho/2}$
2	1

$m = 0$ refers to the conventional demodulator, as no multiplication is applied, and eqn. 9.100 reproduces the coherence factor used earlier, e.g. eqns. 4.26 and 5.25. The result for $m = 1$ has been given in the literature[43] and we see that with $m = 2$ there is no suppression of the wanted modulation.

It has been assumed that the i.f. filter is wide enough for its effect on the modulated carrier to be neglected and, with this proviso, multiplication by the square of the envelope is an optimum procedure in the sense of causing the least degradation of the wanted signal as a result of effects of coherence with other terms in the demodulator output.

A standard detector cannot be improved on when a frequency modulated carrier is only slightly disturbed by noise, but, as we have seen, when the noise increases in level not only does the rather sudden onset of the threshold effect occur, but the wanted signal is subsequently depressed too. The latter effect is minimised by applying the multiplication by squared envelope technique, and, consequently, the greatest advantage from maximising its coherence factor lies in the region of very small carrier-to-noise ratios. The outcome is a re-distribution of the noise and intermodulation components across the baseband frequency range, providing a performance curve that crosses over that of the conventional receiver. When clicks are eliminated by this means, therefore, a carrier-to-noise ratio exists, below which a performance superior to that of the conventional demodulator is realised but above which performance is poorer.

This behaviour is shown on Figs. 9.11 and 9.12 where two typical situations are treated, with the theoretical f.m.f.b. performance shown also.

The behaviour seen in Figs. 9.11 and 9.12, where a consistently poorer performance than that offered by the conventional receiver is achieved for large ρ, is due to an interference term stemming from an interaction between the modulation and the noise. Thus, unless due recognition of the modulating signal is taken in the analysis this important feature will not be revealed.

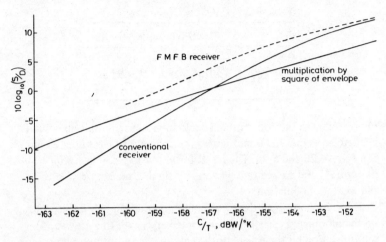

Fig. 9.11 Multiplication by square of envelope in a low deviation case: $\omega_\Delta / p_m = 0.52$

Top channel of 240 channel system baseband range 60 kHz–1052 kHz 200 kHz r.m.s. test-tone deviation

$$C/T \text{ dBW}/^\circ\text{K} = \rho \text{ (dB)} + 10 \log_{10} \left[k \frac{2\omega_B}{2\pi} \right]$$

where k is Boltzmann's constant $(1.38 \times 10^{-23} \text{ J}^\circ\text{K}^{-1})$ and in the present case $2 \omega_B / 2\pi$ = input noise bandwidth = 6.50 MHz

Multiplication by the envelope rather than by its square (Figs. 9.11 and 9.12 refer to the latter) lessens the effect and then the demodulator output can be described by

$$V_1(t) = \frac{P(t)\dot{Q}(t) - Q(t)\dot{P}(t)}{\sqrt{P^2(t) + Q^2(t)}} \tag{9.101}$$

The time dependent denominator $\sqrt{P^2(t) + Q^2(t)}$ proves to be the source of great analytical complication in determining the spectral density of $V_1(t)$ and while some progress can be made with this problem at the extremes of very high carrier-to-noise ratios[40] and zero carrier-to-noise ratio, these do not offer much guidance as to the overall performance. To overcome this difficulty one can resort to the Monte Carlo approach.[41]

In comparison, the output from a demodulator employing multiplication by the square of the envelope, i.e. $P\dot{Q} - Q\dot{P}$, can be analysed easily and this case is instructive as the various terms that arise will have very similar counterparts if other envelope multiplication schemes are examined. Using eqn. 9.97, the output is given by

$$V_2(t) = M(t) + A(t) - B(t) \qquad (9.102)$$

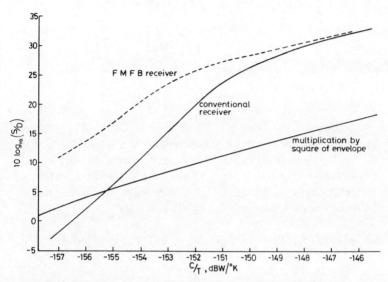

Fig. 9.12 Multiplication by square of envelope in a large deviaton case: $\omega_\Delta/p_m = 2 \cdot 62$

Top channel of 240 channel system baseband range 60 kHz—1052 kHz
1 MHz r.m.s. test-tone deviation

$$C/T \text{ dbW/}^\circ\text{K} = \rho\,(\text{dB}) + 10 \log_{10}\left[k\,\frac{2\omega_B}{2\pi}\right]$$

where k is Boltzmann's constant ($1 \cdot 38 \times 10^{-23}$ J^0 K^{-1}) and in the present case $2\omega_B/2\pi$ = input noise bandwidth = 24 MHz

where

$$A(t) = \frac{\dot{I}_s}{A}\cos\mu(t) - \frac{\dot{I}_c}{A}\sin\mu(t) + M(t)\left(\frac{I_c}{A}\cos\mu(t) + \frac{I_s}{A}\sin\mu(t)\right)$$

$$B(t) = \frac{I_s\dot{I}_c - I_c\dot{I}_s}{A^2}$$

Now, $M(t), A(t)$ and $B(t)$ are mutually uncorrelated and taking $B(t)$ first, its autocorrelation function may be shown (using results given in

Appendix II of Reference 30, for example) to be

$$-\frac{2}{A^4}\,[gg'' - (g')^2]$$

where, for flat noise,

$$g = g(\tau) = \psi_N(0)\,\frac{\sin \omega_B \tau}{\omega_B \tau}$$

The spectral density (in terms of power/rad/s) is then

$$\frac{\omega_B}{3} \cdot \frac{1}{\rho^2}\left(1 - \frac{\omega}{2\omega_B}\right)^3 \tag{9.103}$$

and with flat f.m. the contribution to the distortion-to-signal ratio made by this term is

$$T_3 = \frac{1}{6\rho^2} \cdot \left(\frac{p_m}{\omega_\Delta}\right)^2 \frac{2\omega_B}{p_m}\left(1 - \frac{\omega}{2\omega_B}\right)^3 \tag{9.104}$$

The working for $A(t)$ is more complicated but it is interesting to note that, if $M(t)$ is replaced by $-M(t)$, the resulting form for $A(t)$ is then the derivative of $Q_1(t)/A$ in eqn. 5.19 that was discussed in Section 5.3 on the conventional demodulator. This fact assists in obtaining the following for the autocorrelation function of $A(t)$

$$\frac{1}{A^2}\left[g(\tau)(\psi_M(\tau) - b_1^2) + 2g'(\tau)b_1 - g''(\tau)\right]\exp - [\psi_\mu(0) - \psi_\mu(\tau)] \tag{9.105}$$

[where $b_1 = \langle M(t+\tau)\mu(t)\rangle = \psi'_\mu(\tau)$], as, on changing the sign of b_1, this becomes a perfect second derivative.

The exponential factor multiplying eqn. 9.105 is directly related by eqn. 4.7 to the power spectrum of the modulated carrier and the contribution made to D/S can be written

$$\frac{1}{\rho}\left(\frac{p_m}{2\omega_B}\right) \cdot \left(\frac{p_m}{\omega_\Delta}\right)^2 \frac{1}{p_m^2}\int_{\omega-\omega_B}^{\omega_B}\left\{\frac{G(q)}{\frac{1}{2}A^2}\right\}(2q - \omega)^2\,dq \tag{9.106}$$

To evaluate the integral, a knowledge of $G(q)$ is required, but two results that hold generally, are

$$\int_{-\infty}^{+\infty}\left\{\frac{G(q)}{\frac{1}{2}A^2}\right\}dq = 1$$

and

$$\int_{-\infty}^{+\infty}q^2\left\{\frac{G(q)}{\frac{1}{2}A^2}\right\}dq = \omega_\Delta^2 \tag{9.107}$$

Remembering that virtually all the carrier power is assumed to lie within the band $\pm\omega_B$ centred on ω_0, a reasonable approximation to eqn. 9.106 aimed at covering both large and small deviations is

$$\frac{3}{\rho}\left(\frac{p_m}{2\omega_B}\right) + \frac{1}{\rho}\left(\frac{p_m}{\omega_\Delta}\right)^2 \frac{p_m}{2\omega_B}\left(\frac{\omega}{p_m}\right)^2 = T_1 + T_2$$

Thus

$$\frac{D}{S} = T_1 + T_2 + T_3 \qquad (9.108)$$

T_3 is given by eqn. 9.104 and T_2 will be recognised as the above-threshold expression (see eqn. 5.23) for the conventional demodulator, while T_1, which is also inversely proportional to ρ, is responsible for degrading the performance above threshold. (Reference 42 gives a slightly different derivation of T_1.)

T_1 is the modulation-noise interaction term and it should be noted that there is no dependence on either the deviation ratio or the base-band frequency ω. Thus, the usual situation in which channels situated low in the baseband are less affected than channels further up the band is not the case here nor is it possible to reduce T_1 by increasing the deviation.

The curves shown in Figs. 9.11 and 9.12 are derived from eqn. 9.108, and it might be supposed that, by narrowing the bandwidth before doing the multiplication, some alleviation of the detrimental effect of T_1 could be obtained, so that threshold extension as well as the improved performance at low values of ρ might be achieved. This is not the case, however, for when extra filtering is introduced another contribution to D/S arises from intermodulation distortion. Near threshold, this tends to cancel the benefits of filtering and, incidentally, when a truncating filter is used, the levels that this distortion component adopts can be read directly from Figs. 7.5–7.10. This is because a multiplication by squared envelope technique is an appropriate device for calculating the distortion levels generated by truncating filters (Section 7.5).

A considerable penalty is paid at the larger values of ρ by ensuring that the modulation suffers no degradation, but, when T_3 (the term inversely proportional to ρ^2) is dominant, filtering can be very beneficial, and an optimum narrowing exists where the benefits of excluding input noise balance the intermodulation distortion that is generated.

9.22 Narrowing the input bandwidth

The effect on the spectral density eqn. 9.103 of introducing narrowband filtering (before the multiplication process) is to modify it to

$$\frac{1}{\rho^2}\left(\frac{p_m}{2\omega_B}\right)^2 \frac{1}{p_m^2}\int_{-\infty}^{+\infty}\left|H_1(jx)H_1\left[j(x+\omega)\right]\right|^2 .(2x^2+\omega x)dx$$

(9.109)

where $H_1(j\omega)$ refers to the extra filtering at the i.f. stage. When $H_1(j\omega)$ is a truncating network of bandwidth $2\omega_1$ ($\omega_1 < \omega_B$) the above is simplified, and, in this case, a result for the coherence factor is available in eqn. 7.52. The contribution made to the distortion-to-signal ratio is then

$$T_3' = \frac{\dfrac{1}{6\rho^2}\left(\dfrac{p_m}{\omega_\Delta}\right)^2\dfrac{2\omega_B}{p_m}\left[\dfrac{2\omega_1}{2\omega_B}-\dfrac{\omega}{2\omega_B}\right]^3}{\left\{\dfrac{1}{2}\,\mathrm{erf}\left(\dfrac{\omega_1-\omega}{\omega_\Delta\sqrt{2}}\right)+\dfrac{1}{2}\,\dfrac{\mathrm{erf}}{\mathrm{Erf}}\left(\dfrac{\omega_1}{\omega_\Delta\sqrt{2}}\right)\right\}^2}$$

(9.110)

and to this must be added a contribution from truncation distortion, which can be read directly from curves such as those shown for top channel on Figs. 7.5–7.10.

When the f.m. index is small ($\omega_\Delta/p_m < 1$), the theory is not sufficiently well developed to predict with accuracy the very narrow bandwidths that then appear to be feasible, but bandwidths of twice the highest modulating frequency represent a natural limit as further reduction will severely affect the higher baseband channels.

For large and intermediate indices, T_3' and the truncation distortion are governing, and it is convenient to confine attention to a carrier-to-noise ratio of 0dB ($\rho = 1$). The likely approach is for the bandwidth to be fixed by optimising the top channel, and then, using eqn. 9.110 and Figs. 7.7–7.10, the distortion levels and bandwidth figures of Table 9.3 are found.

Table 9.3   Narrowband filtering followed by multiplication by square of envelope

$\dfrac{\omega_\Delta}{p_m}$	Percentage of Carson bandwidth for optimum performance in top channel with $\rho = 1$	S/D	Without narrowband filtering	
			S/D	S/D for conventional receiver[*]
	%	dB	dB	
1·0	38·4	7·0	−1·5	−8·0
1·5	45·2	9·0	0·2	−5·9
2·0	47·8	9·5	1·4	−4·4
3·0	49·6	10·5	3·2	−2·5

[*]Assuming $\psi_\mu(0) > 5·0$

The entries for the conventional receiver come from eqn. 5.30, and
Fig. 4.3 enables these low S/D ratios to be interpreted in terms of
n.p.r. It is seen (as in Figs. 9.11 and 9.12) that S/D ratios less than
unity can be converted to ratios that exceed unity even if no extra
filtering is introduced.

If the system designer has freedom to choose the deviation ratio,
information on the best choices is supplied in Reference 42.

9.23 Realisation of multiplication

There is some choice as to how the desired multiplication can be
achieved, an obvious way being to use an envelope detector of the
appropriate square law (or linear law) type and apply the output
together with the output from a conventional f.m. receiver to a
multiplier.

A more subtle method relies on the observation that, when the
limiter is omitted, the balanced discriminator output is proportional to
the product of the i.f. envelope and the instantaneous frequency, i.e.
$R(t) \times \dot{\theta}(t)$ (Reference 43). This result depends on there being linear
diodes in the discriminator, if square-law diodes are substituted, the
output is then proportional to $R^2(t) \times \dot{\theta}(t)$ (Reference 42). Omission
of the limiter can therefore lead to realisations of multiplication by
the square of the envelope or by the envelope itself.

Again, a delay-line discriminator in which the received i.f. wave is
simply multiplied by a delayed version of itself, can provide $R(t) \times
R(t - \tau) \sin [\theta(t + \tau) - \theta(t)]$ as an output. The delay τ is usually
comparable to the reciprocal of the intermediate frequency and so
this output is given, effectively, by $\tau R^2(t) \dot{\theta}(t)$.

By redesigning the limiter so that it has a soft rather than a hard
characteristic, it is possible to produce an effect such as multiplying
by the square of the envelope when an envelope dip occurs while
ensuring conventional operation when the envelope is at full strength.
In this way, a device which may be described as a switching demodulator can be realised by preceding the discriminator with an i.f. amplifier
having a suitably shaped characteristic. (The hybrid receiver of
Reference 40 has a similar aim.)

With such a switching arrangement, the nonlinearity $F[R(t)]$ of
eqn. 9.96 has the form

$$F[R(t)] = 1 \qquad R(t) \geqslant k_0$$
$$= \left(\frac{R(t)}{k_0}\right)^2 \quad R(t) < k_0$$

where k_0 is the level at which switching occurs. Information on the resulting coherence factor and the performance is given in Reference 41.

9.24 References

1 KLAPPER, J., and FRANKLE, J.T.: 'Phase-locked and frequency-feedback systems' (Academic Press, New York and London, 1972)

2 LINDSEY, W.C., and TAUSWORTHE, R.C.: 'A bibliography of the theory and application of the phase-lock principle'. Jet propulsion Laboratory, California Institute of Technology, April 1973, (NASA-CR-133225 JPL-TR-32-1581)

3 ARNDT, G.D., and LOCH, F.J.: 'Correlation detection of impulse noise for FM threshold extension', *Proc. IEEE*, 1970, **58**, pp. 1141–3

4 MALONE, M.J.: 'FM threshold extension without feedback', *Proc. IEEE*, 1968, **56**, pp. 200–201

5 GLAZER, A.: 'Bound on FM threshold extension when using click elimination', IEEE National Telemetering Conference Record, 1971, pp. 89–93

6 CALANDRINO, L., and IMMOVILLI, G.: 'Coincidence of pulses in amplitude and frequency deviations produced by a random noise perturbing an FM wave: an amplitude-phase correlation FM demodulator', *Alta Freq.*, 1967, **36**, (8), pp. 170E–175E

7 CALANDRINO, L., and IMMOVILLI, G.: 'On the performance of amplitude-phase correlation FM demodulators', *Alta Freq.*, 1968, **37**, (2), pp. 19E–25E

8 CLARKE, K.K., and HESS, D.T.: 'Frequency locked loop FM demodulator', *IEEE Trans.*, 1967, **COM-15**, (4), pp. 518–524

9 MUEHLDORF, E.I.: 'FM threshold reduction by optimum filtering', *Proc. IEEE*, 1966, **54**, pp. 1972–1973

10 WAINSTEIN, L.A., and ZUBAKOV, V.D.: 'Extraction of signals from noise' (Prentice Hall, 1962)

11 GLAZER, A.: 'Distribution of click amplitudes', *IEEE Trans.*, 1971, **COM-19**, pp. 539–543

12 ROBERTS, J.H.: 'Frequency-feedback receiver as a low-threshold demodulator in f.m. f.d.m. satellite systems', *Proc. IEE*, 1968, **115**, (11), pp. 1607–1618

13 STOJANOVIC, Z.D.: 'Non-linear distortion analysis in the frequency demodulator using feedback', *IEEE Trans.*, 1975, **COM-23**, pp. 884–890

14 HOFFMAN, E., and SCHILLING, D.L.: 'Distortion in the frequency demodulator using feedback', *IEEE Trans.*, 1972, **COM-20**, pp. 157–162

15 BAX, F.G.M.: 'Analysis of the FM receiver with frequency feedback'. Phillips Research Reports Supplement 8, 1970

16 OGI, M., and SEKIZAWA, T.: 'Solid-state broad-band FM modulator and demodulator', *Fujitsu Sci. & Tech. J.*, 1966, (2), pp. 27–47

17 ROBERTS, J.H.: 'Dynamic tracking filter as a low-threshold demodulator in f.m. f.d.m. satellite systems', *Proc. IEE*, 1968, **115**, (11), pp. 1597–1606

18 LOCKYER, K.S.: 'Threshold extension of an f.m. demodulator using a dynamic tracking filter', *Proc. IEE*, 1968, **115**, (8), pp. 1102–1108

19 GUPTA, S.C.: 'Phase locked loops', *Proc. IEEE*, 1975, **63**, pp. 291–306

20 WEINBERG, A., and LIU, B.: 'Discrete time analysis of non-uniform sampling first and second order digital phase locked loops', *IEEE Trans.*, 1974, **COM-22**, pp. 123–137

21 GILL, G.S., and GUPTA, S.C.: 'First order discrete phase locked loop with applications to demodulation of angle-modulated carrier', *IEEE Trans.*, 1972, **COM-20,** pp. 454–462

22 TAUB, H., and SCHILLING, D.L.: 'Principles of communication systems' (McGraw-Hill, 1971)

23 ABRAMS, B.S., OBERST, J.F., BERKOFF, M., and SCHILLING, D.L.: 'Phase-lock loop threshold investigations', Technical Memorandum 73, June 1965, Polytechnic Institute of Brooklyn, Research Report PIBMRI-1274-65

24 DEVELET, J.A.: 'A threshold criterion for phase-lock demodulation', *Proc. IEEE*, 1963, **51,** (2), pp. 349–356

25 CARASSA, F., and ROCCA, F.: 'Advances in phase-lock demodulation', *IEEE Trans.*, 1970, **COM-18,** (3), pp. 182–191

26 JAFFE, R., and RECHTIN, E.: 'Design and performance of phase lock circuits capable of near-optimum performance over a wide range of input signals and noise levels', *IRE Trans.*, 1955, **IT-1,** pp. 66–76

27 NELSON, W.L.: 'Phase lock loop design for coherent angle error detection in the Telstar Satellite tracking system', *Bell Syst. Tech. J.*, 1963, **42,** (5), pp. 1941–1975

28 FRAZIER, J.P., and PAGE, J.: 'Phase lock frequency acquisition study', *IEEE Trans.*, 1962, **SET-8,** pp. 210–227

29 GARDNER, F.M.: 'Phase lock techniques' (Wiley, New York, 1966)

30 RICE, S.O.: 'Statistical properties of a sine-wave plus random noise', *Bell System. Tech. J.*, 1948, **27,** pp. 109–157

31 GRADSHTEYN, I.S., and RYZHIK, I.M.: 'Tables of integrals series and products' (Academic Press, 1965)

32 VITERBI, A.J.: 'Phase locked loop dynamics in the presence of noise by Fokker-Planck techniques', *Proc. IEEE*, 1963, **51,** (12), pp. 1737–1753

33 ROBERTS, J.H.: 'Phase-lock-loop statistics without recourse to Fokker-Planck techniques', *Electron. Lett.*, 1975, **11,** (12), pp. 267–268

34 TIKHONOV, V.I.: 'The effects of noise on phase lock oscillation operation', *Automatika i Telemakhanika*, 1959, **22,** (9), pp. 1188–1196

35 TIKHONOV, V.I.: 'Phase lock automatic frequency control application in the presence of noise', *Automatika i Telemakhanika*, 1960, **23,** (3), pp. 301–309

36 HOLMES, J.K.: 'On a solution to the second-order phase locked loop', *IEEE Trans.*, 1970, **COM-18,** (2), pp. 119–126

37 STRÖM, T.: 'Approximation of the probability density function for a phase-locked loop', *Ericsson Tech.*, 1972, **28,** (1)

38 CHARLES, F.J., and LINDSEY, W.C.: 'Some analytical and experimental phase locked loop results for low signal-to-noise ratios', *Proc. IEEE*, 1966, **54,** (9), pp. 1152–1166

39 SMITH, B.M.: 'A semi-empirical approach to the PLL threshold', *IEEE Trans.*, 1966, **AES-2,** (4), pp. 463–468

40 PARK, J.H.: 'An FM detector for low S/N', *IEEE Trans.*, 1970, **COM-18,** (2), pp. 110–118

41 ROBERTS, J.H.: 'Variants of conventional f.m. demodulation having the aim of improving poor signal-to-noise ratios', Proceedings of IEE Conference on radio receivers and associated systems, Swansea, July 1972

42 ROBERTS, J.H.: 'Multiplication by square of envelope as a means of improving detection below the FM threshold', *IEEE Trans.*, 1971, **COM-19,** pp. 349–353

43 BLACHMAN, N.M.: 'Noise and its effect on communication' (McGraw-Hill, 1966)

Chapter 10

Digital f.m. and p.m.

10.1 Notation

In this chapter the subject matter is concerned with digital modulating
waveforms rather than analogue types and so the information-bearing
phase or frequency modulation which has hitherto been taken to be a
band of Gaussian noise is now a train of pulses derived from a stream of
binary digits.

In this stream, at intervals of T seconds ($1/T$ is the data rate), the
change from mark to space, or space to mark, may or may not occur,
and the usual assumption will be made that such changes are
equiprobable and are independent events.

The expression for the transmitted signal (in which ϕ_a is an arbitrary
phase angle) is again of the narrowband type

$$V(t) = A \cos \left[\omega_0 t + \mu(t) + \phi_a \right] \qquad (10.1)$$

but $\mu(t)$ now has the representation

$$\mu(t) = \sum_n b_n s(t - nT) \qquad (10.2)$$

where $s(t)$ specifies the shape of a signalling pulse. The frequency
modulation is therefore

$$\dot{\mu}(t) = \sum_n b_n \dot{s}(t - nT) \qquad (10.3)$$

Information is conveyed by the b_n which in the case of binary data will
take only two values, and, in order to clarify the notation used in
eqns. 10.2 and 10.3, suppose $\mu(t)$ is sampled at $t = NT + t_1$ where
$0 < t_1 < T$. Then b_n fixes the polarity of the current pulse and, in
expanded form, $\mu(NT + t_1)$ becomes

$$\mu(NT + t_1) = \ldots b_{-1}s(\overline{N+1}\,T + t_1) + b_0 s(NT + b_1) + \ldots$$

$$\ldots b_{N-1}s(T + t_1) + b_N s(t_1) \qquad (10.4)$$

Correspondingly

$$\dot{\mu}(NT + t_1) = \ldots b_{-1}\dot{s}(\overline{N+1}\,T + t_1) + b_0\dot{s}\,(NT + t_1) + \ldots$$

$$\ldots + b_{N-1}\dot{s}\,(T + t_1) + b_N\dot{s}\,(t_1) \qquad (10.5)$$

If, for example, the pulse $\dot{s}(t)$ has a duration of $2T$, then only $\dot{s}(t_1)$ (the current pulse) and $\dot{s}(T + t_1)$ will be non-zero. Thus, in writing $\dot{\mu}(t) = \sum_n b_n \dot{s}(t - nT)$ the upper limit of the summation depends on the time at which $\dot{\mu}(t)$ is considered and contributions to the sum from pulses other than the current one are due to pulses overlapping. The same upper limit pertains to the summation for $\mu(t)$, but as $\mu(t) = \int^t \dot{\mu}(x)dx$, the terms $s(2T + t_1), s(3T + t_1)\ldots$ appearing in eqn. 10.4 are each equal to the area under an $\dot{s}(t)$ pulse.[*]

The system design may involve the specification of $s(t)$ or $\dot{s}(t)$. A commonly encountered case is phase-shift keying (p.s.k.) in which $\mu(t)$ assumed the value $+\pi/2$ or the value $-\pi/2$ (initially, switching between these two will be assumed to occur instantaneously, and, although 0 and π are equally tenable values, we choose $\pm\pi/2$ because the ensemble average of $\mu(t)$ is then zero), and $s(t)$ is a rectangular pulse of duration T.

In systems using frequency-shift keying (f.s.k.) it is $\dot{s}(t)$ that is specified and this shaping is often defined to be the response of a lowpass filter to a rectangular pulse of duration T. Then $\dot{s}(t)$ is given by the difference of two step responses spaced in time by T and $1/T \int_0^\infty \dot{s}(x)dx = 1$, or, more realistically, $1/T \int_0^l \dot{s}(x)dx = 1$ where lT is the effective duration of a pulse. Typical values for l are 1, 2 or 3, and this normalisation, whereby the area under an $\dot{s}(t)$ pulse equals T, will be retained in the following.

The task of the receiver is to retrieve the train of digits $\ldots$, $b_{n-2}, b_{n-1}, b_n, b_{n+1}, \ldots$ and make as few errors as possible in identifying marks and spaces. A digital data system, unlike an analogue system, can be assigned a precise measure of performance which is the probability P_e that a detection error will be caused by extraneous interference. However, before consideration is given to the calculation of P_e in some representative cases, the power spectrum of $V(t)$ as given by eqn. 10.1 will be discussed.

---

[*] Any contribution to $\mu(t)$ arising from the arbitrary lower limit of integration can be regarded as part of ϕ_a in eqn.10.1.

It is usual to consider two situations where digital f.m. or p.m. spectra are concerned, namely the cases of discontinuous or continuous phase transitions. The former is associated with the use of two or more oscillators operating on slightly different carrier frequencies, the information being conveyed by switching between the oscillator outputs, so causing the phase to be discontinuous at the switching instances.[1,2] When a single oscillator is used, however, the phase is continuous at all times, and because a more compact r.f. spectrum can then be achieved, continuous phase operation is the more widely used. It is certainly the more interesting from a theoretical viewpoint, and attention will be confined to it here.

A characteristic of analyses of the power spectra of continuous phase f.m. or p.m. carriers is the extreme length of the formulae that emerge giving the spectral levels. These formulae, which may involve tabulated functions such as Fresnel integrals or Anger functions, reveal a complicated spectral structure of peaks and troughs, and, while present day computing facilities enable such expressions to be evaluated easily, it is difficult to obtain a feel for the modifications to be expected when simple changes in the modulating arrangements are made. However, examination of exactly calculated cases suggests that for large values of q (the radian frequency departrure from the carrier) the spectra often obey a law of the form

$$G(q) \approx \frac{f(q)}{q^{2(m+1)}} \qquad (10.6)$$

where m is an integer and $f(q)$ a trigonometric function. Here, and in future, large values of q can be taken to comply with $qT \geqslant 20$.

Often, interest lies solely in the tail region of the spectrum and then knowledge of m and the form of $f(q)$ suffices. Some examples of eqn. 10.6 are given later (Section 10.4).

10.2 $\Phi(u_1, u_2)$ and the characteristic function of $\mu(t + \tau) - \mu(t)$

As with analogue systems, certain circuit elements may be nonlinear or significant filtering may be introduced by the receiver input stages (the latter causes the current pulse to be affected by neighbouring pulses; intersymbol interference is the name given to this type of system imperfection) and a knowledge of only the power spectrum of $V(t)$ is unlikely to be adequate to assess detrimental effects on performance in all cases.

The bi-variate characteristic function of $V(t)$ carries within it information on the autocorrelation function, and therefore the power spectrum, as a special case of the information it provides about all the second-order moments between $V(t)$ and $V(t + \tau)$ (typified by $\langle V^n(t) \cdot V^m(t + \tau) \rangle$) and this function, $\Phi(u_1, u_2)$, is the key to investigating a variety of nonlinear operations that may be applied to $V(t)$ (see Section 2.6). Recalling eqns. 2.7 and 2.15, equating $R(t)$ and $R(t + \tau)$ to A, and $\theta(t)$ to $\mu(t)$, we have

$$\Phi(u_1, u_2) = \sum_{m=-\infty}^{+\infty} (-1)^m J_m(AU_1) J_m(AU_2) e^{jm\omega_0\tau} \langle e^{jm[\mu t+\tau)- \mu(t)]} \rangle \tag{10.7}$$

In obtaining this result, a time average over many cycles of cos $\omega_0 t$ has been performed leaving a time average over the slower variation of the modulation $\mu(t)$ to be done, plus an ensemble average over the b_n. These two operations are indicated by the angle brackets in eqn. 10.7 and it is seen that knowledge of the univariate characteristic function of $[\mu(t + \tau) - \mu(t)]$ provides $\Phi(u_1, u_2)$. Further, the general development leading from eqn. 4.1 to 4.3 shows that a direct calculation of the autocorrelation function of $V(t)$ relies on obtaining a result for $\langle \cos [\mu(t + \tau) - \mu(t)] \rangle$ and this will be seen to constitute the terms in $m = \pm 1$ of eqn. 10.7. Note that only the phase difference $\mu(t + \tau) - \mu(t)$ appears in eqn. 10.7 so that the arbitrary phase angle ϕ_a of eqn. 10.1 could be omitted (it was not included in eqn. 4.1).

Let $$\Phi_\mu(u) = \langle \exp ju \, [\mu(t + \tau) - \mu(t)] \rangle \tag{10.8}$$

The time average may be taken over an interval of length LT (with L a large integer), and written

$$\lim_{L \to \infty} \frac{1}{L} \sum_{N=0}^{L-1} \frac{1}{T} \int_0^T \exp ju \, [\mu(NT + x + \tau) - \mu(NT + x)] \, dx \tag{10.9}$$

Thus, it suffices to consider $t = NT + x$ $(0 < x < T)$ and also, for reasons that will be clear in a moment, we take $\tau = QT + \tau_1$ with $0 < \tau_1 < T$, $Q = 0, 1, 2, 3$ etc., and break the x integration into two parts as follows

$$\frac{1}{T} \int_0^{T-\tau_1} \exp (juF_1) dx + \frac{1}{T} \int_{T-\tau_1}^T \exp (juF_2) dx \tag{10.10}$$

where F_1 and F_2 represent $\{\mu(NT + x + \tau) - \mu(NT + x)\}$ in the two ranges. The time $t + \tau$ may be supposed to lie in the interval MT to $(M + 1)T$ so writing $t + \tau = MT + v$ (where v, like x and τ_1, lies in the range 0 to T)

$M = N + Q$ if $x < T - \tau_1$ $(v = x + \tau_1$: the F_1 region)

$M = N + Q + 1$ if $x > T - \tau_1$ $(v = x + \tau_1 - T$: the F_2 region)

Then using eqn. 10.2 with $\tau = QT + \tau_1$ and $Q \neq 0$, the following[*] are obtained for F_1 and F_2 of eqn. 10.10.

$$F_1 = \sum_{m=0}^{Q-1} b_{N+Q-m} s(x + \tau_1 + mT) + \sum_{m=0}^{N} b_{N-m}$$

$$\{s[x + \tau_1 + (Q+m)T] - s(x + mT)\} \qquad (10.11)$$

$$F_2 = \sum_{m=0}^{Q} b_{N+Q+1-m} s(x + \tau_1 - T + mT) + \sum_{m=0}^{N} b_{N-m}$$

$$\{s[x + \tau_1 - T + (Q+m+1)T] - s(x + mT)\}$$

$$(10.12)$$

$Q = 0$ is a special case for which $0 < \tau < T$ and

$$F_1 = \sum_{m=0}^{N} b_{N-m} \{s(x + \tau + mT) - s(x + mT)\} \qquad (10.13)$$

$$F_2 = b_{N+1} s(x + \tau - T) + \sum_{m=0}^{N} b_{N-m}$$

$$\{s[x + \tau - T + (m+1)T) - s(x + mT)\} \qquad (10.14)$$

For illustrative purposes, the binary f.s.k. situation will be taken in which each b_n is assumed to adopt the values $\pm \omega_1$ with equal probability. The ensemble averaging over the b_n of $\exp(juF_1)$ with $Q \neq 0$ then gives

$$\prod_{m=0}^{Q-1} \cos [u\omega_1 s(x + \tau_1 + mT)]$$

$$\cdot \prod_{m=0}^{N} \cos(u\omega_1 [s\{x + \tau_1 + (Q+m)T\} - s(x + mT)])$$

$$(10.15)$$

and for $\exp(juF_2)$ with $Q \neq 0$

$$\prod_{m=0}^{Q} \cos [u\omega_1 s(x + \tau_1 - T + mT)]$$

$$\prod_{m=0}^{N} \cos(u\omega_1 [s\{x + \tau_1 - T + (Q+1+m)T\} - s(x + mT)])$$

$$(10.16)$$

While, with $Q = 0$ the corresponding expressions are

$$\prod_{m=0}^{N} \cos [u\omega_1 \{s(x + \tau + mT) - s(x + mT)\}] \qquad (10.17)$$

---

[*] The arbitrary lower limit on the summation in eqn. 10.2 has been taken as $n = 0$

and

$$\cos\left[u\omega_1 s(x+\tau-T)\right] . \prod_{m=0}^{N} \cos\left(u\omega_1\left[s\{x+\tau-T+(m+1)T\}\right.\right.$$

$$\left.\left. -s(x+mT)\right]\right) \qquad (10.18)$$

In the above, the pulse duration is general, but, as mentioned earlier, $\dot{s}(t)$ may usually be attributed a finite duration such as T, $2T$ or $3T$ and $s(lT)-s(0)=T$ $(l=1, 2,$ or $3)$ The working can be carried through for any l but $l=1$ is of most interest and this case will be pursued here with the further simplifying assumption that $s(0)$ is zero. Then, the $s(t)$ with arguments that equal or exceed T can be replaced by T so simplifying the expressions above. The first (eqn. 10.15), for example, becomes

$$\cos\left[u\omega_1 s(x+\tau_1)\right]\cos^{Q-1}(u\omega_1 T)\cos\left[u\omega_1\{T-s(x)\}\right] \quad (10.19)$$

This holds for $0<x<T-\tau_1$ and will be seen to be independent of N. A like result is obtained in the other cases and $\Phi_\mu(u)$ for a general pulse $s(t)$ of duration T, i.e. the non-overlapping situation, can be written[*]

$$\Phi_\mu(u)=\frac{1}{T}\int_0^{T-\tau}\cos\left[u\omega_1\{s(x+\tau)-s(x)\}\right]dx$$

$$+\frac{1}{T}\int_{T-\tau}^{T}\cos\left[u\omega_1 s(x+\tau-T)\right]\cos\left[u\omega_1\{T-s(x)\}\right]dx \quad (10.20)$$

$$\text{for } 0<\tau<T$$

While for $\tau=QT+\tau_1$ $(0<\tau_1<T)$

$$\Phi_\mu(u)=\frac{1}{T}\int_0^{T-\tau_1}\cos\left[u\omega_1\{T-s(x)\}\right]\cos\left[u\omega_1 s(x+\tau_1)\right]dx\cos^{Q-1}(u\omega_1 T)$$

$$+\frac{1}{T}\int_{T-\tau_1}^{T}\cos\left[u\omega_1\{T-s(x)\}\right]\cos\left[u\omega_1 s(x+\tau_1-T)\right]dx\cos^Q(u\omega_1 T)$$

$$(10.21)$$

On placing $u=m$, a result is available to be substituted in to eqn. 10.7, while $u=1$ gives $\langle\cos\left[\mu(t+\tau)-\mu(t)\right]\rangle$, but it is clear that, unless $s(t)$ has a very simple form, the integrals in the result for $\Phi_\mu(u)$ will be tedious to evaluate (if this is possible without resorting to the aid of a computer) and a blossoming into expressions containing many terms rapidly ensues.

The simplest cases are

$$s(t)=T \qquad 0<t<T$$
$$\text{and}$$
$$s(t)=t \qquad 0<t<T$$

[*] As $\phi_\mu(u)$ depends only on τ, the phase difference is a wide-sense stationary process[3,45]

The former corresponds to p.s.k. with rectangular phase transitions. Note that $\dot{s}(t)$ then consists of two delta functions, one at $t = 0$ and another of opposite polarity at $t = T$, and although eqn. 10.19 has been developed for an f.s.k. situation it is seen that ω_1 is merely a scaling factor. By defining it so that $\omega_1 T = \pi/2$, the p.s.k. case with rectangular phase transitions can be handled, and then

$$\Phi_\mu(u) = \left(1 - \frac{\tau}{T}\right) + \frac{\tau}{T} \cos\left(\frac{\pi}{2}u\right) \quad 0 < T < T \qquad (10.22)$$

$$= \left[1 - \frac{2\tau_1}{T}\sin^2\left(\frac{\pi}{4}u\right)\right] \cos^Q\left(\frac{\pi}{2}u\right) \quad \tau = QT + \tau_1 \qquad (10.23)$$

When u is an integer, as is required in eqn. 10.7,

$$\Phi_\mu(4m) = 1$$

$$\Phi_\mu[2(2m + 1)] = S(\tau) \quad \begin{array}{l}\text{where } S(\tau) \text{ is a triangular wave with} \\ \text{period } T\,[S(0) = 1, S(T/2) = 0, \\ S(T/2) = -1]\end{array}$$

$$\Phi_\mu(2m + 1) = 1 - \frac{\tau}{T} \qquad 0 < \tau < T$$

$$= 0 \qquad \text{otherwise} \qquad (10.24)$$

In this case $\Phi(u_1, u_2)$, the bivariate characteristic function for binary p.s.k. with rectangular switching, can be written

$$\Phi(u_1, u_2) = \tfrac{1}{4}[1 + S(\tau)]\{J_0[A\sqrt{f(\cos z)}] + J_0[A\sqrt{f(-\cos z)}]\}$$
$$+ \tfrac{1}{4}[1 - S(\tau)]\{J_0[A\sqrt{f(\sin z)}] + J_0[A\sqrt{f(-\sin z)}]\}$$
$$+ \tfrac{1}{2}\left[1 - \frac{\tau}{T}\right]\{J_0[A\sqrt{f(\cos z)}] - J_0[A\sqrt{f(-\cos z)}]\} \qquad (10.25)$$

Where $f(\cos z) = u_1^2 + u_2^2 + 2u_1 u_2 \cos z$, $z = \omega_0 \tau$ and $1 - \dfrac{\tau}{T}$ is zero if $\tau > T$. In the f.s.k. situation for which $s(t)$ varies linearly with t, ω_1 governs the deviation that is applied and it is usual to define a deviation ratio k by $k\pi = \omega_1 T$. So for f.s.k. with linear phase transitions

$$\Phi_\mu(u) = \left[1 - \frac{\tau}{2T}\right]\cos\left(u\pi k \frac{\tau}{T}\right) + \frac{\sin\left(u\pi k \dfrac{\tau}{T}\right)}{2u\pi k} \quad \text{for } 0 < \tau < T \qquad (10.26)$$

and when $\tau = QT + \tau_1$

$$\Phi_\mu(u) = \left\{ \frac{1}{2} \left(1 - \frac{\tau_1}{T}\right) \cos\left[u\pi k \left(1 + \frac{\tau_1}{T}\right)\right] \right.$$

$$\left. + \frac{\left[\sin u\pi k \left(1 - \frac{\tau_1}{T}\right)\right]}{2u\pi k} \right\} \cos^{Q-1}(u\pi k)$$

$$+ \left\{ \frac{1}{2}\left(\frac{\tau_1}{T}\right) \cos\left(u\pi k \frac{\tau_1}{T}\right) \right.$$

$$\left. + \frac{\sin\left(u\pi k \frac{\tau_1}{T}\right)}{2u\pi k} \right\} \cos^Q(u\pi k) \qquad (10.27)$$

10.3 Digital r.f. spectra

Formal progress can be made with the calculation of the power spectrum $G(q)$ without specifying $s(t)$, and corresponding[*] to eqn. 4.6

$$\left\{ \frac{G(q)}{\frac{1}{2}A^2} \right\} = \frac{1}{\pi} \int_0^\infty \Phi_\mu(\tau, 1) \cos q\tau d\tau \qquad (10.28)$$

where $\Phi_\mu(\tau, 1)$ stands for $\Phi_\mu(u)$ with $u = 1$, as given by eqn. 10.8. When $\Phi_\mu(u)$ is provided by eqns. 10.22 and 10.23, and $u = 1$

$$\left\{ \frac{G(q)}{\frac{1}{2}A^2} \right\} = \frac{1}{\pi} \int_0^T \left(1 - \frac{\tau}{T}\right) \cos q\tau d\tau = \frac{T}{2\pi} \left(\frac{\sin q\frac{T}{2}}{qT/2}\right)^2 \qquad (10.29)$$

This well-known $(\sin x/x)^2$ spectrum for binary p.s.k. with rectangular transitions can, of course, be obtained in other ways (References 1 to 9 discuss the calculation of the spectrum, the so-called direct method being the most widely used alternative) and $[\sin (qT/2)/qT/2]$ is recognised as the Fourier transform of the phase modulating pulse or, equally in this instance, the amplitude modulating pulse. The spectrum falls away according to q^{-2} and so, in eqn. 10.6, $m = 0$, and $f(q) = (2/\pi T)\sin^2 (qT/2)$, although eqn. 10.29 holds for all q and is not confined to large values of q as in eqn. 10.6.

In the general case $\Phi_\mu(\tau, 1)$ has a differing dependence on τ according to the integer Q for which $\tau = QT + \tau_1$. The integration over τ

---

[*] It may be helpful to remark that $G(q)$ is measured in power/rad/s so $G(q)$. $2\pi/T$ is a power level

in eqn. 10.28 is then taken over contiguous portions of length T, and the r.f. spectrum of $V(t)$, with generally shaped non-overlapping phase transitions, can be written

$$\left\{ \frac{G(q)}{\frac{1}{2}A^2} \right\} = \frac{1}{\pi} \int_0^T (I_1 + I_2) \cos q\tau d\tau$$

$$+ \frac{1}{\pi} \int_0^T (I_3 + I_4 \cos k\pi) F(qT, q\tau_1, k) d\tau_1 \tag{10.30}$$

where, provided $|\cos \omega_1 T| = |\cos k\pi| < 1$

$$F(qT, q\tau_1, k) = \frac{\cos q\tau_1 (\cos qT - \cos k\pi) - \sin q\tau_1 \sin qT}{1 - 2\cos k\pi \cos qT + \cos^2 k\pi}$$

If $|\cos k\pi| = 1$

$$F(qT, q\tau_1, k) = \cos k\pi \left[\pi \cos q\tau_1 \sum_{n=-\infty}^{+\infty} \delta(qT + k\pi - 2n\pi) \right.$$

$$\left. - \frac{\sin\left[q\left(\dfrac{T}{2} + \tau_1 \right) + k\dfrac{\pi}{2} \right]}{2\sin\left(\dfrac{qT + k\pi}{2} \right)} \right]$$

I_1, I_2, I_3 and I_4 are identified from eqns. 10.20 and 10.21. I_3, for example, is given by the first of the two terms in eqn. 10.21, and

$$I_3 = \frac{1}{T} \int_0^{T-\tau_1} \cos \left[k\pi \left\{ 1 - \frac{s(x)}{T} \right\} \right] \cos \left[\frac{k\pi}{T} s(x + \tau_1) \right] dx \tag{10.31}$$

It is seen that lines appear in the spectrum when $|\cos k\pi| = 1$. The simplest case of this occurs when $k = 0$ (the carrier is unmodulated). Then, the $n = 0$ term of the summation of Delta functions provides $\left\{ \dfrac{G(q)}{\frac{1}{2}A^2} \right\} = T\delta(qT)$ For $k = 1, 2, 3$ etc., a continuous spectrum is present together with lines, and the amplitudes of the lines fall away rapidly as separation from the carrier increases. With rectangular f.s.k. there are a finite number of lines and with $k = 1$, for example, there is one line at $q/2\pi = 1/2T$ and another at $q/2\pi = -1/2T$. Half the power resides in these two lines and while they convey no digital information they can provide timing information (Section 10.13).

Eqn. 10.30 shows that the spectrum is determined in particular cases by evaluating double integrals over the square of side T and this is true also of more complicated cases in which pulse overlapping occurs, i.e. $l = 2, 3$ etc. A very general analytical result for the spectrum of continuous phase f.m. or p.m., which is not confined to binary data, has been given by Anderson and Salz[7] and so the general forms of these double integrals are available for study.

In view of eqn. 10.6 it seems likely that repeated integration by parts to yield a form in inverse powers of q could be fruitful, and starting from the Anderson and Salz result, this method of attack has been successfully applied by Baker[10] to identify the form of $f(q)$ in eqn. 10.6.

Before describing these results, however, we remind ourselves of a theorem in Fourier analysis[11] which states that, if the mth derivative of a function [$V(t)$ in this case] is the first derivative to have a discontinuity[the $(m + 1)$th derivative becomes impulsive], then the magnitude of its Fourier transform $F(j\omega)$ decreases at the rate $\omega^{-(m+1)}$, as ω goes to infinity. The power spectrum is proportional to the squared magnitude of $F(j\omega)$ and so it decreases according to a $\omega^{-2(m+1)}$ law. If

$$V(t) = A \cos [\omega_0 t + \mu(t)]$$

then

$$\dot{V}(t) = -A[\omega_0 + \dot{\mu}(t)] \sin [\omega_0 t + \mu(t)]$$

$$\ddot{V}(t) = -A[\omega_0 + \dot{\mu}(t)]^2 \cos [\omega_0 t + \mu(t)] - A\ddot{\mu}(t)\sin [\omega_0 t + \mu(t)]$$

etc. (10.32)

and it is the continuity of the in-phase and quadrature components of $V^{(n)}(t)$ that must be examined. Stated another way, the value of m is decided by the lowest-order derivative of $s(t)$, $0 \leqslant t \leqslant lT$, that is non-zero at the points where $t = 0$ and $t = lT$. In the example of binary p.s.k. considered earlier, $\dot{s}(t) = 0$ except at $t = 0$ and $t = T$ so $m = 0$ and the spectrum falls away according to q^{-2}. With binary f.s.k. and rectangular switching [$\dot{s}(t) = 1$ for $0 < t < T$, i.e. $l = 1$], $\ddot{s}(t)$ and all higher derivatives equal zero. Hence, $m = 1$ and the spectrum falls away according to q^{-4}. Two further examples are:

(a) $\dot{s}(t)$ has a sinusoidal form, and $l = 1$.

$$\dot{s}(t) = \frac{\pi}{2} \sin \left(\pi \frac{t}{T}\right)$$

$$\ddot{s}(t) = \frac{\pi^2}{2T} \cos \left(\pi \frac{t}{T}\right)$$

$$\dddot{s}(t) = \frac{-\pi^3}{2T^2} \sin \left(\frac{\pi t}{T}\right)$$

the first derivative to be non-zero when $t = 0$ and $t = T$ is the second, so $m = 2$ and the spectrum falls away as q^{-6} for large q.

(b) Binary f.m. with cosinusoidal transitions and $l = 2$

$$\dot{s}(t) = \frac{1}{2}\left[1 - \cos\left(\frac{\pi t}{T}\right)\right]$$

$$\ddot{s}(t) = \frac{\pi}{2T}\sin\left(\frac{\pi t}{T}\right)$$

$$\dddot{s}(t) = \frac{1}{2}\left(\frac{\pi}{T}\right)^2 . \cos\left(\frac{\pi t}{T}\right) \quad \dddot{s}(0) = \dddot{s}(0) = \frac{1}{2}\left(\frac{\pi}{T}\right)^2 .$$

Thus, $m = 3$ so showing that the spectrum falls away as q^{-8} for large q (Reference 10).

Evidently the value of m does not depend on the deviation ratio k, and thus it is suggested that $V(t)$ be expanded in an approximate form appropriate to low deviation ratios.

$$V(t) \approx A\cos\omega_0 t - A\mu(t)\sin\omega_0 t \qquad (10.33)$$

The second of these terms provides the contribution at large q and the r.f. spectrum will therefore follow the power spectrum of $\mu(t)$ reflected about the carrier frequency. $1/q^2$ times this spectrum gives the spectrum of $\dot{\mu}(t)$ which, in the case of cosinusoidal frequency transitions, will be proportional to

$$k^2\left[\frac{\sin qT}{qT\left\{\frac{(qT)^2}{\pi^2} - 1\right\}}\right]^2 \qquad (10.34)$$

This varies as q^{-6} for large q and, thus, in total, the r.f. spectrum falls away according to q^{-8}, as stated for case *(b)* above.

10.4 Forms of $f(q)$

From the above it is seen that the value of m does not depend on the deviation ratio. This is not the case with $f(q)$, however, and results such as eqn. 10.34 refer to leading terms in expansions of $f(q)$ for small k.

(i) Binary f.s.k.
Baker finds the general form of $f(q)$, and for binary f.s.k. with rectangular transitions ($|\cos k\pi| \neq 1$), gives

$$\left\{ \frac{G(q)}{\frac{1}{2}A^2 T} \right\} \approx \frac{1}{q^4} \left(\frac{2\pi k^2}{T^4} \right) \frac{[\cos k\pi - \cos qT]^2}{[1 - 2\cos k\pi \cos qT + \cos^2 k\pi]} \quad (10.35)$$

The exact result which is provided by eqn. 10.30 reproduces eqn.

10.35, except that q^4 is replaced by $\left[q^2 - \left(\frac{k\pi}{T} \right)^2 \right]^2$. If k is so small

that $\cos k\pi$ can be replaced by unity, the right-hand side of eqn.
10.35 becomes

$$\frac{1}{q^2} \left(\frac{\pi k^2}{2T^2} \right) \left(\frac{\sin \frac{qT}{2}}{q \frac{T}{2}} \right)^2 \quad (10.36)$$

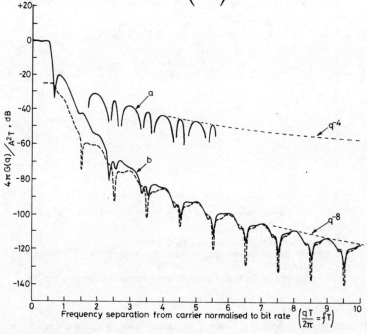

Fig. 10.1 Two examples of binary f.m. spectra

a Rectangular pulses in frequency. Deviation ratio = 0·7, pulse duration = T

b Raised-cosine pulses in frequency. Deviation ratio = 0·7, pulse duration = $2T$

With curve *a* the spectrum has zeros when the abscissa scale takes the value $n \pm 0·35$

$n = 1, 2, 3 \ldots$, and its level at the origin is

$20 \log_{10} \frac{2}{k\pi} = -1$ dB when $k = 0·7$

The dashed curve underlying curve *b* shows the asymptotic result (Reference 10)

which may be compared with eqn. 10.29 for binary p.s.k. Fig. 10.1 is
for the case of binary f.m. with cosinusoidal frequency transitions and
shows how the asymptotic formula for this case (see Expression 33 of
Reference 10) approaches the exact result. A portion of the spectrum
for rectangular switching is also shown.

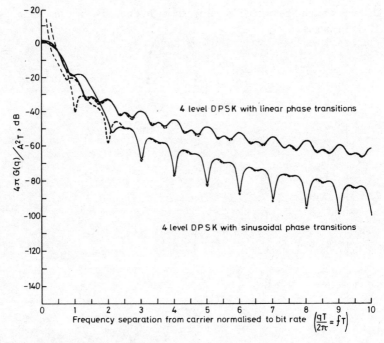

Fig. 10.2 Two examples of four-phase DPSK spectra
Broken curves are asymptotic results (Reference 10)*, full curves are
exact spectra
* Courtesy Institute of Electrical and Electronic Engineers Inc.

(ii) Four-phase cases
Differentially coherent reception of phase shift keyed signals is a topic
that will be discussed in Section 10.5. The phase of the presently
received signal is compared to the phase of the previous signal, and in
a four-phase system this phase change is usually arranged to be one of
the four possibilities $-\pi/4, +\pi/4, -3\pi/4$ or $+3\pi/4$. The power
spectrum for this transmission has a neat asymptotic form when
$s(t) = t$ i.e. linear phase transitions. The result[10] is

$$\left\{\frac{G(q)}{\frac{1}{2}A^2T}\right\} \approx \frac{\pi}{(2qT)^4}\{5 + 2\sqrt{2}\cos qT + 2\cos 2qT\} \quad (10.37)$$

If, however, the sinusoidal form considered in (*a*) in Section 10.3 is adopted for the $s(t)$ pulses

$$\left\{\frac{G(q)}{\frac{1}{2}A^2T}\right\} \approx \frac{\pi^5}{(2qT)^6}\{5 - 2\sqrt{2}\cos qT - 2\cos 2qT\} \quad (10.38)$$

As mentioned earlier, these results are expected to be acceptable for $qT \geqslant 20$ or a $qT/2\pi$ (i.e. fT) of three and greater. A comparison of eqns. 10.37 and 10.38 with the exact results is shown on Fig. 10.2.

A large literature exists dealing with the spectra of digital f.m. and p.m. transmissions. The reader is referred to References 1–9 where extensions to multilevel f.s.k., the effects of correlation between successive pulses, pulse trains in which the pulses may overlap and have different shapes, and preferred algorithms for computation of the formulae, are treated.

10.5 Modulation and demodulation methods

The material of this section is intended to be a review of the many ways of transmitting and then retrieving digital data that are now commonly implemented. In general terms, the receiver aims to reconstitute the stream of binary digits by performing operations on the recovered waveform that allow $\mu(t)$ or functions of $\mu(t)$ such as $\sin\mu(t)$ and $\cos\mu(t)$, or $\sin[\mu(t + T) - \mu(t)]$ and $\cos[\mu(t + T) - \mu(t)]$, to be examined, and which, in absence of noise or other interference, would never result in a mark being mistaken for a space, or vice versa.

The design of the decision circuitry and of the chain comprising the pre-modulator filter, bandpass filter, detector, and post detector filter is governed by what impairments the signal may suffer before its reception. How the receiver may then be persuaded to respond to intended signal changes but ignore perturbations due to noise and other interference is indicated by statistical decision theory.

One of the leading considerations concerns the information made available at the receiver regarding both the frequency and the phase of the wanted signal. If both are known then coherent detection may be implemented by multiplying the received signal with a local reference followed by removal of the component at twice the intermediate frequency; absolute changes in phase can be detected so the information can be applied at the transmitter in such a form.

As has been seen, a phase lock loop can be used to provide the local reference that is locked in phase and hence in frequency, to the carrier used for transmission, except for a phase error $\phi(t)$ due to noise. Hopefully this error is small, and the quasi-coherent or partially coherent detection that is then achieved will provide satisfactory performance, i.e. the presence of $\phi(t)$ does not cause too many additional detection errors.

M-ary is the term coined for systems that use an alphabet of *M* symbols, and $\mu(t)$ then has *M* distinct states at a sampling instant. An example of this is known as four-phase c.p.s.k. (coherent phase shift keying) in which $\mu(t)$ takes one of the four values $\pm \pi/4, \pm 3\pi/4$. It will be noticed that these angles are uniformly spaced around the unit circle and $M = 4 = 2^2$. The alphabet in this case stems from considering the binary digits in pairs, and $\pi/4, -\pi/4, 3\pi/4$, and $-3\pi/4$ usually correspond to 11, 10, 01 and 00, respectively. It is then convenient to speak of a symbol error and this would occur when $\pi/4$ is signalled, for instance, if the phase is judged by the decision circuitry not to lie in the first quadrant. Thus, the usual x and y axes form convenient decision boundaries in this case.

If the necessary stability to preserve phase is not available at the receiver, coherent detection may become impracticable (considerations of cost and equipment complexity may also rule out coherent or partially coherent detection) and an alternative that is often turned to is comparison or differential detection. Here, a phase reference is derived from past signalling intervals and the receiver examines the phase change that occurs over the digit period *T*. Thus, it is the value of

$$\Delta_s(\overline{N+1\,T}) = \mu(t + \overline{N+1\,T}) - \mu(t + NT) \qquad N = 0, 1, 2, \ldots$$
(10.39)

that carries the information (in future the $N = 0$ sample of Δ_s will be assumed typical) and this phase difference can be made available in terms of $\sin \Delta_s(T)$ and $\cos \Delta_s(T)$ through multiplying the received waveform by a version of itself having a time difference of *T*. If this operation is applied to the received signal when it is written as in eqn. 1.3

$$V(t)V(t + T) = R(t)\cos[\omega_0 t + \theta(t)] . R(t + T)$$

$$\cos[\omega_0(t + T) + \theta(t + T)]$$

$$= \frac{R(t)R(t + T)}{2}\cos[\omega_0 T + \theta(t + T) - \theta(t)]$$
(10.40)

plus a term in $2\omega_0 t$ which is filtered out. A version of eqn. 10.40 with sine instead of cosine can be produced by introducing a $\pi/2$ phase shift before multiplication, and so an examination of the polarities of the sine and cosine outputs* allows the signalled phase change to be allotted to the corresponding quadrant. When both are negative it is concluded that the signalled phase change was $- 3\pi/4$, for example. The original data stream has to be pre-coded and, as with coherent detection cases, binary or *M*-ary forms of differential encoding can be used (binary d.p.s.k. or *M*-ary d.p.s.k.). Note that $\omega_0 t + \theta(t + T) - \theta(t)$ in eqn. 10.40 is an angle reduced modulo 2π, also $\theta(t + T)$ and $\theta(t)$ are not necessarily independent phase angles when noise is the cause of them differing in value from $\mu(t + T)$ and $\mu(t)$. Two examples of the transmitted spectrum are shown on Fig. 10.2.

An incoherent method of detection is one in which all features of the wanted signal except its phase are known at the receiver and an example of this can arise with the transmission of binary data by on-off switching between the outputs of two oscillators sited at the transmitter. The receiver has two filters, one tuned to the frequency used for space and the other tuned to the frequency used for mark, and the filter outputs are envelope detected, or squared and then smoothed (energy detection). Marks and spaces are declared by subtracting the processed signals and comparing the result with a zero threshold.

Owing to the phase discontinuities that occur at the switching instants, the power spectrum falls away only as q^{-2} at frequencies remote from the carriers used for mark and space, but using a single oscillator with phase continuity, a q^{-4} law (or better) is achievable; this is much more attractive when channels are to operate in the presence of neighbouring transmissions. A shift to a frequency above the carrier standing for a mark with a shift to a position below the carrier standing for a space is an obvious arrangement, and a conventional discriminator (an incoherent form of detection) will provide the waveform $\dot{\mu}(t)$ which, when correctly sampled, can be used to separate a mark $[\dot{\mu}(t) > 0]$ from a space $[\dot{\mu}(t) < 0]$, or a post-detection filter may delay the decision until $\dot{\mu}(t)$ has been filtered.

The timing information for sampling might be extracted from the residual carrier (this implies some pre-arranged relationship between the carrier frequency and the data rate), from a preamble, or from particular periodic sequences of digits sent in-between-times when no messages are sent. The consequences of errors in timing at the detector output can be investigated analytically without too much difficulty, but the corresponding analysis for the output of the post-detector filter is usually best accomplished by simulation or Monte Carlo means. This is because the instantaneous frequency is

---

* $\omega_0 T$ can be eliminated using obvious trigonometrical identities

non-Gaussian. With simulation, if timing errors or other system imperfections are rare events ($P_e < 10^{-4}$) very large sample populations (long
computer runs) are necessary to ensure significance of the results and
the programs become expensive to run. However, ways of partly over-
coming this difficulty have been proposed.[12]

Bandpass filters play an important role in digital system design, and
expressions for $P(t)$ and $Q(t)$, the inphase and quadrature signal
components at the output of a bandpass filter, are obtained by substituting eqn. 10.2 in eqn. 7.1. In general, the forms, being of such complexity, serve best as an aid in developing computer similation or Monte
Carlo-type programs that model system operation. However, when
noise is added to the filtered signal, considerable information about the
statistical properties of the detected wave can be obtained and
expressed formally in terms of $P(t)$ and $Q(t)$ (or their differentiated
and delayed versions), and so we tend to concentrate attention on the
detector output. Section 10.19 discusses the post-detector filter which,
as implied above, presents extreme theoretical difficulty.

The optimisation problem that confronts the designer is how to
ensure that the signal occupies a bandwidth that is sufficiently narrow
for the effects of noise and adjacent channel interference to be minimal
and yet is not so narrow that intersymbol interference introduces an
unacceptable number of detection errors.

The intersymbol interference referred to here is of two kinds.
Firstly, if the pulses making up $\mu(t)$ of eqn. 10.2 overlap, then some
intersymbol interference is sure to be present unless by careful design
Nyquist's laws can be exploited (Section 5.3 of Reference 13). The
pre-modulator filter is responsible for shaping the baseband pulses
$s(t)$ and so governs this design aspect. The second kind of intersymbol
interference and the one more difficult to control is that additionally
present after any bandpass filter stages and the demodulator have been
traversed. It is $P(t)$ and $Q(t)$ that contain the information as to how
this extra intersymbol interference affects the error count, and where
possible, general guide lines to the resulting nonlinear problem of the
best choice for the receiver bandpass filter will be given, but each case
encountered should, ultimately, be considered on its own merits*. The
memory of the filter means that the intersymbol interference
experienced at any sampling instant depends on the particular pattern
of bits that led up to that point and so an average is usually to be taken

---

* The reader interested in detailed investigations into the effects of intersymbol
interference is directed to the numerous papers that appeared in *Alta Frequenza*
over the period 1971–73, where results provided by special-purpose computer
programs are described.

over all possible patterns of foregoing bits. Thus, the application of pre-modulator shaping to realise a spectrum with more steeply falling skirts [examples (*a*) and (*b*) of Section 10.3] may result in unacceptable levels of intersymbol interference at the sampler.

Designs have been proposed[14,15] which aim to achieve complete freedom from intersymbol interference when the instantaneous frequency of a filtered rectangularly switched f.s.k. wave is sampled. It is clear from the general expression eqn. 7.7 that while $M(t)$ is constant $[M(t) = \pm \omega_1$, say], provided the impulse response function of the i.f. filter has decayed to zero within the time T, the instantaneous frequency will be free of intersymbol interference. Thus, a bandwidth in excess of $1/T$ Hz is indicated and the more detailed investigations identify i.f. transfer characteristics that are rather wider than are required when noise has to be excluded too. Obviously, freedom from intersymbol interference is highly desirable when it would otherwise far outweigh other causes of detection errors, but more often a design is sought which strikes a good compromise between filtering out noise, and introducing errors from spectrum truncation effects.

There are a variety of criteria that can be applied when comparisons are made between modulation methods (systems can be compared on the basis of a common data rate, a specified bandwidth occupancy, at some fixed value of carrier-to-noise ratio or carrier to interferer ratio etc.) and clear cut preferences are seldom to be identified. There have been many comparisons made that assume Gaussian noise to be the only kind of system interference[16−19] but this is unlikely to be realistic except perhaps for a satellite link, and the effects of fading, echoes, impulse noise and adjacent channel interference etc. can have great bearing on system design. The inevitable presence of Gaussian (thermal) noise means that it should never be ignored entirely, but a situation in which the signal is disturbed to a much greater extent by the unwanted presence of a c.w. tone can be a good model of jamming, for example, and so, rather than go over ground that has been well covered in the past, we aim to provide results which extend earlier material and which touch on these other forms of system imperfections.

10.6 Coherent and partially coherent detection

The first example to be treated will be that of the coherent or partially coherent detection of a binary phase shift keyed (p.s.k.) transmission.

Then, the received sum of carrier plus r.f. interference may be written

$$V(t) = A \cos [\omega_0 t + \mu(t)] + X(t) \cos \omega_0 t - Y(t) \sin \omega_0 t$$

$$= R(t) \cos [\omega_0 t + \theta(t)] \tag{10.41}$$

and the system could be designed so that binary information is conveyed by switching $\mu(t)$ between the two values 0 and π or, as will be assumed here, $+\pi/2$ and $-\pi/2$. Rectangular switching like this or, more accurately, a close approximation to it, is quite frequently used in practice although there is a large bandwidth requirement. Eqn. 10.29 shows that the power spectrum has a $[(\sin x/2)/(x/2)]^2$ shape with $x = qT$, q being measured from the carrier and $1/T$ Hz being the data rate.

As was described in Section 9.13 of the previous Chapter, a phase lock loop can provide a local reference that is locked in both phase and frequency to the carrier of the received transmission except for a phase error $\phi(t)$ due to the presence of noise. If this reference is used to implement coherent detection at the receiver, the output from the phase comparator when sampled at $t = T$ will be proportional to $R(T) \sin [\theta(T) - \phi(T)]$. With rectangular switching of the type currently under investigation if a $+\pi/2$ phase shift is signalled then $\theta(T)$ would, ideally, be equal to $\pi/2$, but owing to the presence of noise or r.f. interference (and, perhaps, to intersymbol interference) a departure from this value is likely to have taken place. An error will be made by the decision circuitry, however, only if $R(T) \sin [\theta(T) - \phi(T)]$, or equally, $\theta(T) - \phi(T)$, is judged to be negative [where $\theta(T) - \phi(T)$ is a phase angle reduced modulo 2π].

If the reference signal provided by the p.l.l. is noise free, then perfectly coherent detection is achievable and the probability of error P_e (assuming marks and spaces to be equilikely) is given by the probability that $R(T) \sin \theta_{\pi/2}(T)$ is negative. The suffix $\pi/2$ has been added to indicate that this probability is to be evaluated conditional upon the (arbitrary) choice that a $\pi/2$ phase shift has been signalled. Then, when the input bandwidth is large enough for any intersymbol interference effects to be ignored, $R(T) \sin \theta_{\pi/2}(T) = A + Y(T)$ (in the notation of eqn. 10.41), and so, if $Y(t)$ should be the quadrature component of narrowband Gaussian noise

$$P_e = \tfrac{1}{2} [1 - \text{erf} (\sqrt{\rho})] \tag{10.42}$$

where $\text{erf} (x) = \dfrac{2}{\sqrt{\pi}} \int_0^x e^{-y^2} dy$ and $\rho = \dfrac{A^2}{2\langle I_s^2 \rangle}$ is the carrier-to-noise power ratio. The result corresponding to eqn. 10.42 for coherent f.s.k.* is equally easy to derive and only requires ρ to be replaced by $\rho/2$

Jain[20] shows that if a binary p.s.k. signal plus noise (the carrier to noise ratio being ρ) is hard limited and retransmitted (with amplitude K) but is re-received in the presence of noise (carrier-to-noise ratio $b\rho$, say) then, when coherent detection is achieved, the probabaility of error P_B is given by

$$P_B = \tfrac{1}{2}[1 - \sqrt{1 - k^2} I_e(k, x)] \qquad (10.43)$$

where $\qquad k = \dfrac{1-b}{1+b}$ and $x = \rho \dfrac{(1+b)}{2}$

Even if the received signal and noise are passed through a second limiter and again contaminated with noise, the error probability is still given by eqn. 10.43 with b suitably interpreted. This is typical of the situation in which a satellite transponder is of the hard-limiting type and the reader may care to see how eqn. 10.43 can be obtained from eqn. 2.17, the integral result eqn. 2.18, and the remarks above eqn. 2.18. One of the signals used in the bivariate characteristic function is the reference, $V \cos \omega_0 t$ say, and the other is the sum of noise and a constant amplitude transmission (a hard limited version of p.s.k. signal-plus-noise with composite amplitude K) that enters the receiver.

$Y(t)$ in eqn. 10.41 could be the quadrature component of an unwanted adjacent channel or co-channel transmission, but if its amplitude relative to A is less than unity it cannot cause an error in the sign of $A + Y(t)$. When this relative amplitude exceeds unity, $Y(t)$ may be given the density function:

$$p(Y) = \frac{1}{\pi \sqrt{(rA)^2 - Y^2}}, |Y| < rA$$

i.e. $Y(t)$ is a randomly phased sinusoid of amplitude rA. Then

$$P_e = \text{Prob}\,[A + Y(t) < 0] = \frac{1}{2} - \frac{1}{\pi}\sin^{-1}\left(\frac{1}{r}\right) \qquad r > 1$$

$$(10.44)$$

When more than one interferer is present the extension of eqn. 10.44 is obtained by using the density function of the sum of the corresponding number of incommensurate sinusoids. These distributions for large numbers of equi-amplitude tones are shown in Fig. 7.2, and it is then highly likely that the Central Limit theorem will

* The switch from one frequency state to the other is often arranged to coincide closely with a zero of the carrier so as to reduce the spread of spectral components

be judged to hold sufficiently well for the error probability to be given by a expression like eqn. 10.42.

Small numbers of interferers (less than five, say) require special treatment (the distribution of the sums are shown in References 21 and 22) and it has been well established that attempts to replace the interference by an equivalent amount of noise tend to err on the pessimistic side regarding the number of errors that will be experienced on average.[23]

Note that when no phase relationship is assumed to exist between the wanted and unwanted signals the amounts by which the interfering signals are offset in frequency from the carrier of the wanted transmission do not enter the calculation of P_e for coherent reception.

10.7 Useful bounding technique

An exact calculation of P_e when noise and several interfering signals enter the receiver has been carried through in Reference 24 where up to four interferers and multi-phase-shift keying (four, eight and sixteen phase systems) are treated. The working is necessarily complicated so some simpler computational approach would be valuable, and with the aim of bounding P_e in a realistic manner References 25 and 26 have described an extremely useful technique which can also include the effects of intersymbol interference.

The method presupposes that the samples $S(t)$ that are examined by the decision circuitry can be expressed as follows

$$S(t) = C + I + N \qquad (10.45)$$

Here C is the symbol[*] that is transmitted, N is a Gaussian noise component but I is some form of interference (due to extraneous signals or intersymbol interference) that does not have a Gaussian distribution of its amplitudes and, in fact, the distribution of I is largely unknown. Taking a binary case for illustrative purposes, the probability, conditional on some value for I that $S(t)$ has a sign opposite to that of C, is given by

$$P(I) = \frac{1}{4}\left[\operatorname{erfc}\left(\frac{C+I}{\sigma_N\sqrt{2}}\right) + \operatorname{erfc}\left(\frac{C-I}{\sigma_N\sqrt{2}}\right)\right] \qquad (10.46)$$

where $\sigma_N^2 = \langle N^2 \rangle$, and $\operatorname{erfc}(y) = 1 - \operatorname{erf}(y)$

[*] $C = \pm A$ in the notation of Section 10.6

To obtain the averaged error probability, P is now to be averaged over the non-Gaussian distribution of I. When I has but a few possible values (intersymbol interference, for example, in which only the immediately neighbouring pulses contribute) this is not too difficult but the cases frequently met in practice fall in between this situation and the one where the Central Limit theorem might be invoked to argue that I is nearly normal.

The authors of References 25 and 26 suppose that three statistical parameters of I can be determined without undue difficulty. These are its mean value, its variance, and its peak value (the latter is the sum of the amplitudes when several c.w. interferers constitute I). Armed with this information, distributions are identified which share these parameters with the true distribution of I but which produce lower and upper bounds on the averaged value of P.

Without loss of generality, the mean value of I will be assumed to be zero and the peak value will be called I_m; thus I never has an excursion outside the interval $-I_m$ to $+I_m$. Letting $f(x)$ be the (unknown) probability density function of I

$$\int_{-I_m}^{I_m} f(x)dx = 1 \qquad \int_{-I_m}^{I_m} xf(x)dx = 0 \qquad \int_{-I_m}^{I_m} x^2 f(x)dx = \sigma_I^2$$

(10.47)

where σ_I^2 is the mean square value of I

It is shown in Reference 26 that, of all admissible density functions $f(x)$ that satisfy eqn. 10.47,

$$f(x) = \left[1 - \left(\frac{\sigma_I}{I_m}\right)^2\right] \delta(x) + \frac{1}{2}\left(\frac{\sigma_I}{I_m}\right)^2 \delta(x - I_m) + \frac{1}{2}\left(\frac{\sigma_I}{I_m}\right)^2 \delta(x + I_m)$$

(10.48)

is the one that causes $\bar{P} = \int_{-I_m}^{I_m} P(I)f(I)dI$ to be maximised, while

$$f(x) = \frac{1}{2}\left[\delta(x - \sigma_I) + \delta(x + \sigma_I)\right]$$

(10.49)

causes $\bar{P}$ to be minimised.

These maximising and minimising densities are seen to be extremely simple, and they mean that $\bar{P}$ can be bounded merely by giving I the values zero, $\pm\sigma_I$ and $\pm I_m$, in eqn. 10.46. They apply for large values of $|C|/\sigma_N$ (corresponding to error probabilities less than 10^{-2}, say) but this is usually the region of greatest interest. A treatment of the larger error-probabilities is also given in References 25, 26, and subject to the constraints of eqn. 10.47, the resulting bounds are the tightest that can be obtained.

Results provided by this technique can be compared with data given in Reference 23. From there, $\bar{P}$ is shown in Fig. 10.3 together

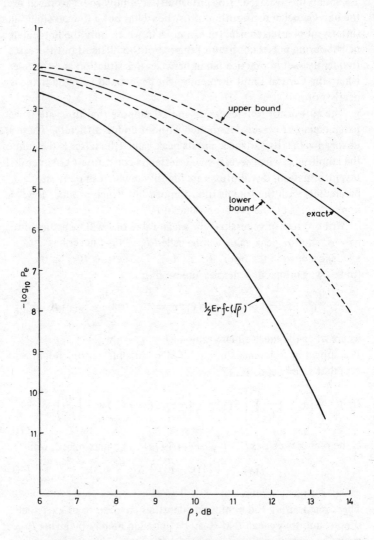

Fig. 10.3 Probability of error for coherent binary phase-shift keying
Curve labelled exact refers to a p.s.k. signal disturbed by noise and two
equi-amplitude interferers. Each interferer lies 13 dB below the signal
(Reference 23)*. The dashed curves are upper and lower bounds derived
from the theory of Section 10.7, and the lower full curve refers to a
p.s.k. signal disturbed only by noise
* Courtesy Institute of Electrical and Electronic Engineers Inc.

with the upper and lower bounds that are obtained in the case of a binary p.s.k. signal accompanied by noise and two equi-amplitude interferers. The power of each interferer lies 13 dB below the carrier power. Usually these bounds prove to be sufficiently tight for design purposes; more sophisticated bounding techniques are described in References 27, 28.

This method has an interesting extension in the case of coherent detection of binary or M-ary p.s.k. signals operating in an additive mixture of Gaussian and impulsive noise. It has been shown[29] that, in absence of intersymbol interference, the probability of error can be expressed as a weighted sum of terms like eqn. 10.42. Consequently, with additive intersymbol interference as in eqn. 10.45, the error probability can be bounded by using eqns. 10.48 and 10.49, and the combined effect of Gaussian noise, impulsive noise, and intersymbol interference may be investigated straightforwardly.

10.8 Use of the Tikhonov distribution

When the p.l.l. reference is noisy, the Tikhonov density function discussed in Chapter 9 may be ascribed to $\phi(T)$. Then, assuming the derivation of the reference signal to be a process that is statistically unrelated to operation of the decision circuitry, the probability of error conditional upon $\pi/2$ having been signalled,* can be written

$$P_B = \frac{1}{2} - \frac{1}{4\pi} \int_{-\pi}^{\pi} \text{sgn}\left(\frac{\pi}{2} - |\phi|\right) \text{ erf}\left(\sqrt{\rho}\,|\cos\phi|\right) \frac{e^{a_1 \cos\phi}}{I_0(a_1)}\, d\phi$$

$$(10.50)$$

This result assumes no intersymbol interference is present but that the p.s.k. carrier is received along with noise (the carrier-to-noise ratio is ρ) and a_1 is the parameter of the Tikhonov density function. The equation has its greatest area of application with space communication links nearly all of which use coherent detection.

Usually Gaussian noise is the sole interference on such links, but cases can arise with deep space probes where transmission through turbulent media causes the channel to become time varying (the fading amplitude is then likely to be governed by the m-distribution described in Section 10.15) and so a further averaging of eqn. 10.50 accounting for the way this fading affects both a_1 and ρ is in order. However, this case will not be taken further here.

---

* Assuming $-\pi/2$ is as likely as $+\pi/2$, P_B is also the averaged probability of error

The values of a_1 and ρ determine the quality of performance and when $\rho \ll a_1$ P_B will approach P_e as given by eqn. 10.42. At the other extreme ($\rho \gg a_1$) the argument of the error function may be supposed always large, so

$$P_B \simeq \frac{1}{2} - \frac{1}{4\pi} \int_{-\pi}^{\pi} \text{sgn}\left(\frac{\pi}{2} - |\phi|\right) \frac{e^{a_1 \cos\phi}}{I_0(a_1)} \, d\phi \qquad (10.51)$$

This integral defines a Struve function, however, and[20]

$$P_B \simeq \frac{1}{2}\left[\frac{I_0(a_1) - L_0(a_1)}{I_0(a_1)}\right] \qquad (10.52)$$

Here $L_0(a_1)$ is the modified Struve function of zero order, and $I_0(a_1) - L_0(a_1)$ is given, for example, in Table 12.1 of Reference 30.

Eqn. 10.52 may be termed the irreducible error probability as it represents a limit imposed by the p.l.l. on receiver performance. In the intermediate region where $\rho \simeq a_1$, eqn. 10.50 can be expressed as an infinite series whose terms involve $I_n(\rho/2)$ and $I_{2n+1}(a_1)$ (Reference 20).

10.9 Differentially coherent detection

With differentially coherent detection, the information lies in changes of phase and, as in eqn. 10.40, the phase change occurring over the time T can be expressed as $\theta(t+T) - \theta(t)$, or in the more symmetrical form $\theta(t+T/2) - \theta(t-T/2)$. A binary case will be taken for the initial presentation.

Let $$d = \{\theta(t+T/2) - \theta(t-T/2) + Z\} \qquad (10.53)$$

where Z is a general threshold (Z will be made zero later), and the curly bracket contains an angle that is reduced modulo 2π. The probability that d is negative is then given (see eqn. 2.17) by

$$Pr[d<0] = \frac{1}{2}\left[1 - \frac{1}{2\pi}\iint_{-\infty}^{+\infty} \frac{\partial\phi(u_1,u_2)}{\partial Z} \frac{du_1 du_2}{u_1 u_2}\right] \qquad (10.54)$$

Any appropriate one of the bivariate characteristic functions listed in eqns. 2.10 to 2.13 can be substituted into this result, but eqn. 2.10 (with $\tau = T$, and t replaced by $t - T/2$) is chosen for its generality

The case under examination then corresponds to a differentially encoded p.m. signal disturbed by filtering or by the effects of fading, so that its amplitude is no longer constant, and received in the presence

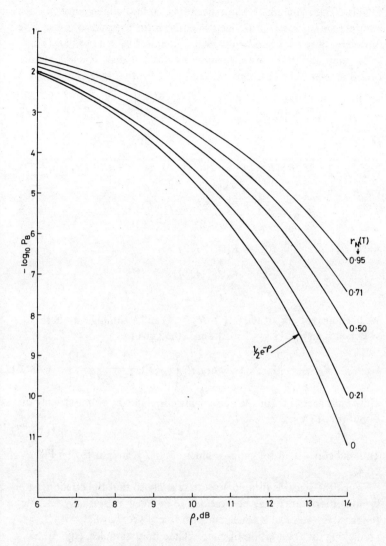

Fig. 10.4 Probability of error for binary differential phase shift keying in the
presence of additive Gaussian noise
$r_N(T)$ is the correlation coefficient of noise at spacing T seconds

of noise. The signal phase is also perturbed so that intersymbol interference is experienced independently of the presence of noise. The time-varying envelope and phase will be denoted by $R_s(t)$ and $\theta_s(t)$.

If, temporarily, the averaging indicated by the angle brackets is not executed, eqn. 2.18 of Chapter 2 can be used with $Z = 0$ to give

$$P_B = \frac{1}{2}\left[1 - \langle \frac{R_1 R_2}{2\alpha\psi_N(0)} \cdot \frac{|\sin \Delta(T)|}{\sqrt{1 - r_N^2(T)}} I_e\left(\frac{\beta}{\alpha}, \alpha\right)\rangle\right] \quad (10.55)$$

where $\beta =$

$$\frac{\sqrt{R_1^4 + R_2^4 + 2R_1^2 R_2^2 [2r_N^2(T) + \cos 2\Delta(T)] - 4r_N(T)R_1 R_2 (R_1^2 + R_2^2)\cos \Delta(T)}}{4\psi_N(0)[1 - r_N^2(T)]}$$

$$\alpha = \frac{R_1^2 + R_2^2 - 2R_1 R_2 r_N(T)\cos \Delta(T)}{4\psi_N(0)[1 - r_N^2(T)]}$$

and
$$R_1 = R_s(t - T/2)$$
$$R_2 = R_s(t + T/2)$$
$$\Delta(T) = \theta_s(t + T/2) - \theta_s(t - T/2)$$

With a constant amplitude ($R_1 = R_2 = A$) and assuming a π-phase switched signal $[\Delta(T) = \pm \pi/2]$ eqn. 10.55 gives

$$P_B = \frac{1}{2}\left[1 - \sqrt{1 - r_N^2(T)}I_e\left\{r_N(T), \frac{\rho}{1 - r_N^2(T)}\right\}\right] \quad (10.56)$$

This result accounts for the noise being correlated at a time spacing of T, but if $r_N(T) = 0$

$$P_B = \frac{1}{2}e^{-\rho} \quad (10.57)$$

This and eqn. 10.56 for various values of $r_N(T)$, are plotted on Fig. 10.4.

When the signal is filtered not too severely so that the effect of inter-symbol interference may be expected to be small, it is usually realistic to regard R_1 and R_2 as equal, and also to put $\frac{1}{2}R_1^2/\psi_N(0) = \rho$. Then, on making the assumption of uncorrelated noise samples, eqn. 10.55 gives

$$P_B \simeq \frac{1}{2}\langle 1 - |\sin \Delta(T)|I_e[\cos \Delta(T), \rho]\rangle \quad (10.58)$$

If $\Delta(T)$ is written as $\Delta(T) = \pi/2 - x(T)$ where $x(T)$ arises from inter-symbol interference, an approximate development of P_B is

$$P_B = \frac{1}{2}e^{-\rho}[1 + \langle x^2(T)\rangle(1 + \rho/2)\rho/2 + \ldots] \quad (10.59)$$

The square bracket gives the increase over eqn. 10.57 that occurs in the error probability, this is characteristic of the way intersymbol interference affects P_B, and higher-order terms will involve higher moments of $x(T)$. The term shown requires the mean square value of x to be calculated, and this first relies upon using the characteristic of the filter that introduces intersymbol interference (as it appears in eqn. 7.1 for example) to formulate an expression for $x(T)$.

Note the similarity of eqns. 10.56 and 10.58 if $r_N(T)$ and $\cos \Delta(T)$ have like values. This offers an alternative to using eqn. 10.59 in that eqn. 10.56 can be computed with r_N equated to the r.m.s. value of $x(T)$ and the curves for $r_N(T) \neq 0$ shown on Fig. 10.4 are provided for this purpose. Another use of these curves is to indicate the degredation of the error probability if the data rate is increased, with the amount of noise that contaminates the carrier remaining unchanged. By reducing T, some intersymbol interference will also be suffered but a non-zero $r_N(T)$ arises because the noise becomes increasingly self-correlated at time spacing T. This illustrates a general maxim for differentially encoded systems in that it is desirable for the data rate and input noise bandwidth to correspond to a zero in the autocorrelation function of the noise.

10.10 Adjacent channel interference in binary d.p.s.k. systems

The interferer will be supposed unmodulated and the detector input is written as

$$V(t) = A \cos [\omega_0 t + \mu(t)] + rA \cos [\overline{\omega_0 + \omega_D} t + \alpha] \quad (10.60)$$

It is required to calculate the probability that the presence of the interferer (relative amplitude r, frequency separation ω_D) causes an error in detecting the differentially encoded binary information conveyed by $\mu(t)$. Eqn. 10.54 is to be used with $\phi(u_1, u_2)$ given by eqn. 2.13 ($\omega_0 \tau = Z$ and $\tau = T$), but on making a comparison with eqn. 3.26, it is evident that the working that led to eqn. 3.29 for the expected number of zeros per second of $V(t)$ contains all the analysis that is presently required. This working is halted at eqn. 3.28 (because h is not reduced to zero but is replaced by T), and letting $C + D = 4$ with $C - D = 4 \cos [\omega_D T]$ we find

$$P_B = \tfrac{1}{2} [1 - \operatorname{sgn}(\omega_D \Delta) T_1 - T_2] \quad (10.61)$$

where $\Delta = \pm \pi/2$, and where

$$T_1 = \left\{ 0, \frac{1}{\pi} \cos^{-1} \left[\frac{\frac{1}{r^2}\left(\frac{1}{C} + \frac{1}{D}\right) - 1}{\frac{1}{r^2}\left|\frac{1}{C} - \frac{1}{D}\right|} \right] \text{ or } 1 \right\}$$

the alternatives being taken according as 1 lies below, between, or above

$$\frac{2}{Cr^2} \quad \text{and} \quad \frac{2}{Dr^2}$$

$$T_2 = \left\{ 0, \frac{1}{\pi} \cos^{-1} \left[\frac{r^2(C+D) - 4}{r^2 |C - D|} \right] \text{ or } 1 \right\}$$

The alternatives being taken according as 1 lies below, between, or above $\frac{C}{2}r^2$ and $\frac{D}{2}r^2$. (Note, the argument of the inverse cosine of T_2 simplifies to $(r^2 - 1)/(r^2 |\cos \omega_D T|)$.)

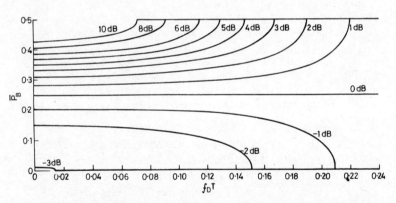

Fig. 10.5 Averaged probability of error for binary DPSK in the presence of a pure tone interferer
$f_D T$ = product of carrier separation and bit duration
Indicated figure in decibels is ratio of interfering carrier amplitude to wanted carrier amplitude at detector input

The average probability of error $\bar{P}_B$ (assuming Δ adopts the values $\pm \frac{\pi}{2}$ with equal probability) is given by

$$\bar{P}_B = \tfrac{1}{2}[1 - T_2] \qquad (10.62)$$

$\bar{P}_B$ is plotted in Fig. 10.5, it is unchanged if $\omega_D T$ is replaced by $\omega_D T \pm k\pi$ and it has symmetry about the points where $\omega_D T = k\pi/2$ (k any integer)

With reference to Fig. 10.5, when the probability of error rather suddenly changes to one half, the effect can be attributed to the unwanted signal capturing the receiver (Section 5.7).

10.11 Four-phase d.p.s.k.

Let $\Delta(T)$ stand for the detected phase change occurring over the time T. Then in absence of noise or interference, $\Delta(T)$ is one of $\pm \pi/4$, $\pm 3\pi/4$ and with four-phase d.p.s.k. (as with most types of M-ary modulation schemes) the probability of error is determined by calculating the likelihood of $\Delta(T)$ lying outside certain decision boundaries. When $\pi/4$ is signalled, for example, provided $\Delta(T)$ is judged to lie between 0 and $\pi/2$, i.e. in the first quadrant, no error will be suffered.

In such cases, eqn. 2.25 of Chapter 2 may be used as it applies to angles that are reduced modulo 2π, and when $\alpha = 0 \quad \beta = \pi/2$, it is seen that $(\beta - \alpha)/2\pi = 1/4$ which reminds us that the probability of mistaking a symbol (one of $\pm \pi/4$, $\pm 3\pi/4$) lies between 0 and $1 - \frac{1}{4} = \frac{3}{4}$.

An exact calculation of P_s, the probability of a symbol error, requires an evaluation of the double integrals of eqn. 2.25 and the working when noise is the source of errors proceeds as with the left-hand side of eqn. 2.18 except that the integration ranges are 0 to ∞ instead of $-\infty$ to ∞. This circumstance prevents the results from being presented in a neat form, but when the carrier-to-noise ratio ρ is large it is clear that the few errors that then occur come almost entirely from situations in which $\Delta(T)$ lies just outside the boundaries in question; in the case quoted earlier, $\Delta(T)$ is either slightly negative or exceeds $\pi/2$ by a small amount.

The probability of mistaking $\pi/4$ when it is signalled may therefore be approximated by

$$P_{\pi/4} = \langle \frac{1}{2} \left[1 - \text{sgn} \left\{ \frac{\pi}{2} - \Delta(T) \right\} \right] \rangle + \langle \frac{1}{2} [1 - \text{sgn} \{\Delta(T)\}] \rangle$$

$$(10.63)$$

The second of the two members of eqn. 10.63 contributes when $\Delta(T)$ lies in the range 0 to $-\pi$, and the first contributes when $\Delta(T)$ exceeds $\pi/2$, but is less than $3\pi/2$ ($3\pi/2$ is identical to $-\pi/2$ when angles reduced modulo 2π are under consideration). The approximation involved in using eqn. 10.63 therefore amounts to the region π to

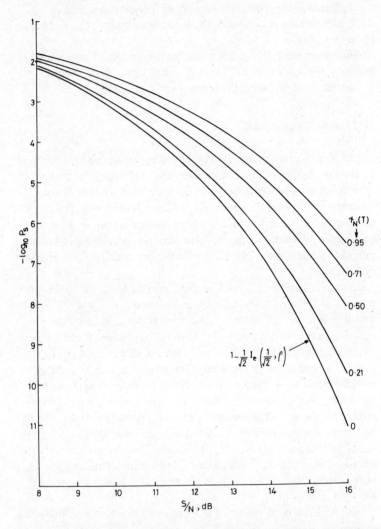

Fig. 10.6 Probabaility of error for four-phase differentially coherent phase shift
keying in the presence of additive Gaussian noise
$r_N(T)$ is the correlation coefficient of noise at spacing T seconds. See
Section 10.11 for the definition of S/N

$3\pi/2$ (or, equivalently, $-\pi/2$ to $-\pi$) being included twice, but the error incurred is small when $\Delta(T)$ lies in this region on only a relatively small proportion of occasions. Using eqn. 2.18 and assuming a constant amplitude signal then gives[*]

$$P_s = 1 - \frac{1}{2\sqrt{2}} \, I_e\left(\frac{1}{\sqrt{2}}, \rho\right)$$

$$- \frac{1}{4\sqrt{2}} \frac{\sqrt{1 - r_N^2(T)}}{\left(1 + \frac{1}{\sqrt{2}} r_N(T)\right)} I_e\left[\frac{\left|r_N(T) + \frac{1}{\sqrt{2}}\right|}{1 + \frac{1}{\sqrt{2}} r_N(T)}, \frac{\left\{1 + \frac{1}{\sqrt{2}} r_N(T)\right\}}{1 - r_N^2(T)} \rho\right]$$

$$\text{(10.64)}$$

$$- \frac{1}{4\sqrt{2}} \frac{\sqrt{1 - r_N^2(T)}}{\left(1 - \frac{1}{\sqrt{2}} r_N(T)\right)} I_e\left[\frac{\left|r_N(T) - \frac{1}{\sqrt{2}}\right|}{1 - \frac{1}{\sqrt{2}} r_N(T)}, \frac{\left\{1 - \frac{1}{\sqrt{2}} r_N(T)\right\}}{1 - r_N^2(T)} \rho\right]$$

For uncorrelated noise $[r_N(T) = 0]$, this takes the simple form

$$P_s = 1 - \frac{1}{\sqrt{2}} \, I_e\left(\frac{1}{\sqrt{2}}, \rho\right) \quad \rho > 4, \text{ say} \qquad \text{(10.65)}$$

The asymptotic form of $I_e(k, x)$ for large x (see the Appendix) when applied to eqn. 10.65 gives

$$P_s = \frac{(1 + \sqrt{2}) e^{-\rho(1 - 1/\sqrt{2})}}{\sqrt{\pi \rho \sqrt{2}}} \qquad \text{(10.66)}$$

As each symbol refers to two binary digits, it is usual to call $\rho/2$ (the carrier power to the noise power measured in twice the data rate) the signal-to-noise ratio S/N, and then to plot P_s against S/N. Fig. 10.6 shows such a plot where eqn. 10.64 has been evaluated for five values of $r_N(T)$.

It may be noted that in terms of S/N eqn. 10.66 is in agreement with Expression 10.49 of Reference 13, but the simple nature of eqn. 10.65 from which it comes was not there mentioned.

Further, the symbol error probability P_s is usually converted into an equivalent binary error probability by using a Gray coding (p. 219 of Reference 13).

[*] The probability of mistaking $\pi/4$ is the same as mistaking $-\pi/4$ and the probability of mistaking $3\pi/4$ is the same as mistaking $-3\pi/4$

10.12 Adjacent channel interference and four-phase d.p.s.k.

Again the bivariate characteristic function of eqn. 2.13 can be used,
this time in eqn. 2.25, to examine the effect of c.w. interference on a
four-phase d.p.s.k. signal.

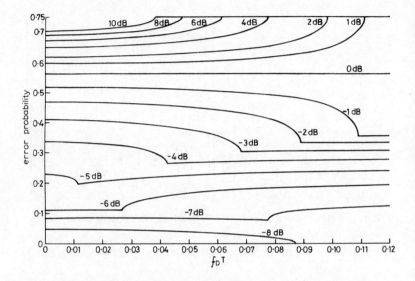

Fig. 10.7 Average probability of error for four-phase DPSK in the presence of a
pure tone interferer
$f_D T$ = product of carrier separation and bit duration
Indicated figure in decibels is ratio of interfering carrier amplitude to
wanted carrier amplitude at detector input

The double integrals can be calculated with the help of eqn. 3.27,
and the working is straightforward but very lengthy. The probability
of error is not the same for each of the four-phase states, and it is
necessary to calculate four conditional error probabilities and then
average their sum.

The results are best presented graphically, and Fig. 10.7 shows the
averaged symbol error probability obtained from a computer program
that assisted with the calculations.

Note that P_s is unchanged if $\omega_D T = \omega_D T \pm k\pi/2$ (k any integer),
and P_s has symmetry about the points where $\omega_D T = k\pi/4$. The capture
effect (Sections 5.7 and 10.10) is evident when $r > 1$ and the error
probability attains the value 3/4.

10.13 Limiter-discriminator detection

This section assumes that the information lies in the instantaneous
frequency of the signal, and so a limiter-discriminator combination (the
perfect frequency detector is used at the receiver. Many of the results
obtained in Chapters 3 and 6 have application here, and, when a zero
decision threshold is set, the probability of error when sampling the
instantaneous frequency of such a signal disturbed by noise is given
(take $\omega = 0$ in eqn. 6.6) by

$$P_B = \left\langle \frac{1}{2}\left[1 - \sqrt{1 - \left(\frac{\beta}{\alpha}\right)^2}\, I_e\left(\frac{\beta}{\alpha}, \alpha\right)\right]\right\rangle \qquad (10.67)$$

where

$$\alpha = \frac{R_s^2}{4\psi_N(0)}\left[\frac{-r_N''(0) + (\dot{\theta}_s)^2 + \left(\frac{\dot{R}_s}{R_s}\right)^2}{-r_N''(0)}\right] \qquad (10.68)$$

$$\beta = \frac{R_s^2}{4\psi_N(0)} \frac{\left\{\left[-r_N''(0) - (\dot{\theta}_s)^2 - \left(\frac{\dot{R}_s}{R_s}\right)^2\right]^2 + 4\left(\frac{\dot{R}_s}{R_s}\right)^2[-r_N''(0)]\right\}^{1/2}}{-r_N''(0)}$$

$$(10.69)$$

As was noted in Chapter 6, the right-hand side of eqn. 10.67 takes the
special form $\langle \frac{1}{2} e^{-\alpha}\rangle$ with $\alpha = R_s^2/[2\psi_N(0)]$ when $\beta = 0$.

With R_s equal to the carrier amplitude A, the probability of error
becomes $\frac{1}{2}e^{-\rho}$, and is seen to be the same as for the best performance
achievable with binary d.p.s.k. (see eqn. 10.57 and Fig. 10.4). The
simple exponential is to be compared with eqn. 10.42 which, for large
ρ, is well approximated by $\frac{1}{2}e^{-\rho}/(\sqrt{\pi\rho})$. This form has been derived
and discussed many times in the literature,[16-18] and it represents the
best possible performance, the next best being $\frac{1}{2}e^{-\rho}$ (see, for
example, Fig. 10.12 of Reference 13, Fig. 1 of Reference 17, or Fig.
7.5.1 of Reference 32). With the particular filtering arrangements that
cause β to be zero, therefore, incoherent reception using the limiter-
discriminator can match the optimum performance of binary
differential phase shift keying. Thus, the minimisation of β in eqn.
10.67 would seem a worthwhile design aim, and this has been
recognised in References 31 and 32 (pp. 338–339).

As the square root of eqn. 10.69 contains a sum of two positive
terms, a necessary condition for $\beta = 0$ is $\dot{R}_s = 0$. Then, in absence of
intersymbol interference, so that with binary f.s.k. and a deviation
ratio k, we have $\dot{\theta}_s = \pm k\pi/T$, it is evident that the choice
$k\pi/T = \sqrt{-r_N''(0)}$ will make β zero.

Now $-r_N''(0)$ is directly related by eqn. 5.17 to the i.f. bandwidth so with a specified deviation there is a corresponding ratio of i.f. bandwidth to data rate that causes β to be zero. With a rectangular filter, for example, $-r_N''(0) = \omega_B^2/3$, where $2\omega_B$ is the filter bandwidth, and k is to be chosen so that $(k\pi/T)^2 = \omega_B^2/3$. A rectangular or truncating filter is a convenient shape to postulate from the point of view of identifying the band that contains a large proportion of the transmitted power and, in the present context, $2\omega_B$ can be viewed as the noise bandwidth of a general filter.

Early studies of the r.f. spectra of binary f.m., using analysis of the kind outlined in Section 10.3, revealed that a compact spectrum, i.e. one for which a reasonably flat distribution of spectral levels covers a band equal to the data rate, and the spectrum falls away steeply outside, is obtained when k is chosen near to 0·7. The spectra shown on Fig. 10.1 are drawn for this case.

On checking back against the requirement that $\beta = 0$ there is found to be a close compatibility (a rectangular i.f. bandwidth of $1\cdot21/T$ Hz corresponds to $k = 0\cdot7$) and so $k \approx 0\cdot7$ could be advantageous from both error probability and spectrum occupancy viewpoints.

Note that the necessary condition $\dot{R}_s = 0$ need hold only at sampling instants, and so it can be closely complied with even when the i.f. filter introduces a significant disturbance to the amplitude (and, therefore, the phase) of the f.s.k. wave. However, the pointed brackets surrounding eqn. 10.67 remind us that the memory of the filter necessitates an average over the pre-history of the data stream leading up to the sampling instant, and so, when intersymbol interference is present, we cannot ensure that $(\dot{\theta}_s)^2$ equals $-r_N''(0)$ for every sample.

The amount of intersymbol interference that can be allowed to arise is to be balanced against the advantage gained by narrowing the bandwidth to exclude noise, and two studies[33,34] that have investigated this aspect reveal that preferred deviations and bandwidths differ little from those identified when intersymbol interference is ignored and the relationship between deviation and i.f. bandwidth is the one making $\beta = 0$.

Tjung and Wittke[33] have reported that there is a well-defined minimum in the signal power needed to realise a binary error probability of 10^{-4} if the deviation ratio is chosen near to 0·7 and the noise bandwidth of a (Gaussian or rectangular) i.f. filter is in the region of $1/T$ Hz. Bobilin[34] identifies the third-order Butterworth network with 3 dB bandwidth of $1\cdot1/T$ Hz (noise bandwidth $1\cdot15/T$ Hz) as a good choice for the combination of transmitter and receiver filters (well defined minima in the error probability again being demonstrated), with the deviation ratio chosen as 0·72.

Both the quoted sources assume a post discriminator filter of the integrate and dump variety (Section 10.20) with integration time equal to T, and also take averages over all possible sequences of foregoing bits. This is needed to comply with the angle brackets surrounding eqn. 10.67 which refer to R_s, $\dot{R}_s$ and $\dot{\theta}_s$ being dependent not only on the current digit but past ones as well.

Use of the integrate and dump filter causes the decision between mark and space to be based on phase differences (see eqn. 10.85) rather than instantaneous frequency so the information is coded in the d.p.s.k. format. Nevertheless, it seems a fair assumption that a minimisation of the error probability before the post detector filter, i.e. at the discriminator output where eqn. 10.67 applies, is also achieved by these choices of deviation, bandwidths, and filter types.

At the close of Chapter 9 (Section 9.23) the performance offered by demodulators that provide $R(t)\dot{\theta}(t)$ or $R^2(t)\dot{\theta}(t)$ as an output were discussed in relation to analogue f.m. If devices having these same outputs are used in digital f.m. systems then, with binary data [$\dot{\theta}(t)$ is to be declared positive or negative], the probability of error is the same as for the limiter-discriminator and is given by eqn. 10.67. This is not the case with multilevel f.s.k. or a duo-binary f.m. system, however, for non-zero thresholds have to be set. The calculation of P_e then involves the envelope $R(t)$.

In discussing the choice of deviation it is pertinent to mention the case made out by de Buda[35] for using continuous phase binary f.s.k. with a deviation ratio of one half (the r.f. spectrum is narrow and given by a much simplified formula, as eqn. 10.35 shows).* $k = 1/2$ is a very special case when $\dot{s}(t)$ has a rectangular form for then the correctly sampled output from an integrate and dump filter is always an odd or even multiple of $\pi/2$ and, as eqns. 10.26 and 10.27 show, $\langle \cos[\mu(t + \tau) - \mu(t)]\rangle \equiv 0$ for $\tau > 2T$. Also, by including a squarer in the receiver, the two spectral lines of the $k = 1$ case (Section 10.3) can be made to appear and these may be used for timing purposes.

De Buda identifies an optimum receiver structure for $k = 1/2$ in which the in-phase and quadrature components of the received wave are multiplied by locally generated reference signals and then integrated over a time $2T$ which, as we see, is the time separation beyond which these components become completely uncorrelated.

It is the clear-cut directive to integrate over $2T$ (see pp. 341–342 of Reference 32) which makes de Buda's receiver novel (integration over a time T might seem always appropriate as the data rate is $1/T$ Hz and

* $k = 1/2$ is a deviation ratio that is gaining in popularity and often designated m.s.k. (minimum shift keying)

successive bits are assumed independent) and the dual advantages of continuous phase (a narrow spectrum) and coherent detection (fewer decision errors) are claimed.

However, being a coherent method of detection, the receiver structure is more complicated than the conventional limiter-discriminator incoherent receiver we wish to examine subsequently, and so we return to eqn. 10.67 recalling that the conditions

$$k\pi/T \approx \sqrt{-r_N''(0)}, \quad k \approx 0.7 \tag{10.70}$$

appear to represent an excellent basis from which to search for an optimum design (Section 10.19).

10.14 Effect of an echo on binary f.m.

When a binary system is designed with the aim of making β as small as possible, fading or the presence of an echo of the wanted signal will give rise to additional detection errors.

It will be assumed that the deviation and i.f. bandwidth of a rectangularly-switched binary f.s.k. signal have been chosen to comply with $(k\pi/T)^2 = -r_N''(0)$ but a randomly phased echo of delay τ_0 accompanies the signal and noise at the receiver input. The sum of signal and echo when written as in eqn. 5.32 then gives the following for R_s and $\dot\theta_s$ which appear in eqns. 10.68 and 10.69:

$$R_s = A\sqrt{1 + 2r\cos\epsilon_1(t) + r^2} \tag{10.71}$$

$$\dot\theta_s = \frac{M(t)[1 + r\cos\epsilon_1(t)] + rM(t-\tau_0)[r + \cos\epsilon_1(t)]}{1 + 2r\cos\epsilon_1(t) + r^2} \tag{10.72}$$

with

$$\epsilon_1(t) = \omega_0\tau_0 + \mu(t) - \mu(t-\tau_0) \tag{10.73}$$

$M(t)$ is the instantaneous frequency of the signal when sampled, and, in the rectangularly switched case, $M(t-\tau_0)$ can equal either $+M(t)$ or $-M(t)$. When $M(t)$ and $M(t-\tau_0)$ are equal, $\dot\epsilon_1(t) = 0$ [so $\dot R_s(t) = 0$] and

$$\dot\theta_s = M(t) = \frac{k\pi}{T} = \sqrt{-r_N''(0)}$$

Then, using eqn. 10.67

$$P_B = \tfrac{1}{2}\langle \exp - \rho[1 + 2r\cos\epsilon_1(t) + r^2]\rangle \tag{10.74}$$

The random phasing of the echo means that $\epsilon_1(t)$ is assumed to be uniformly distributed in $-\pi$ to $+\pi$. Then the angle brackets refer to an average over $\epsilon_1(t)$, and we have the short delay formula

$$P_B = \tfrac{1}{2} e^{-\rho(1+r^2)} I_0(2r\rho) \qquad (10.75)$$

When τ_0 exceeds T it is equi-probable that $M(t - \tau_0)$ is $+M(t)$ or $-M(t)$. When $M(t - \tau_0) = -M(t)$, it is found, using eqn. 10.68, that $\alpha = \rho(1 + r^2)$, and using eqn. 10.69, $\beta = 2r\rho$. Then eqns. 10.75 and 10.67 give

$$
P_B = \frac{1}{4} e^{-\rho(1+r^2)} I_0(2r\rho)
$$

$$
+ \frac{1}{4} \left[1 - \sqrt{1 - \frac{4r^2}{(1+r^2)^2}} \; I_e \left\{ \frac{2r}{1+r^2} \,, \rho(1+r^2) \right\} \right]
$$

$$(10.76)$$

As noted by Schneider,[36] this expression can be written very neatly in terms of a Marcum Q function (see eqns. 6.7 and 6.8) and

$$P_B = \tfrac{1}{2} Q[r\sqrt{2\rho}, \sqrt{2\rho}] \qquad (10.77)$$

To maintain an error probability of 10^{-4}, for example, this shows that 10 dB more signal power is required to combat the effect of an echo of half the signal power.[36] This well illustrates the severe degradation in performance that can be caused by an echo of relatively small amplitude.

10.15 Nonselective fading

A fading medium is described as non-selective if only the amplitude of the received transmission fluctuates and the phase is undisturbed.

In this section, an expression of pleasing simplicity is obtained for the binary error probability under fading conditions when the error probability for the non-fading signal is given by an exponential, as in eqn. 10.57.

It has been reported[37] that, over a wide range of frequencies in the v.h.f. and u.h.f. bands, the received amplitude R has a probability density function $p(R)$ that can be well approximated by

$$
p(R) = \frac{2m^m R^{2m-1}}{\Gamma(m) \Omega^m} \exp - \left(\frac{m}{\Omega} R^2 \right) \qquad (10.78)
$$

where $\qquad \Omega = \overline{R^2} \quad$ and $\quad m = \dfrac{(\overline{R^2})^2}{\overline{R^4} - (\overline{R^2})^2} \geqslant \dfrac{1}{2}$

The cumulative distribution (Prob $R > R_0$) is given by

$Q\left[\dfrac{2mR_0^2}{\Omega}\middle| 2m\right]$ where $Q[\chi^2 | v]$ is the cumulative sum of the Poisson

distribution and is shown, for example, in Table 26.7 of Reference 30.

Eqn. 10.78 is known as Nakagami's m distribution and a value for m can nearly always be found that causes a close fit to a measured density function for R.

The distribution has the property that for $m = 1$ it is the Rayleigh distribution density, for $m = 1/2$ it is a one-sided Gaussian density, while for large $m(m > 4$, say) a shape closely resembling the density function for the Rician fading channel (envelope of signal plus noise) is adopted; this density is given in Expression 9.50 of Reference 45, and, from its second and fourth moments, it is found that $m = \dfrac{(1 + \rho)^2}{1 + 2\rho}$,

$\Omega = 2\psi_N(0)(1 + \rho)$. This flexibility of Nakagami's distribution is attractive from a theoretical viewpoint, and if it is used to implement the $\langle\rangle$ brackets of eqn. 10.67 in the $\beta = 0$ situation

$$P_B = \int_0^\infty \frac{1}{2}\exp - \frac{R^2}{2\psi_N(0)} \cdot \frac{2m^m R^{2m-1}}{\Gamma(m)\Omega^m}\ \exp - \left(\frac{m}{\Omega}\,R^2\right) dR$$

$$= \frac{1}{2}\left\{1 + \frac{\Omega}{2m\psi_N(0)}\right\}^{-m} \tag{10.79}$$

Here $\dfrac{\Omega}{2\psi_N(0)} = \dfrac{\overline{R^2}}{2\psi_N(0)}$ can be interpreted as the mean carrier-to-noise (power ratio), the mean being calculated across all possible fading amplitudes.

The conclusion likely to be drawn from use of eqn. 10.79 is that performance will be unacceptably poor unless steps (diversity reception, for example, see Section 5.2 of Reference 38) are taken to combat the effects of fading.

10.16 Multi-path example

With the current interest in ground-to-air communication through a satellite (the L-band aeronautical satellite channel, for example), a useful model of the received signal is provided by forming the sum of the steady undistorted signal, a diffuse scattered signal, and noise.

Retaining the modulation methods and model of Section 10.15 means that the components of the scattered signal have sufficient coherence for their overall effect to amount to an echo with a relative amplitude that is specified statistically. When the delay τ_0 exceeds the bit duration T, the echo process behaves like extra noise and if r is Rayleigh distributed ($\overline{r^2} = k_0$), for example, eqn. 10.77 can be averaged over r to give

$$\bar{P}_B = \frac{1}{2} \exp - \left(\frac{\rho}{1 + \rho k_0} \right) \qquad (10.80)$$

This exhibits an irreducible error probability given by $1/2 \exp - (1/k_0)$ as $\rho k_0 \to \infty$. More often, the delay spread of the multipath amounts to only a fraction of the bit duration and it is appropriate to average eqn. 10.75 in like fashion. Then

$$\bar{P}_B = \frac{1}{2} \cdot \frac{1}{1 + \rho k_0} \exp - \left(\frac{\rho}{1 + \rho k_0} \right) \qquad (10.81)$$

Here the averaged error probability decreases to zero as $\rho k_0 \to \infty$. Eqn. 10.81 has been attributed to Jones.[39]

10.17 Adjacent channel interference in binary f.s.k.

The averaged probability of error when a two-state f.s.k. signal (the instantaneous radian frequency switches between $\pm \omega_a$) is disturbed by adjacent channel interference, can be obtained from eqn. 3.29 in the same way that eqn. 10.61 was obtained from eqn. 3.28; or from eqn. 6.10 with $[B(t)]/[R_s(t)] = r$. We find that the averaged probability of error is given by

$$\bar{P}_B = \langle \tfrac{1}{2}[1 - T_2] \rangle \qquad (10.82)$$

where $T_2 = \left(0, \dfrac{1}{\pi} \cos^{-1} \left\{ \dfrac{1 + \left(1 - \dfrac{2}{r^2}\right)\left(\dfrac{\omega_a}{\omega_D + \dot{\alpha}}\right)^2}{\left| 1 - \left(\dfrac{\omega_a}{\omega_D + \dot{\alpha}}\right)^2 \right|} \right\} \text{ or } 1 \right)$

the alternatives being taken according as 1 lies below, between, or above r^2 and $\left| \dfrac{r(\omega_D + \dot{\alpha})}{\omega_a} \right|^2$

Here $\omega_D + \dot{\alpha}$ is the off-set frequency of the interferer at the sampling instant ($\dot{\alpha} = 0$ if the interferer is unmodulated).

The angle brackets of eqn. 10.82 refer to an average over the possible values of $\dot{\alpha}$. When $\dot{\alpha}$ has a Gaussian distribution, then the interferer could be a large capacity analogue f.m. f.d.m. transmission, but note that the model assumes the interfering signal suffers no bandwidth restriction due to filtering at the input of the interfered-with receiver.

When the interferer is another rectangularly-switched f.s.k. signal and $\dot{\alpha}$ adopts just two values ($\pm \omega_1$, say) with equal probability, the averaging brackets are easily implemented by giving ω_D firstly the value $\omega_D + \omega_1$ and then the value $\omega_D - \omega_1$, and taking one half the sum of the resulting error probabilities.

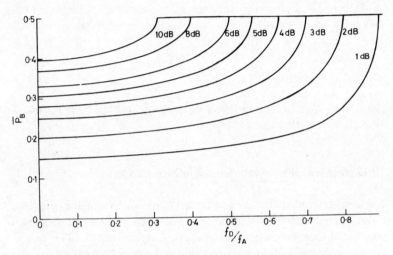

Fig. 10.8 Average probability of error for binary frequency shift keying in the presence of a pure tone interferer

f_D/f_A = ratio of carrier separation to absolute value of imposed carrier frequency deviation

$2f_A T$ = deviation ratio

Indicated figure in decibels is ratio of unwanted carrier amplitude to wanted carrier amplitude at input to the detector

Fig. 10.8 shows $\bar{P}_B$ plotted for $r > 1$ and an unmodulated interferer. It is clear that the case of the f.s.k. interferer described above can be easily handled using this figure, and the capture effect (Sections 5.7, 10.10, 10.12) is evident again.

When r is less than unity, $(\omega_D + \dot{\alpha})/(\omega_a)$ has to be large enough to ensure $[r(\omega_D + \dot{\alpha})]/\omega_a > 1$ for a significant error count to arise, and the reader is reminded of the underlying assumption that the interferer is the principal source of errors, and noise is being ignored. Eqn. 6.10 allows the error probability conditioned on a positive ($+\omega_a$) or negative ($-\omega_a$) signal deviation to be written (compare eqn. 10.61) as

$$P_B = \frac{1}{2}\left[1 - \text{sgn}\left(\frac{\omega_D + \dot{\alpha}}{\omega_a}\right)T_1 - T_2\right]$$

where

$$T_1 = \left\{0, \frac{1}{\pi}\cos^{-1}\left[\frac{\left(\frac{\omega_D + \dot{\alpha}}{\omega_a}\right)^2(1 - 2r^2) + 1}{\left|1 - \left(\frac{\omega_D + \dot{\alpha}}{\omega_a}\right)^2\right|}\right] \text{ or } 1\right\}$$

the alternatives being taken according as 1 lies below, between or above

the two values $1/r^2$ and $\left[\left(\frac{\omega_a}{\omega_D + \dot{\alpha}}\right)\frac{1}{r}\right]^2$

10.18 Three levels

Three-level systems $(-1, 0 \text{ and } +1)$ can be viewed and realised in a number of ways and are known under such names as duo-binary, bi-ternary or partial response methods.[40]

The original formulation arose with linear modulation techniques in an endeavour to overcome the practical difficulties presented by Nyquist's conclusion that maximum transmission rate of binary information with complete freedom from intersymbol interference demands rectangular filters and therefore no phase variations with frequency, or timing inaccuracies.

By allowing the filter skirts to decay gradually (the so-called roll-off factor: p. 56 of Reference 13), the zero crossings can still be equally spaced so that no intersymbol interference need be suffered and the rigid requirement on timing accuracy is relaxed, but more bandwidth is then demanded.

The methods referred to above take the process a stage further by recognising the inevitable presence of intersymbol interference if shaped pulses are initiated as frequently as a data rate corresponding to twice the rectangular bandwidth and they deliberately exploit this fact to realise extra signalling levels. With three levels, the third (zero) level, for instance, is produced by the overlap of consecutive antipodal pulses and a coding is usually applied at the transmitter that causes the two outer levels to both refer to binary mark (say) with the zero level referring to space.[41]

The Nyquist ideal of two bits per Hertz of lowpass bandwidth can then be achieved, but, because three levels have to be distinguished rather than two, there is more scope for noise to cause detection errors.

We shall not be concerned further with particular details of shaping and generating the three-level pulse train, supposing that it is used to frequency modulate a carrier that is received with additive noise. When the discriminator output is sampled, therefore, three levels $\pm (k\pi)/T$ and zero are to be distinguished, and the average probability that a detection error occurs will be considered. Two thresholds at $\pm r_0 (k\pi)/T$ are to be set and $r_0(0 < r_0 < 1)$ is to be chosen optimally.

The general form for the distribution of $\dot{\theta}$ shown in eqn. 6.6 can be used to obtain an expression for $\bar{P}_e$ the averaged probability of error (we calculate the probabilities of error conditional on each of the three levels having been sent, and form the sum weighted by 1/2, 1/4 and 1/4; the zero level appears twice as often as the two outer levels). It is not possible to force $\bar{P}_e$ to be governed by the desirable $\beta = 0$ form of the $\dot{\theta}$ distribution, but the approximation eqn. 6.16 is applicable here since the inequality eqn. 6.20 is found to be met.

Then, for large carrier-to-noise ratios ($\rho > 2$, say) the optimum value of r_0 is given by

$$r_0 = \frac{1}{2} + \frac{d^2}{8\rho} \log_e 2 \qquad (10.83)$$

where

$$d = \frac{2T}{k\pi} \sqrt{-r_N''(0)}$$

Thus, $r_0 = \frac{1}{2}$ is close to the optimum when unintentional intersymbol interference (as opposed to the intentional intersymbol interference that gives the third signalling level) is ignored, and then

$$\bar{P}_e \approx \frac{1}{\sqrt{\pi\rho}} \left\{ \frac{1}{2d} + \frac{3}{4} d \right\} \exp - \left(\frac{\rho}{1 + d^2} \right) \qquad (10.84)$$

Thung *et al.*[41] have found that $r_0 \approx 0\cdot 4$ is the best choice when intersymbol interference is taken into consideration.

The dependence of r_0 on ρ means that the threshold setting has to be continually varied if optimum performance is to be maintained when the level of the received signal fluctuates. Under fading conditions, therefore, a conventional binary f.m. system with a zero decision threshold may well be preferred.

10.19 Post detection filtering

The question of post detector filtering is a vexed one. In the case of analogue f.m. its use incurs no advantage or disadvantage as the filter will affect the spectral densities of the signal and the interference equally so leaving their ratio and S/D (as defined in Section 4.4) unchanged. In the case of digital p.m. or f.m., when the filter input can be written as a sum of signal and (Gaussian) noise components, there is no difficulty in handling the filter output, but frequently this is not possible and the statistical properties of the filtered wave are extremely difficult to determine. Consequently, it is equally difficult to ascertain if any advantage will be gained by excluding noise in relation to the extra intersymbol interference that will be introduced.

Again, if a performance can be realised which is known to be near-optimum in the absence of post detector filtering (as with eqn. 10.57, for example) then extra filtering is unlikely to produce further improvement.

In digital systems it is customary to include a post detector filter and its form is often the same as the filter used at the transmitter to shape $s(t)$ in the baseband pulse train (the pre-modulator filter). The optimum overall shaping of the chain comprising the pre-modulator filter, bandpass filter (often split between transmitter and receiver) and post detector filter is not easy to identify. The following list is typical of current engineering opinion regarding the parameters to be used for a binary f.s.k. link operating in Gaussian noise.

Deviation ratio $k = 0.7$
Pre-modulator and post discriminator low pass filters both Gaussian
    with 3 dB width equal to $0.57 \times 1/T$ Hz
Bandpass filter, 6 element Butterworth 3 dB bandwidth equal to
    $1.3 \times 1/T$ Hz, giving $\rho = 10.6$ dB for $P_B = 10^{-4}$. 99.4% of
    transmitted power lies in $1.2/T$ Hz

A linear and therefore much simplified design problem for the post detector filter is encountered with those coherent modulation methods in which rectangular switching of the phase leads to rectangular waveforms for the in-phase and quadrature signal components. Then, the signal may often be viewed as a form of suppressed-carrier a.m. transmission, so allowing freedom from intersymbol interference to be sought by basing the design on Nyquist's laws[13] or similar rules.[14,15]

An approach that is sometimes taken when the phase transitions are shaped is to ignore the nonlinearities and proceed as if it were an a.m. signal rather than an f.m. signal that is to be optimally processed. This technique will be most successful when the deviation applied is small enough for the transmission to be written as in eqn. 10.33 whereupon the signal has much in common with an amplitude modulation wave.

10.20 Integrate and dump filter

A commonly used post descriminator filter is the integrate and dump network whose output may be described by

$$y(T) = \int_0^T \dot{\theta}(t)dt = \theta(T) - \theta(0) \qquad (10.85)$$

Integration of the discriminator output effects a return to the phase plane, but $\theta(T) - \theta(0)$ is an angle which is not reduced modulo 2π. As is well known, the distribution of $y(T)$ is an unsolved problem.[42]

However, when attention is confined to very large values of the carrier to noise ratio ($\rho > 10$, say) $\theta(T)$ and $\theta(0)$ lie in the same 2π interval except for rare excursions which may be ignored initially. Then the results shown in Chapter 2 are directly applicable, for $\theta(T) - \theta(0)$ is now viewed as an angle reduced modulo 2π. From eqns. 2.17 and 2.18[*] on assuming a constant amplitude signal and $r_N(T) = 0$, i.e. the noise which is added to the signal is uncorrelated at spacing T:

$$\Pr\left[Z + \theta(T) - \theta(0) < 0\right] = \tfrac{1}{2}\left[1 - |\sin(\Delta_s + Z)| I_e\left\{\cos(\Delta_s + Z), \rho\right\}\right] \qquad (10.86)$$

Here Δ_s is the value of $\theta(T) - \theta(0)$ in the absence of noise [$\Delta_s = \mu(T) - \mu(0)$ in the notation of eqn. 10.39] and eqn. 10.86 is a compact form for the distribution exploited in Reference 42 to show that with low-deviation multilevel f.s.k., even when account is taken of the multiples of 2π that might be present in $\theta(T) - \theta(0)$ (attributable to the clicks netted during integration over T), there arises a negligible modification to the error probability as predicted by eqn. 10.86. For handling the larger Δ_s situations, Section 6.3 has shown that

$$\dot{\theta}(t) = \dot{\mu}(t) + \frac{i_s}{A} \qquad (10.87)$$

is a first approximation to $\dot{\theta}(t)$, provided the following inequality is satisfied (ω of eqn. 6.20 is taken as zero since a binary system employing a zero threshold is to be considered)

$$\frac{1}{\rho} < \frac{[\dot{\mu}(t)]^2}{-r_N''(0)} < 1 \qquad (10.88)$$

For ρ in the click region, therefore, use of eqn. 10.87 gives

[*] Put $K_1 = K_2 = \psi_N(0)$, $C = 0$, $R_1 = R_2 = A$, and $\Delta = \Delta_s$

$$y(T) \approx [\mu(T) - \mu(0)] + \left[\frac{I_s(T) - I_s(0)}{A}\right] + [p(T) - n(T)]\, 2\pi$$

$$(10.89)$$

Here $[p(T) - n(T)]$ is the net number (positive or negative) of spikes that have appeared in the time T, and this term is not accounted for by the distribution eqn. 10.86.

$p(T)$ refers to positive-going spikes $[n(T)$ to negative-going spikes] and on viewing these trains as being independent and constituting time-dependent Poisson processes the probability density function of $Z(T) = [p(t) - n(T)]$ is given by convolution,[42] and

$$p(Z) = e^{-y_- + y_+} \sum_{q=-\infty}^{+\infty} \delta(Z - q) \left(\sqrt{\frac{y_+}{y_-}}\right)^q I_q(2\sqrt{y_+ \cdot y_-}) \quad (10.90)$$

where

$$y_- + y_+ = \int_0^T (v_- + v_+)dt \quad [(v_- + v_+) \text{ being given by eqn. 5.10}]$$

$$y_- - y_+ = \int_0^T (v_- - v_+)dt$$

$$= \left[\frac{\mu(T) - \mu(0)}{2\pi}\right] e^{-\rho} \text{ from eqn. 5.15}$$

$$= \langle Z \rangle$$

$$\langle Z^2 \rangle - (\langle Z \rangle)^2 = y_- + y_+$$

Thus $y(T)$ can be written

$$y(T) = [\mu(T) - \mu(0)](1 - e^{-\rho}) + \left[\frac{I_s(T) - I_s(0)}{A}\right] + 2\pi Z'(T)$$

$$(10.91)$$

$Z'(T)$ is now a zero-mean discrete variable and $(1 - e^{-\rho})$ will be recognised as the coherence factor (eqns. 4.27 and 5.30)

Temporarily ignoring the noise term $[I_s(T) - I_s(0)]/A$, it is evident that, if one click occurs (so making $Z'(T)$ either $+1$ or -1), there is the possibility of an error being caused in the sign of $y(T)$ owing to the presence of $\pm 2\pi$.

This has been referred to in the literature [43,44] as a deviation threshold because in the case of a rectangularly switched f.s.k. signal $\mu(T) - \mu(0) = \pi k$ and, unless k is so large that $2\pi Z'(T)$ cannot cause a sign change, the possibility of error exists. k must exceed two, for example, for such error to be impossible when one click arises.

More often, interest lies in the error probability when it is averaged over the possible values of $Z'(T)$. The similarity of eqn. 10.91 to eqn.

10.45 (identify $[\mu(T) - \mu(0)](1 - e^{-\rho})$ with C, $[I_s(T) - I_s(0)]/A$ with N, and $2\pi Z'(T)$ with I) then shows that the probability of a binary error conditional on a value for I is given by eqn. 10.46. The averaging in question can be done using eqn. 10.90. It is found that with practical ρs the $q = 0$ term, which is then close to unity, is dominant and, usually, the contribution made by clicks to binary systems may be ignored when the inequality 10.88 is satisfied.

Note that eqn. 10.91 is in a form appropriate to binary d.p.s.k. and that σ_N in eqn. 10.46 is given by

$$\sigma_N^2 = \left\langle \left[\frac{I_s(T) - I_s(0)}{A} \right]^2 \right\rangle = \frac{1}{\rho} (1 - r_N(T))$$

and so noise correlation at spacing T can be simply incorporated.

The inequality 10.88 can be satisfied for both large and small deviation cases; $\sqrt{-r_N''(0)} = \omega_B/\sqrt{3}$ for a rectangular receiver filter of width $2\omega_B$, so, in the f.s.k. case, k is to satisfy $k < (\omega_B T)/(\pi\sqrt{3})$. For low deviations, if conditions prevail that minimise the error probability at the discriminator output (as discussed in Section 10.5 $\omega_B T/\pi = 1\cdot2$ is then typical), clicks can be ignored if $2k^2 < 1$, i.e. k is less than about $0\cdot7$.

As a summarising statement we may say that $k = 0\cdot7$ represents a plateau below which the Gaussian noise component causes the majority of errors and above which the click-type of disturbance can be an important source of errors at the output of the integrate and dump filter.

10.21 Distribution of the filter output

This concluding section describes a general method for handling the output from a filter and determining, in an approximate way, its probability distribution at any time instant t. The input is non-Gaussian and, typically, is the result of applying some instantaneous nonlinear operation (such as squaring or frequency detection) to the sum of signal and noise. The output $x(t)$ is represented by a sum of samples of the input, each weighted by the impulse response function of the filter, and the time spacing between samples is chosen to be $1/2W$ seconds, where W is some realistic estimate of the highest significant frequency in the noise. The sum is presumed to be a good approximation to the convolution integral that specifies the filter output at t, and the sampling theorem (p. 312 of

Reference 45) is appealed to as reason for assuming that the terms
making up the sum are statistically independent.

With $\phi(u)$ as the univariate characteristic function of the output,
this function is equated to the product of the characteristic functions
of each term in the sum (eqn. 2.9 is an example of this multiplicative
property) and the probability that the filter response at the time in
question lies below a threshold L can then be written

$$P_r[x(t) < L] = \frac{1}{2} - \frac{1}{2\pi} \int_{-\infty}^{+\infty} \frac{\phi(u)}{ju} e^{-juL} du \qquad (10.92)$$

The principal value of this integral is to be taken (the form can be
compared with eqns. 3.25 and 3.60) but it is likely that the evaluation
will have to be done numerically. Reference 46 offers an example of
this where the general method is shown to be very successful for
examining the effects of post detection filtering on an incoherent
f.s.k. system.

An important parameter is the time-bandwidth product (given by
$2WT$ in the case of the integrate and dump filter of eqn. 10.85), and,
when this is large, it is frequently the case that the sum of samples has
a distribution which is nearly normal, as suggested by the Central Limit
theorem. Large in this context depends on how small the probabilities
of interest are, the smaller the probabilities, the larger $2WT$ has to be,
but $2WT > 50$ is a working guide in most practical situations.

While there is no guarantee that a normal distribution will be
approached by the sum (which may have negative as well as positive
terms due to oscillations in the filter impulse response) it is more likely
to happen when the carrier-to-noise ratio ρ is large, as with the example
considered in Section 10.20. Then each sample of the input is
well-behaved in the sense of having a finite variance [$\sigma^2(WT)$, say] and
in eqn. 10.92 $\phi(u) \approx \exp - [u^2 \sigma^2 (WT)WT]$.

A case in which this is not true arises when $\rho = 0$, and the instantaneous frequency of narrowband noise is filtered. As eqns. 2.1 and 6.9
show, each input sample has a characteristic function $\phi_s(u)$ that can be
specified neatly, and

$$\phi_s(u) = u\sqrt{-r_N''(0)} \cdot K_1(u\sqrt{-r_N''(0)}) \qquad (10.93)$$

where $K_1(x)$ is a Bessel function of the second kind of imaginary
argument. However, the coefficient of u^2 in $\phi_s(u)$ is infinite, and so we
cannot expect the normal limit to be approached, and the distribution
of the filter output depends heavily on the particular filter used.

In practice the very large frequency excursions that give rise to the
infinite variance will be tempered by the finite bandwidth of the

discriminator, but such perverse cases as this are best handled through two lines of attack so that the results provided by each can be compared. Here, as elsewhere, bringing to bear the complementary strengths of analysis and simulation can offer a powerful way of making accurate assessments of system performance.

10.22 References

1 BENNETT, W.R., and RICE, S.O.: 'Spectral density and autocorrelation functions associated with binary frequency shift keying', *Bell Syst. Tech. J.*, 1963, **42** pp. 2355–2385
2 PELCHAT, M.G.: 'The autocorrelation function and power spectrum of PCM/FM with random binary modulating wave-forms.' *IEEE Trans.* 1964, **SET-10**, (1), pp. 39–44
3 LANGSETH, R.E.: 'Spectrum of a carrier frequency modulated by a Poisson pulse train with application to feedback diversity.' *IEE Trans.* 1972, **COM-20**, pp. 1015–1021
4 TJUNG, T.T.: 'Power spectra and power distributions of random binary f.m. signals with premodulation shaping,' *Electron. Lett.*, 1965, **1**, (6), pp. 176–178
5 POSTL, W.: 'Die specktrale leistungsdichte bei Frequenzmodulation eines tragers mit einem Stochastischen Telegraphiesignal', *Frequenz*, 1963, **17**, pp. 107–110
6 SHIMBO, O.: 'General formula for power spectra of digital f.m. signals,' *Proc. IEE*, 1966, **113**, (11), pp. 1783–1789
7 ANDERSON, R.R., and SALZ, J.: 'Spectra of digital f.m.' *Bell Syst. Tech. J.*, 1965, **44**, (6), 1965, pp. 1165–1189
8 ROWE, H.E., and PRABHU, V.K.: 'Power spectrum of a digital frequency modulation signal', *Bell Syst. Tech. J.*, 1975, **54**, (6), pp. 1095–1125
9 BENEDETTO, S., and BIGLIERI, E.: 'A spectral analysis technique for digital non-stationary random processes', Second International Symposium on Information Theory, Tsahkadsor, Armenia, Sept. 1971
10 BAKER, T.J.: 'Asymptotic behaviour of digital FM spectra'. *IEEE Trans.*, 1974, **COM-22** (10), pp. 1585–1594
11 COHEN, S.A.: 'The Fourier transform asymptotic behaviour theorem', *IEEE Trans.*, 1969, **E-12**, pp. 56–57
12 BIGLIERI, E., CASTELLANI, V., RAMELLO, B., and SANT' AGOSTINO, M.: 'Extremal statistics and computer simulaton', *Alta Freq.*, 1970, **39**, pp. 273E–282E
13 BENNETT, W.R., and DAVEY, J.R.: 'Data transmission' (McGraw-Hill, 1965)
14 TOMLINSON, M.: 'Realizable filters which give zero intersymbol interference in an FSK system', *Int. J. Circuit Theory & Appl.*, 1974, **2**, (3) pp. 291–297
15 O'MAHONY, M.J., and CATTERMOLE, K.W.: 'Distortionless frequency-shift keying: further results', *Electron. Lett.*, 1975, **11**, (24), pp. 605–606
16 REIGER, S.: 'Error probabilities of binary data transmission systems in the presence of random noise', *IRE National Convention Record 1953*, Pt. 8, pp. 72–79

17 EDWARDS, J.R.: 'A comparison of modulation schemes for binary data transmission', *Radio & Electron Eng.*, 1973, **43**, (9), pp. 562–568

18 ARTHURS, E., and DYM, H.: 'On the optimum detection of digital signals in the presence of white noise – a geometric interpretation and a study of three basic data transmission systems', *IRE Trans.*, 1962, **CS-10**, pp. 336–372

19 HELSTROM, C.: 'A comprison of digital communication systems', *IRE Trans.*, 1960, **CS-8** pp. 141–150

20 JAIN, P.C.: 'Error probabilities in binary angle modulation', *IEEE Trans.*, 1974, **IT-20**, (1), pp. 36–42

21 SLACK, M.: 'Probability distributions of sinusoidal oscillations combined in random phase', *J. IEE*, 1946, **93**, Pt. III, pp. 76–86

22 BENNETT, W.R.: 'Distribution of the sum of randomly phased components', *Q. Appl. Maths.*, 1948, **5**, p. 385

23 ROSENBAUM, A.S.: 'Binary PSK error probabilities with multiple co-channel interferences', *IEEE Trans.*, 1970, **COM-18** (3), pp. 241–253

24 SHIMBO, O., and FANG, R.: 'Effects of co-channel interference and Gaussian noise in M-ary PSK systems', *COMSAT Tech. Rev.*, 1973, **3**, (1), pp. 183–207

25 GLAVE, F.E.: 'An upper bound on the probability of error due to intersymbol interference for correlated digital signals', *IEEE Trans.*, 1972, **IT-18**, pp. 356–363

26 MATTHEWS, J.W.: 'Sharp error bounds for intersymbol interference', *IEE Trans.*, 1973, **IT-19**, (4), pp. 440–447

27 ROSENBAUM, A.S., and GLAVE, F.E.: 'An error probability upper bound for coherent phase shift keying with peak-limited interference', *IEEE Trans.*, 1974, **COM-22**, (1), pp. 6–16

28 GLAVE, F.E., and ROSENBAUM, A.S.: 'An upper bound analysis for coherent phase shift keying with co-channel, adjacent channel and intersymbol interference', *IEEE Trans.*, 1975, **COM-23**, (6) pp. 586–597

29 CHAKRABARTI, N.B., and GANGOPADHYAY, R.: 'Error probabilities for ASK/PSK, systems in an additive mixture of Gaussian and impulsive noise', *Electron. Lett.*, 1976, **12**, (9), pp. 227–229

30 ABRAMOWITZ, M., and STEGUN, I.A. (Eds.): 'Handbook of mathematical functions with formulas, graphs and mathematical tables', (NBS, New York, 1965)

31 SALZ, J.: 'Performance of multi level narrow band FM digital communications systems', *IEEE Trans.*, 1965, **COM-13**, pp. 420–424

32 SCHWARTZ, M., BENNETT, W.R., and STEIN, S.: 'Communication systems and techniques', (McGraw-Hill, 1966)

33 TJUNG, T.T., and WITTKE, P.: 'Carrier transmission of binary data in a restricted band', *IEEE Trans.*, 1970, **COM-18**, pp. 295–304

34 BOBILIN, R.T.: 'Distortion analysis of digital FM systems'. Ph.D. thesis, Electrical Engineering Dept., Purdue University, June 1970 (Available through University Microfilms)

35 de BUDA, R.: 'Coherent demodulation of frequency shift keying with low deviation ratio', *IEEE Trans.*, 1972, **COM-20**, pp. 429–435

36 SCHNEIDER, H.L.: 'Click comparison of digital and matched filter receivers', *Bell Syst. Tech. J.*, 1968, **47**, pp. 301–313

37 NAKAGAMI, M.: 'The m-distribution: a general formula of intensity distribution of rapid fading', *in* HUFFMAN, W.C. (Ed.): 'Statistical methods in radio wave propagation (Pergamon Press, 1960)

38 JAKES, W.C. Jnr. (Ed.): 'Microwave mobile communications' (Wiley, 1974)

39 JONES. J.J.: 'Multi channel FSK and DPSK reception with three component multi path', *IEEE Trans.*, 1968, **COM-16**, (6), pp. 808–821

40 SCHMIDT, K.H.: 'Data transmission using controlled intersymbol interference', *Electri. Commun.*, 1973, **48**, pp. 121–133

41 TJUNG, T.T., WEE, B.L., CHIA, T.S., and TAN, O.H.: 'Error rates for biternary frequency modulation', *Electron. Lett.*, 1974, **10**, (15), pp. 295–296

42 MAZO, J.E., and SALZ, J.: 'Theory of error rates for digital FM', *Bell Syst. Tech. J.*, 1966, **45**, pp. 1511–1535

43 KLAPPER, J.: 'Demodulator threshold performance and error rates in angle modulated digital signals', *RCA Rev.*, 1966, **27**, pp. 226–244

44 COHN, J.: 'A new approach to FM threshold reception', Proceedings National Electronics Conference 1956, 12, pp. 221–236

45 MIDDLETON, D.: 'An introduction to statistical communication theory' (McGraw-Hill, 1960)

46 MILSTEIN, L.B., and AUSTIN, M.C.: 'Performance of non coherent FSK and AM-FSK systems with post detection filtering', *IEEE Trans.*, 1975, **COM-23**, pp. 1300–1306

Table of $I_e(k,x)$

The function $I_e(k, x)$ is defined by

$$I_e(k, x) = \int_0^x e^{-u} I_0(ku)du \quad 0 \leqslant k \leqslant 1$$

and is tabulated here for x in the range 0 to 39 [0 (0·1) 3, 3 (0·2) 9, 9 (0·1) 39] and for $k = 0·1, 0·2, 0·4, 0·6, 0·75, 0·85, 0·9, 0·95, 0·99$ and 1·00. The following special cases are given in Appendix 1 of Reference 1 where a short table of $I_e(k, x)$ is also shown.

$$I_e(0, x) = 1 - e^{-x}$$

$$I_e(1, x) = xe^{-x}[I_0(x) + I_1(x)]$$

$$I_e(k, \infty) = \frac{1}{\sqrt{1 - k^2}}$$

together with

$$I_e(k, x) \approx \frac{1}{\sqrt{1 - k^2}} - \frac{1}{\sqrt{2k(1 - k)}} \cdot \text{erfc}\,[\sqrt{x(1 - k)}]$$

which may be used when both x and kx are large (> 3, say). The I_e function can be expressed in terms of the Marcum Q function as follows

$$I_e(\sin 2\theta, \tfrac{1}{2}R^2) \cos 2\theta = 1 + e^{-R^2/2} I_0(\tfrac{1}{2}R^2 \sin 2\theta) - 2Q(R \sin \theta, R \cos \theta)$$

(see eqns. 6.7 and 6.8 of the text) and it can be related to other tabulated integrals. An example is given following the tables.

RICE IE FUNCTION IE(K,X)

IE(K,X)= INTEGRAL FROM ZERO TO X OF EXP(-V)*IO(K*V)*DV
WHERE IO IS THE MODIFIED BESSEL FUNCTION OF ZERO ORDER

x	0.100000	0.200000	0.400000	0.600000	0.750000	0.850000	0.900000	0.950000	0.990000	1.000000
0.1	0.095163	0.095167	0.095175	0.095190	0.095206	0.095218	0.095225	0.095232	0.095238	0.095240
0.2	0.181275	0.181292	0.181361	0.181476	0.181593	0.181685	0.181735	0.181788	0.181833	0.181844
0.3	0.259200	0.259254	0.259440	0.259830	0.260196	0.260485	0.260643	0.260813	0.260951	0.260987
0.4	0.329720	0.329839	0.330315	0.331110	0.331917	0.332555	0.332905	0.333275	0.333586	0.333666
0.5	0.393541	0.393757	0.394622	0.396068	0.397536	0.398701	0.399339	0.400015	0.400582	0.400728
0.6	0.451304	0.451651	0.453041	0.455368	0.457737	0.459616	0.460648	0.461740	0.462659	0.462895
0.7	0.503585	0.504008	0.506154	0.509598	0.513111	0.515903	0.517637	0.519063	0.520431	0.520783
0.8	0.550908	0.551620	0.554478	0.559276	0.564177	0.568081	0.570228	0.572506	0.574425	0.574918
0.9	0.593745	0.594689	0.598481	0.604859	0.611389	0.616601	0.619477	0.622521	0.625091	0.625752
1.0	0.632522	0.633729	0.638580	0.646754	0.655144	0.661856	0.665557	0.669494	0.672815	0.673670
1.1	0.667627	0.669124	0.675148	0.685320	0.695790	0.704185	0.708823	0.713761	0.717932	0.719006
1.2	0.699402	0.701221	0.708521	0.720878	0.733633	0.743887	0.749562	0.755612	0.760728	0.762047
1.3	0.728183	0.730332	0.739007	0.753712	0.768943	0.781222	0.788029	0.795297	0.800951	0.803039
1.4	0.754236	0.756742	0.766861	0.784075	0.801958	0.816417	0.824449	0.833037	0.840319	0.842198
1.5	0.777826	0.780700	0.792342	0.812194	0.832888	0.849671	0.859014	0.869019	0.877032	0.879709
1.6	0.799188	0.802451	0.815604	0.838270	0.861919	0.881162	0.891897	0.903412	0.913204	0.915715
1.7	0.818531	0.822190	0.837025	0.862683	0.889218	0.911043	0.923247	0.936359	0.947527	0.950410
1.8	0.836049	0.840011	0.856600	0.884997	0.914930	0.939452	0.953197	0.967989	0.980609	0.983877
1.9	0.851914	0.856383	0.874561	0.905955	0.939187	0.966510	0.981862	0.998411	1.012559	1.016220
2.0	0.866283	0.871163	0.891042	0.925489	0.962106	0.992325	1.009347	1.027733	1.043472	1.047755
2.1	0.879298	0.884588	0.906177	0.943716	0.983792	1.016992	1.035743	1.056033	1.073434	1.077953
2.2	0.891086	0.896786	0.920085	0.960743	1.004508	1.040508	1.061151	1.083393	1.102519	1.107491
2.3	0.901786	0.907871	0.932874	0.976664	1.023831	1.063219	1.085584	1.109881	1.130794	1.136237
2.4	0.911437	0.917946	0.944641	0.991567	1.042346	1.084924	1.109168	1.135559	1.158819	1.164246
2.5	0.920200	0.927104	0.955473	1.005530	1.059951	1.105775	1.131941	1.160483	1.185146	1.191578
2.6	0.928139	0.935432	0.965451	1.018024	1.076709	1.125827	1.153955	1.184702	1.211322	1.218272
2.7	0.935332	0.943005	0.974647	1.030914	1.092677	1.145312	1.175258	1.208260	1.236890	1.244574
2.8	0.941842	0.948893	0.983128	1.042459	1.107906	1.163734	1.195894	1.231209	1.261889	1.269920
2.9	0.947753	0.956159	0.990952	1.053312	1.122444	1.181676	1.215900	1.253553	1.286352	1.294960
3.0	0.953104	0.961861	0.998175	1.063523	1.136332	1.198996	1.235312	1.275357	1.310312	1.319482

RICE IE FUNCTION IE(K,X)

IE(K,X)= INTEGRAL FROM ZERO TO X OF EXP(-V)*IO(K*V)*DV
WHERE IO IS THE MODIFIED BESSEL FUNCTION OF ZERO ORDER

X \ K	0.100000	0.200000	0.400000	0.600000	0.750000	0.850000	0.900000	0.950000	0.990000	1.000000
3.2	0.962347	0.971772	1.011010	1.082105	1.162316	1.231903	1.272482	1.317429	1.356831	1.367193
3.4	0.969938	0.979987	1.021079	1.098789	1.186135	1.262700	1.307430	1.357627	1.401665	1.413250
3.6	0.976174	0.986799	1.031371	1.113573	1.208024	1.291595	1.340949	1.396127	1.444920	1.457817
3.8	0.981297	0.992452	1.039425	1.126772	1.228184	1.318763	1.372602	1.433079	1.486798	1.501029
4.0	0.985508	0.997147	1.046345	1.138580	1.246789	1.344358	1.402730	1.468611	1.527397	1.543011
4.2	0.988960	1.001048	1.052298	1.149163	1.263980	1.368512	1.431453	1.502836	1.566822	1.583862
4.4	0.991814	1.004292	1.057427	1.158662	1.279915	1.391341	1.458879	1.535850	1.605163	1.623670
4.6	0.994153	1.006991	1.061851	1.167202	1.294682	1.412946	1.485103	1.567738	1.642498	1.662512
4.8	0.996077	1.009238	1.065673	1.174890	1.308397	1.433420	1.510206	1.598576	1.678897	1.700457
5.0	0.997660	1.011110	1.068978	1.181818	1.321137	1.452842	1.534263	1.628430	1.714421	1.737565
5.2	0.998962	1.012669	1.071839	1.188070	1.332995	1.471286	1.557342	1.657360	1.749125	1.773890
5.4	1.000053	1.013970	1.074319	1.193716	1.344040	1.488818	1.579501	1.685421	1.783058	1.809480
5.6	1.000915	1.015056	1.076470	1.198821	1.354336	1.505495	1.600796	1.712660	1.816265	1.844379
5.8	1.001641	1.015962	1.078337	1.203440	1.363842	1.521373	1.621275	1.739121	1.848786	1.878624
6.0	1.002238	1.016719	1.079960	1.207623	1.372910	1.536501	1.640085	1.764846	1.880656	1.912253
6.2	1.002730	1.017351	1.081371	1.211413	1.381289	1.550923	1.659966	1.789871	1.911910	1.945298
6.4	1.003136	1.017880	1.082599	1.214851	1.389123	1.564682	1.678256	1.814229	1.942577	1.977749
6.6	1.003469	1.018323	1.083668	1.217970	1.396451	1.577881	1.695892	1.837952	1.972686	2.009749
6.8	1.003746	1.018693	1.084600	1.220802	1.403310	1.590357	1.712904	1.861069	2.002282	2.041209
7.0	1.003971	1.019003	1.085412	1.223374	1.409733	1.602341	1.729324	1.883606	2.031728	2.072189
7.2	1.004158	1.019262	1.086121	1.225713	1.415751	1.613797	1.745180	1.905587	2.059908	2.102711
7.4	1.004312	1.019480	1.086740	1.227839	1.421392	1.624754	1.760497	1.927037	2.088020	2.132795
7.6	1.004439	1.019662	1.087280	1.229774	1.426681	1.635237	1.775500	1.947977	2.115685	2.162458
7.8	1.004543	1.019815	1.087752	1.231534	1.431643	1.645271	1.789613	1.968425	2.142919	2.191720
8.0	1.004630	1.019944	1.088165	1.233137	1.436300	1.654879	1.803455	1.988403	2.169760	2.220594
8.2	1.004701	1.020051	1.088526	1.234597	1.440671	1.664082	1.818684	2.007926	2.196163	2.249097
8.4	1.004760	1.020142	1.088841	1.235928	1.444777	1.672901	1.829810	2.027012	2.222201	2.277242
8.6	1.004808	1.020218	1.089118	1.237141	1.448634	1.681553	1.842360	2.045677	2.247870	2.305045
8.8	1.004849	1.020282	1.089359	1.238246	1.452258	1.689956	1.854513	2.063934	2.273181	2.332512
9.0	1.004881	1.020335	1.089571	1.239255	1.455665	1.697228	1.866287	2.081799	2.298147	2.359661

END OF PLN AT   15/02/47   ON   29/04/76

RICE IE FUNCTION IE(K,X)

IE(K,X)= INTEGRAL FROM ZERO TO X OF EXP(-V)*IO(K*V)*DV
WHERE IO IS THE MODIFIED BESSEL FUNCTION OF ZERO ORDER

x	0.100000	0.200000	0.400000	0.600000	0.750000	0.850000	0.900000	0.950000	0.990000	1.000000
10.0	1.004977	1.020300	1.090297	1.243119	1.469892	1.731627	1.919948	2.165667	2.418173	2.490960
11.0	1.005014	1.020509	1.090674	1.255576	1.480409	1.759758	1.966055	2.241431	2.531035	2.615667
12.0	1.005029	1.020097	1.090870	1.247746	1.488521	1.782822	2.005864	2.310207	2.657676	2.734686
13.0	1.005034	1.020611	1.090974	1.246154	1.494042	1.801857	2.040774	2.372890	2.738844	2.848732
14.0	1.005036	1.020017	1.091028	1.246803	1.498415	1.817605	2.070393	2.450214	2.855141	2.958381
15.0	1.005037	1.020019	1.091057	1.249222	1.501685	1.850673	2.096580	2.482789	2.922068	3.064106
16.0	1.005038	1.020620	1.091072	1.249674	1.504150	1.861363	2.119482	2.531127	3.015040	3.166300
17.0	1.005038	1.020620	1.091080	1.249670	1.506008	1.870605	2.135554	2.575666	3.099410	3.205290
18.0	1.005038	1.020621	1.091085	1.249784	1.507413	1.858174	2.157180	2.616785	3.184780	3.361376
19.0	1.005038	1.020621	1.091089	1.249859	1.508476	1.864507	2.172684	2.654809	3.258511	3.454744
20.0	1.005038	1.020620	1.091088	1.249908	1.509283	1.869814	2.186342	2.690025	3.353729	3.545731
21.0	1.005038	1.020621	1.091089	1.249939	1.509895	1.874267	2.198391	2.722684	3.408636	3.634402
22.0	1.005038	1.020621	1.091089	1.249940	1.510360	1.878008	2.209032	2.753009	3.476504	3.720940
23.0	1.005038	1.020621	1.091089	1.249974	1.510714	1.881155	2.218442	2.781199	3.544398	3.805549
24.0	1.005039	1.020621	1.091089	1.249983	1.510984	1.883806	2.226771	2.807430	3.610151	3.888298
25.0	1.005038	1.020621	1.091089	1.249989	1.511189	1.886037	2.234150	2.831861	3.673843	3.969522
26.0	1.005038	1.020621	1.091089	1.249993	1.511340	1.889920	2.240692	2.854436	3.735738	4.049722
27.0	1.005039	1.020621	1.091089	1.249905	1.511466	1.889509	2.246498	2.875882	3.795738	4.126559
28.0	1.005039	1.020621	1.091089	1.249997	1.511558	1.890852	2.251654	2.895718	3.854141	4.203031
29.0	1.005039	1.020621	1.091089	1.249998	1.511628	1.891987	2.256236	2.914248	3.910880	4.278097
30.0	1.005039	1.020621	1.091089	1.249999	1.511681	1.892947	2.260311	2.931571	3.966085	4.351868
31.0	1.005038	1.020621	1.091089	1.249999	1.511722	1.893759	2.263936	2.947774	4.019830	4.424410
32.0	1.005038	1.020621	1.091089	1.249999	1.511754	1.894447	2.267163	2.962938	4.072181	4.495780
33.0	1.005038	1.020621	1.091089	1.250000	1.511778	1.895010	2.270037	2.977137	4.123201	4.566030
34.0	1.005039	1.020621	1.091089	1.250000	1.511797	1.895524	2.272598	2.990438	4.172947	4.635220
35.0	1.005039	1.020621	1.091089	1.250000	1.511811	1.895943	2.274882	3.002905	4.221474	4.703398
36.0	1.005038	1.020621	1.091089	1.250000	1.511822	1.896299	2.276918	3.014594	4.268832	4.770597
37.0	1.005039	1.020621	1.091089	1.250000	1.511830	1.896600	2.278735	3.025558	4.315066	4.836061
38.0	1.005038	1.020621	1.091089	1.250000	1.511836	1.896857	2.280357	3.035847	4.360222	4.902230
39.0	1.005039	1.020621	1.091089	1.250000	1.511841	1.897074	2.281806	3.045505	4.404341	4.966739

END OF RUN AT   15/04/38   ON   29/04/76

$$V(K, c) = \frac{2c}{1 + c^2} I_e \left(\frac{1 - c^2}{1 + c^2}, \frac{1 + c^2}{4c^2} K^2 \right)$$

$$= Q \left[\frac{K}{2} \left(\frac{1 + c}{c} \right), \frac{K}{2} \left(\frac{1 - c}{c} \right) \right]$$

$$- Q \left[\frac{K}{2} \left(\frac{1 - c}{c} \right), \frac{K}{2} \left(\frac{1 + c}{c} \right) \right]$$

where $V(K, c)$ is called the circular generalised error function[2] and a table of $V(K, c)$ is given in Reference 3.

$$V(K, 1) = 1 - e^{-K^2/2}$$

$$\lim_{c \to 0} V(K, c) = \text{erf} \left(\frac{K}{\sqrt{2}} \right)$$

This result corresponds to the special case quoted below eqn. 2.18.

11.1 References

1   RICE S.O.: 'Statistical properties of a sine wave plus random noise', *Bell Syst. Tech. J.*, 1948, **27**, pp. 109–157
2   SENDERSKIY V.A.: 'Noise immunity of quasi-coherent detection of P.S.K. signals', *Telecommun. & Radio Eng.*, 1973, **27**, pp. 122–124
3   HARTER H.L.: 'Circular error probabilities', *J. Am. Stat. Assoc.*, 1960, **55**, pp. 723–731

Index